Math **Diagnosis** and **Intervention** System

Booklet B

Basic Facts in Grades K–3

Overview of Math Diagnosis and Intervention System

The system can be used in a variety of situations:

- **During School** Use the system for intervention on prerequisite skills at the beginning of the year, the beginning of a topic, or the beginning of a lesson. Use for intervention during the Topic when more is needed beyond the resources already provide for the lesson.
- **After-school, Saturday school, summer-school (intersession) programs** Use the system for intervention offered in special programs.

The system provides resources for:

- **Assessment** Diagnostic Tests are provided. Each Diagnostic Test assesses the content for a grade. Use a test at the start of the year for entry-level assessment or anytime during the year as a summative evaluation.
- **Diagnosis** An item analysis identifies areas where intervention is needed.
- **Intervention** Booklets A–E in Part 1 and Booklets F–J in Part 2 identify specific concepts and assign a number to each concept, for example, A12 or E10. For each concept, there is a two-page Intervention Lesson that provides an instructional activity followed by practice. References for the Intervention Lessons are provided in teacher materials for *en**Vision**MATH.*
- **Monitoring** The Teacher's Guide provides both Individual Record Forms and Class Record Forms to monitor student progress.

Editorial Offices: Glenview, Illinois • Parsippany, New Jersey • New York, New York

Sales Offices: Boston, Massachusetts • Duluth, Georgia • Glenview, Illinois
Coppell, Texas • Sacramento, California • Mesa, Arizona

ISBN-13: 978-0-328-31129-3
ISBN-10: 0-328-31129-4

21 22 23 V069 15 14 13

Table of Contents

Table of Contents continued

Booklet B: Basic Facts in Grades K-3

Addition

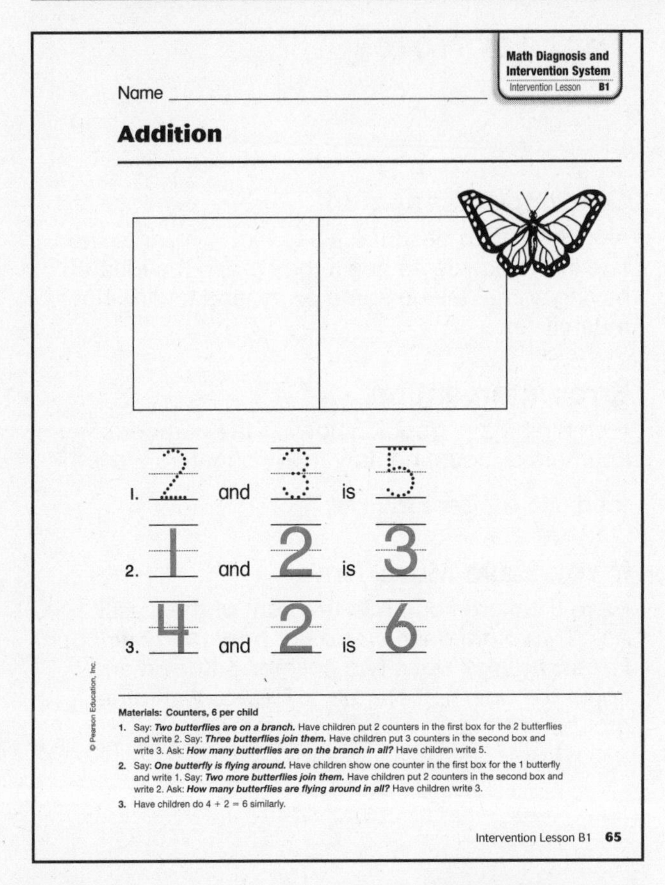

Math Diagnosis and Intervention System
Intervention Lesson B1

Name ______________________

Addition

1. 2 and 3 is 5
2. 1 and 2 is 3
3. 4 and 2 is 6

© Pearson Education, Inc.

Materials: Counters, 6 per child

1. Say: ***Two butterflies are on a branch.*** Have children put 2 counters in the first box for the 2 butterflies and write 2. Say: ***Three butterflies join them.*** Have children put 3 counters in the second box and write 3. Ask: ***How many butterflies are on the branch in all?*** Have children write 5.
2. Say: ***One butterfly is flying around.*** Have children show one counter in the first box for the 1 butterfly and write 1. Say: ***Two more butterflies join them.*** Have children put 2 counters in the second box and write 2. Ask: ***How many butterflies are flying around in all?*** Have children write 3.
3. Have children do 4 + 2 = 6 similarly.

Intervention Lesson B1 **65**

Math Diagnosis and Intervention System
Intervention Lesson B1

Name ______________________

Addition (continued)

Write the numbers.

4. 3 and 2 is 5
5. 2 and 1 is 3
6. 4 and 1 is 5
7. 2 and 3 is 5

© Pearson Education, Inc.

66 Intervention Lesson B1

Teacher Notes

Ongoing Assessment

Make sure children can show the numbers 1 to 5 with counters.

Error Intervention

If children do not know what to put for how many in all,

then have them put the two groups of counters together and count them.

If You Have More Time

Ask children to make up joining stories and share them with the class.

Subtraction

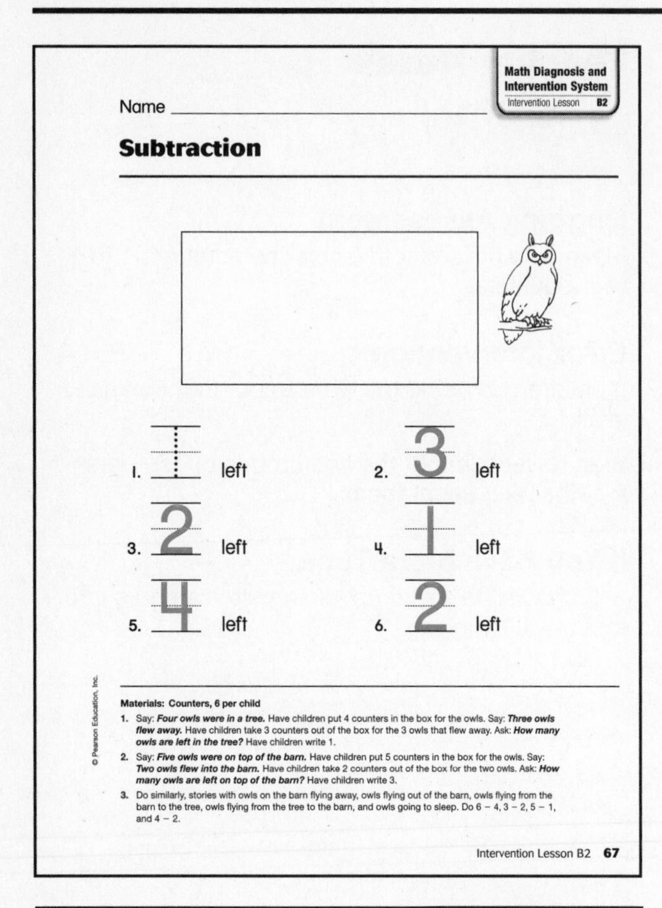
Math Diagnosis and Intervention System
Intervention Lesson B2

Name ______________________

Subtraction

1. 1 left
2. 3 left
3. 2 left
4. 1 left
5. 4 left
6. 2 left

Materials: Counters, 6 per child

1. Say: ***Four owls were in a tree.*** Have children put 4 counters in the box for the owls. Say: ***Three owls flew away.*** Have children take 3 counters out of the box for the 3 owls that flew away. Ask: ***How many owls are left in the tree?*** Have children write 1.
2. Say: ***Five owls were on top of the barn.*** Have children put 5 counters in the box for the owls. Say: ***Two owls flew into the barn.*** Have children take 2 counters out of the box for the two owls. Ask: ***How many owls are left on top of the barn?*** Have children write 3.
3. Do similarly, stories with owls on the barn flying away, owls flying out of the barn, owls flying from the barn to the tree, owls flying from the tree to the barn, and owls going to sleep. Do 6 − 4, 3 − 2, 5 − 1, and 4 − 2.

© Pearson Education, Inc.

Intervention Lesson B2 **67**

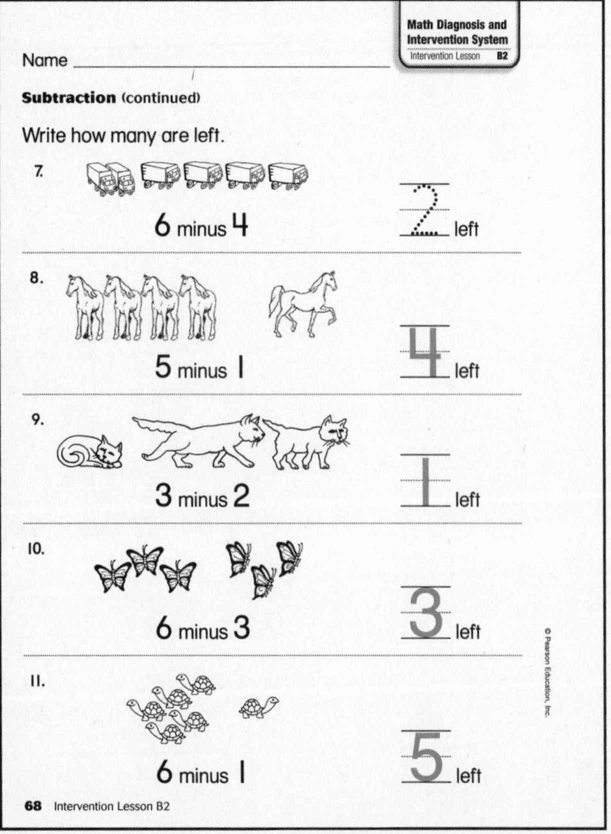
Math Diagnosis and Intervention System
Intervention Lesson B2

Name ______________________

Subtraction (continued)

Write how many are left.

7. 6 minus 4 — 2 left
8. 5 minus 1 — 4 left
9. 3 minus 2 — 1 left
10. 6 minus 3 — 3 left
11. 6 minus 1 — 5 left

© Pearson Education, Inc.

68 Intervention Lesson B2

Teacher Notes

Ongoing Assessment

Ask children to describe a situation similar to the one in the activity to see if they grasp the idea of having some, taking some away, and finding how much is left.

Error Intervention

If children have trouble showing the number of counters or counting how many counters are left,

then use A1: Zero to Five.

If You Have More Time

Have 5 children come to the front of the class. Ask: ***If two children sit down, how many will be left standing?*** Have two children sit down and count the ones left standing. Repeat with other groups of children and other numbers.

Finding Sums

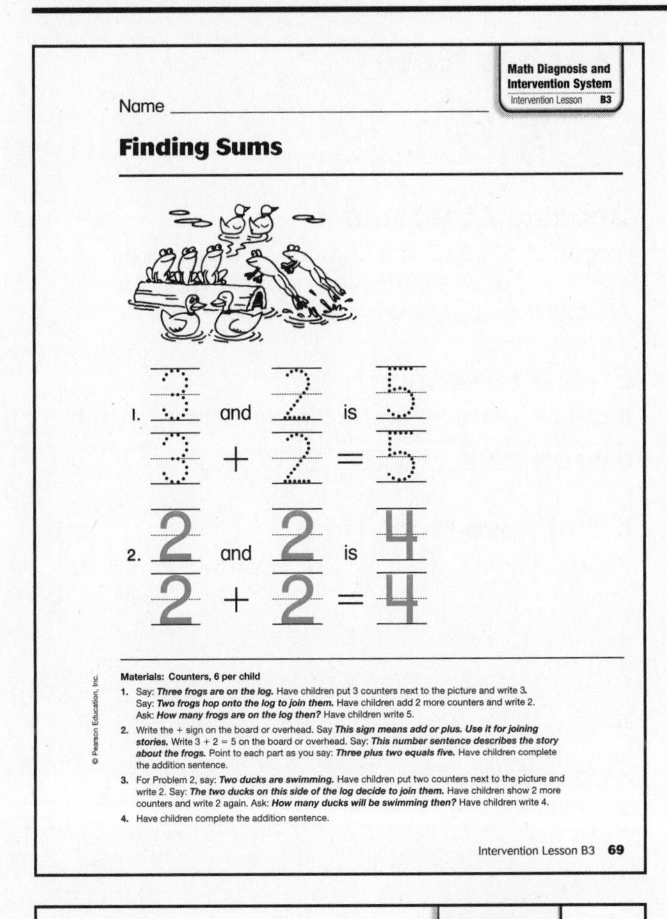

Math Diagnosis and Intervention System
Intervention Lesson B3

Name ______________________

Finding Sums

1. 3 and 2 is 5
$3 + 2 = 5$

2. 2 and 2 is 4
$2 + 2 = 4$

Materials: Counters, 6 per child

1. Say: ***Three frogs are on the log.*** Have children put 3 counters next to the picture and write 3. Say: ***Two frogs hop onto the log to join them.*** Have children add 2 more counters and write 2. Ask: ***How many frogs are on the log then?*** Have children write 5.
2. Write the + sign on the board or overhead. Say ***This sign means add or plus. Use it for joining stories.*** Write 3 + 2 = 5 on the board or overhead. Say: ***This number sentence describes the story about the frogs.*** Point to each part as you say: ***Three plus two equals five.*** Have children complete the addition sentence.
3. For Problem 2, say: ***Two ducks are swimming.*** Have children put two counters next to the picture and write 2. Say: ***The two ducks on this side of the log decide to join them.*** Have children show 2 more counters and write 2 again. Ask: ***How many ducks will be swimming then?*** Have children write 4.
4. Have children complete the addition sentence.

Math Diagnosis and Intervention System
Intervention Lesson B3

Name ______________________

Finding Sums (continued)

Write the numbers.

3. 3 and 1 is 4
$3 + 1 = 4$

4. $2 + 3 = 5$

5. Draw to show each number

$4 + 2 = 6$

Teacher Notes

Ongoing Assessment

Ask children to read a number sentence like 4 + 1 = 5 to see if they understand the symbols.

Error Intervention

If children have trouble finding how many in all,

then use B1: Addition.

If You Have More Time

Write a number sentence like 3 + 1 = 4 on the board or overhead and ask 4 children to come to the front of the class and act it out.

Finding Differences

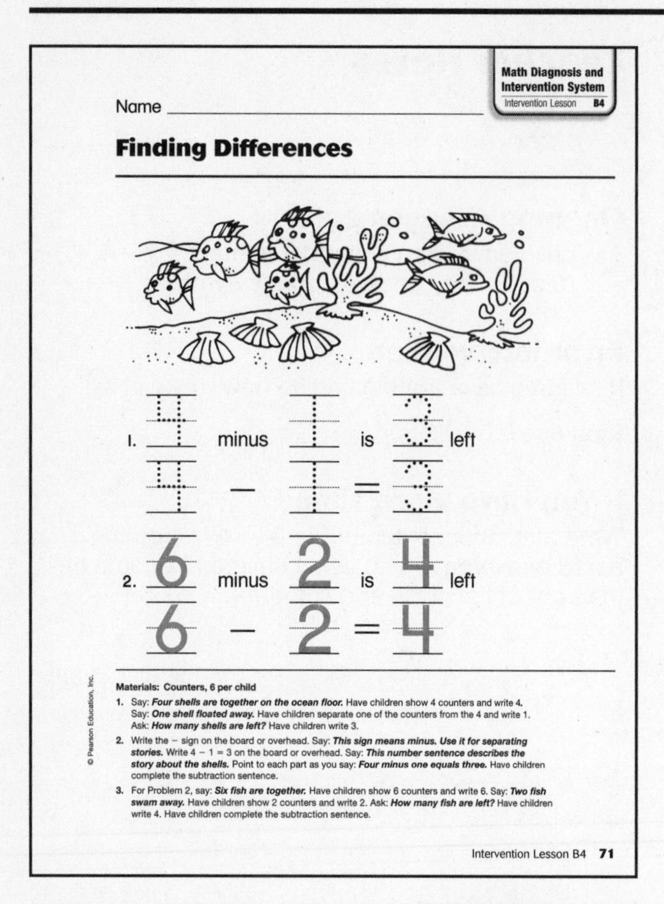

Math Diagnosis and Intervention System
Intervention Lesson B4

Name ______________________

Finding Differences

1. 4 minus 1 is 3 left

4 − 1 = 3

2. 6 minus 2 is 4 left

6 − 2 = 4

Materials: Counters, 6 per child

1. Say: ***Four shells are together on the ocean floor.*** Have children show 4 counters and write 4. Say: ***One shell floated away.*** Have children separate one of the counters from the 4 and write 1. Ask: ***How many shells are left?*** Have children write 3.
2. Write the − sign on the board or overhead. Say: ***This sign means minus. Use it for separating stories.*** Write 4 − 1 = 3 on the board or overhead. Say: ***This number sentence describes the story about the shells.*** Point to each part as you say: ***Four minus one equals three.*** Have children complete the subtraction sentence.
3. For Problem 2, say: ***Six fish are together.*** Have children show 6 counters and write 6. Say: ***Two fish swam away.*** Have children show 2 counters and write 2. Ask: ***How many fish are left?*** Have children write 4. Have children complete the subtraction sentence.

© Pearson Education, Inc.

Intervention Lesson B4 **71**

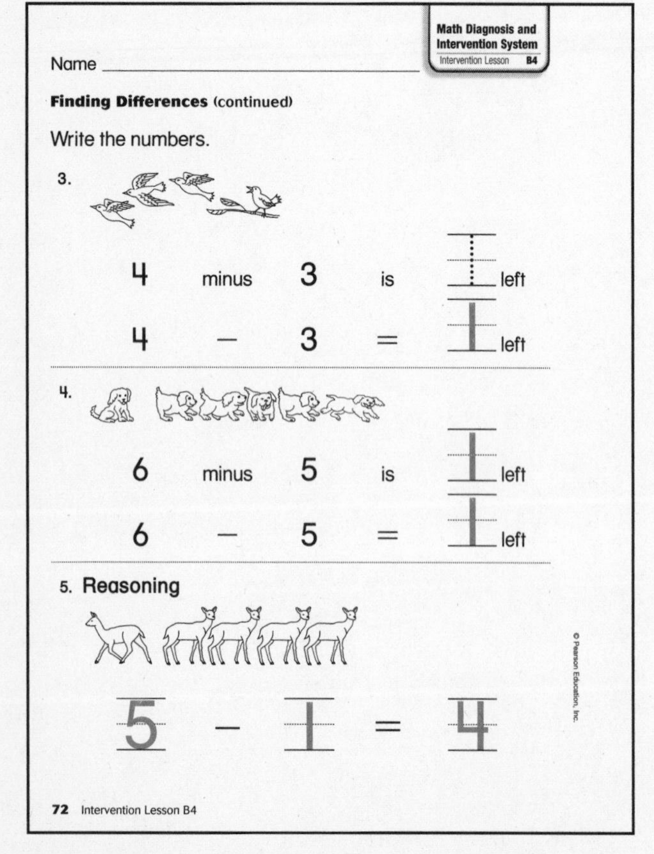

Math Diagnosis and Intervention System
Intervention Lesson B4

Name ______________________

Finding Differences (continued)

Write the numbers.

3. 4 minus 3 is 1 left

4 − 3 = 1 left

4. 6 minus 5 is 1 left

6 − 5 = 1 left

5. **Reasoning**

5 − 1 = 4

© Pearson Education, Inc.

72 Intervention Lesson B4

Teacher Notes

Ongoing Assessment

Ask children to read a number sentence like 4 − 2 = 2 to see if they learned the symbols. Accept minus or take-away for the − sign.

Error Intervention

If children have trouble finding how many are left,

then use B2: Subtraction.

If You Have More Time

Have children draw a picture to show 6 − 3 = 3.

Making 6 and 7

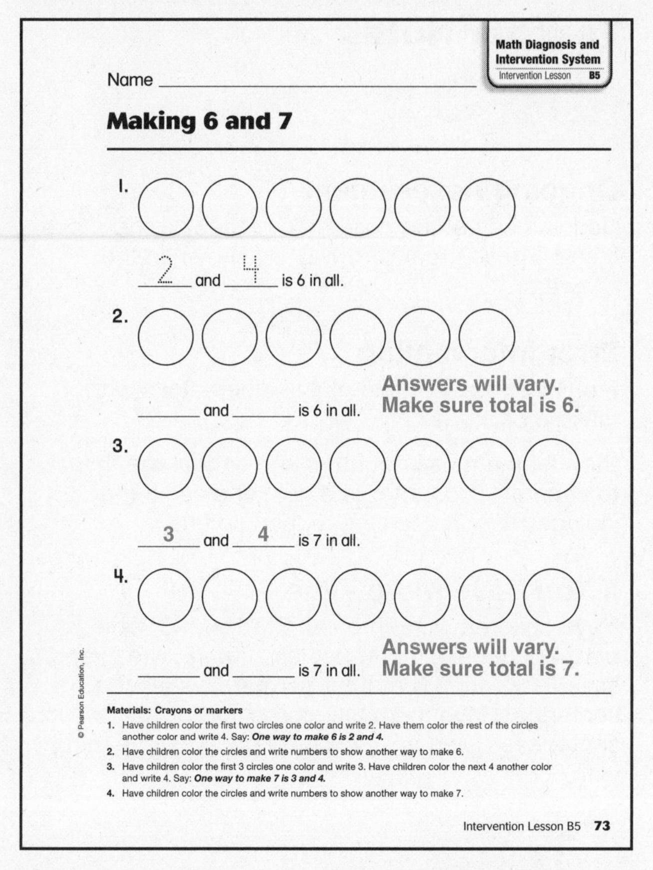

Math Diagnosis and Intervention System
Intervention Lesson B5

Name ____________________

Making 6 and 7

1. ○○○○○○

2 and 4 is 6 in all.

2. ○○○○○○

____ and ____ is 6 in all. **Answers will vary. Make sure total is 6.**

3. ○○○○○○○

3 and 4 is 7 in all.

4. ○○○○○○○

____ and ____ is 7 in all. **Answers will vary. Make sure total is 7.**

Materials: Crayons or markers

1. Have children color the first two circles one color and write 2. Have them color the rest of the circles another color and write 4. Say: ***One way to make 6 is 2 and 4.***
2. Have children color the circles and write numbers to show another way to make 6.
3. Have children color the first 3 circles one color and write 3. Have children color the next 4 another color and write 4. Say: ***One way to make 7 is 3 and 4.***
4. Have children color the circles and write numbers to show another way to make 7.

© Pearson Education, Inc.

Intervention Lesson B5 **73**

Math Diagnosis and Intervention System
Intervention Lesson B5

Name ____________________

Making 6 and 7 (continued)

Find different ways to make 6 and 7.

Order of answers may vary.

5.	6.
1 and 5 is 6.	1 and 6 is 7.
2 and 4 is 6.	2 and 5 is 7.
3 and 3 is 6.	3 and 4 is 7.
4 and 2 is 6.	4 and 3 is 7.
5 and 1 is 6.	5 and 2 is 7.
	6 and 1 is 7.

7.

3 and 2 is 5.

© Pearson Education, Inc.

74 Intervention Lesson B5

Teacher Notes

Ongoing Assessment

Ask: ***What is one way to make 7?*** Sample answer: 3 and 4

Error Intervention

If children have trouble finding ways to make 6 or 7,

then let them use counters.

If You Have More Time

Have 6 children come to the front of the room. Ask one to step away from the rest. Have children in their seats say 1 and 5 is 6. Have another child step away by the first child. Have children in their seats say 2 and 4 is 6. Continue to 5 and 1 is 6. Then repeat with 7 different children to find ways to make 7.

Math Diagnosis and Intervention System
Intervention Lesson B6

Making 8 and 9

Name ______

Making 8 and 9

1. ○○○○○○○○

3 and 5 is 8 in all.

2. ○○○○○○○○

___ and ___ is 8 in all. **Answers will vary. Make sure total is 8.**

3. ○○○○○○○○○

2 and 7 is 9 in all.

4. ○○○○○○○○○

___ and ___ is 9 in all. **Answers will vary. Make sure total is 9.**

Materials: Crayons or markers

1. Have children color the first three circles one color and write 3. Have them color the rest of the circles another color and write 5. Say: ***One way to make 8 is 3 and 5.***
2. Have children color the circles and write numbers to show another way to make 8.
3. Have children color the first 2 circles one color and write 2. Have children color the next 7 another color and write 7. Say: ***One way to make 9 is 2 and 7.***
4. Have children color the circles and write numbers to show another way to make 9.

Name ______

Making 8 and 9 (continued)

Find different ways to make 8 and 9. **Order of answers may vary.**

5.

1 and 7 is 8.

2 and 6 is 8.

3 and 5 is 8.

4 and 4 is 8.

5 and 3 is 8.

6 and 2 is 8.

7 and 1 is 8.

6.

1 and 8 is 9.

2 and 7 is 9.

3 and 6 is 9.

4 and 5 is 9.

5 and 4 is 9.

6 and 3 is 9.

7 and 2 is 9.

8 and 1 is 9.

Teacher Notes

Ongoing Assessment

Notice if any of the children find the ways to make 8 and 9 in an organized way, as shown in the answers.

Error Intervention

If children can not find all the different ways to make 8 or 9,

then let them use counters and encourage them to separate 1 counter at a time and see if they included 1 + 7, then 2 + 6, and so on.

If You Have More Time

Have children work in pairs. Start with 8. One partner chooses a number less than 8, like 2, and says *8 is 2 and.* The other partner finishes the sentence. Have them take turns completing the sentences. Then have children do the same thing with 9.

Joining Stories

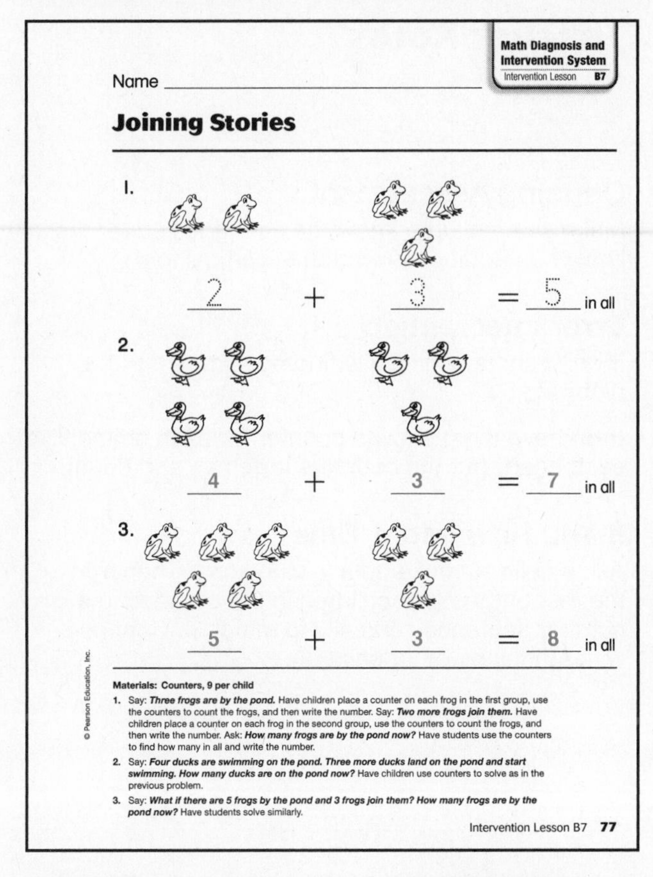
Math Diagnosis and Intervention System
Intervention Lesson B7

Name ________________

Joining Stories

1. 2 + 3 = 5 in all
2. 4 + 3 = 7 in all
3. 5 + 3 = 8 in all

Materials: Counters, 9 per child

1. Say: ***Three frogs are by the pond.*** Have children place a counter on each frog in the first group, use the counters to count the frogs, and then write the number. Say: ***Two more frogs join them.*** Have children place a counter on each frog in the second group, use the counters to count the frogs, and then write the number. Ask: ***How many frogs are by the pond now?*** Have students use the counters to find how many in all and write the number.
2. Say: ***Four ducks are swimming on the pond. Three more ducks land on the pond and start swimming. How many ducks are on the pond now?*** Have children use counters to solve as in the previous problem.
3. Say: ***What if there are 5 frogs by the pond and 3 frogs join them? How many frogs are by the pond now?*** Have students solve similarly.

© Pearson Education, Inc.

Intervention Lesson B7 77

Math Diagnosis and Intervention System
Intervention Lesson B7

Name ________________

Joining Stories (continued)

Write a number sentence for each picture.

4. 2 + 2 = 4
5. 3 + 3 = 6
6. 3 + 2 = 5
7. 3 + 1 = 4
8. 2 + 1 = 3
9. 4 + 1 = 5
10. 2 + 4 = 6
11. 1 + 3 = 4

Reasoning Complete each number sentence.

12. 3 + 2 = 5
13. 3 + 1 = 4

© Pearson Education, Inc.

78 Intervention Lesson B7

Teacher Notes

Ongoing Assessment

Watch children count to see if they are starting with 1 to count or if they are counting on.

Error Intervention

If students do not match the counters to the pictures correctly,

then ask questions like, ***Which picture does this counter match? This one?*** Continue until the child sees that there is either an extra counter or not enough.

If You Have More Time

Have children work in pairs. One partner makes up a word problem like the ones in the lesson and shows it with counters. The other partner solves the problem. Then, they trade roles and repeat.

Adding Across and Down

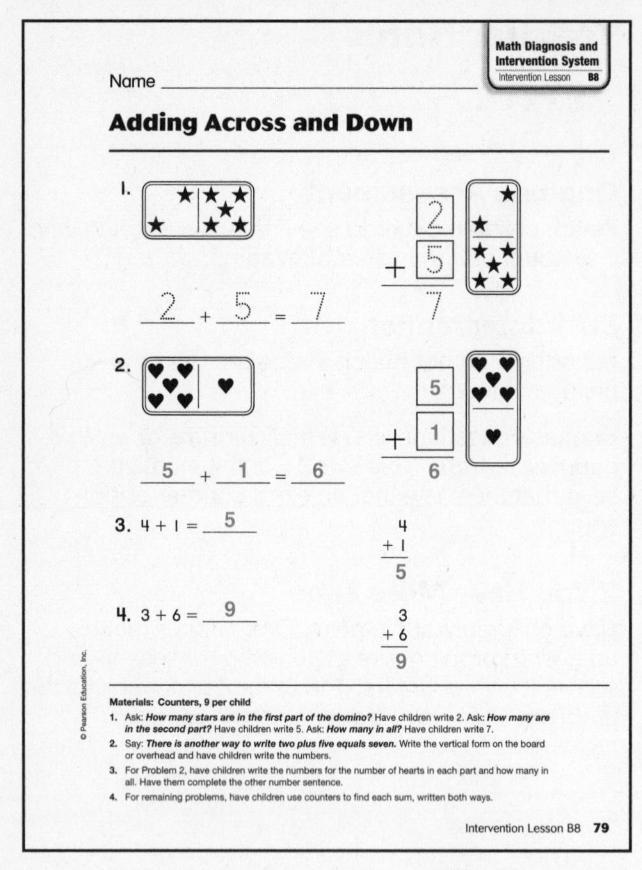
Math Diagnosis and Intervention System
Intervention Lesson B8

Name ______

Adding Across and Down

1. 2 + 5 = 7

   $\begin{array}{r} 2 \\ +\ 5 \\ \hline 7 \end{array}$

2. 5 + 1 = 6

   $\begin{array}{r} 5 \\ +\ 1 \\ \hline 6 \end{array}$

3. 4 + 1 = 5

   $\begin{array}{r} 4 \\ +\ 1 \\ \hline 5 \end{array}$

4. 3 + 6 = 9

   $\begin{array}{r} 3 \\ +\ 6 \\ \hline 9 \end{array}$

Materials: Counters, 9 per child

1. Ask: ***How many stars are in the first part of the domino?*** Have children write 2. Ask: ***How many are in the second part?*** Have children write 5. Ask: ***How many in all?*** Have children write 7.
2. Say: ***There is another way to write two plus five equals seven.*** Write the vertical form on the board or overhead and have children write the numbers.
3. For Problem 2, have children write the numbers for the number of hearts in each part and how many in all. Have them complete the other number sentence.
4. For remaining problems, have children use counters to find each sum, written both ways.

Intervention Lesson B8 79

Teacher Notes

Ongoing Assessment

Make sure children know the sum goes under the line when addition is written in vertical form.

Error Intervention

If children have difficulty finding sums from the pictures,

then have them show a counter for each shape, like each heart, put the counters together, and count.

If You Have More Time

Ask a child to make up a joining story. Then, have the rest of the other children in the class write a number sentence vertically to match it. Continue with stories by other children.

Math Diagnosis and Intervention System
Intervention Lesson B8

Name ______

Adding Across and Down (continued)

Write the numbers. Add.

5. 4 + 3 = 7

   $\begin{array}{r} 4 \\ +\ 3 \\ \hline 7 \end{array}$

Add. Use counters if you like.

6. 6 + 1 = 7	7. 2 + 3 = 5	8. 5 + 3 = 8
9. 3 + 3 = 6	10. 7 + 1 = 8	11. 1 + 3 = 4
12. 6 + 2 = 8	13. 4 + 2 = 6	14. 4 + 1 = 5
15. $\begin{array}{r} 2 \\ +\ 5 \\ \hline 7 \end{array}$	16. $\begin{array}{r} 5 \\ +\ 1 \\ \hline 6 \end{array}$	17. $\begin{array}{r} 2 \\ +\ 2 \\ \hline 4 \end{array}$
18. $\begin{array}{r} 1 \\ +\ 2 \\ \hline 3 \end{array}$	19. $\begin{array}{r} 5 \\ +\ 3 \\ \hline 8 \end{array}$	20. $\begin{array}{r} 3 \\ +\ 2 \\ \hline 5 \end{array}$

80 Intervention Lesson B8

Adding in Any Order

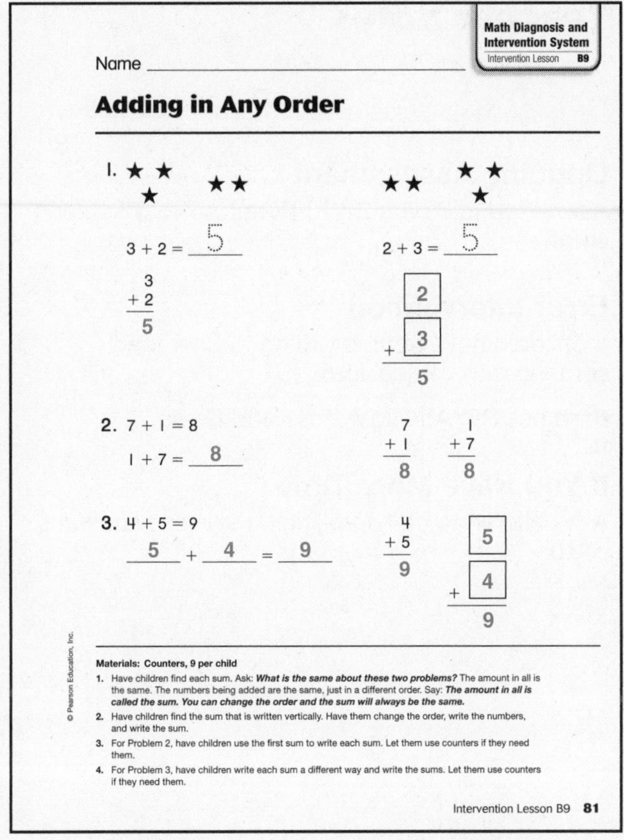

Name ______

Adding in Any Order

1. 3 + 2 = 5 2 + 3 = 5

$\begin{array}{r} 3 \\ +2 \\ \hline 5 \end{array}$ $\begin{array}{r} 2 \\ +3 \\ \hline 5 \end{array}$

2. 7 + 1 = 8
1 + 7 = 8

$\begin{array}{r} 7 \\ +1 \\ \hline 8 \end{array}$ $\begin{array}{r} 1 \\ +7 \\ \hline 8 \end{array}$

3. 4 + 5 = 9
5 + 4 = 9

$\begin{array}{r} 4 \\ +5 \\ \hline 9 \end{array}$ $\begin{array}{r} 5 \\ +4 \\ \hline 9 \end{array}$

Materials: Counters, 9 per child

1. Have children find each sum. Ask: ***What is the same about these two problems?*** The amount in all is the same. The numbers being added are the same, just in a different order. Say: ***The amount in all is called the sum. You can change the order and the sum will always be the same.***
2. Have children find the sum that is written vertically. Have them change the order, write the numbers, and write the sum.
3. For Problem 2, have children use the first sum to write each sum. Let them use counters if they need them.
4. For Problem 3, have children write each sum a different way and write the sums. Let them use counters if they need them.

Teacher Notes

Ongoing Assessment

Observe which children need counters to find the second sums and which ones grasp the Commutative Property.

Error Intervention

If children have difficulty finding the sums with counters,

then use B1: Addition and B3: Finding Sums.

If You Have More Time

Have 7 children stand in front of the class. Put 3 in one group and 4 in another. Have children write a number sentence for the groups of children. Write 3 + 4 = 7 on the board or overhead. Have one child move from the group of 4 to the group of 3. Have children write a number sentence for the groups. Write 4 + 3 = 7 on the board or overhead. Ask if the total number of children changed. Explain if 3 + 4 = 7, then 4 + 3 = 7. Repeat with different groups of 6, 8, and 9 children.

Name ______

Adding in Any Order (continued)

Add. Then change the order.
Use counters if you like.

4. 3 + 4 = 7
4 + 3 = 7

5. 1 + 4 = 5
4 + 1 = 5

6. $\begin{array}{r} 7 \\ +1 \\ \hline 8 \end{array}$ $\begin{array}{r} 1 \\ +7 \\ \hline 8 \end{array}$

7. $\begin{array}{r} 1 \\ +3 \\ \hline 4 \end{array}$ $\begin{array}{r} 3 \\ +1 \\ \hline 4 \end{array}$

8. **Reasoning** Look at the picture. How many butterflies are there in all? Write two addition sentences.

4 + 2 = 6

2 + 4 = 6

9. **Reasoning** If 5 + 3 = 8, what is 3 + 5? 8

Parts of Ten

Math Diagnosis and Intervention System
Intervention Lesson B10

Name ____________________

Parts of Ten

1. 7 + 3 = 10

$$\begin{array}{r} 7 \\ + 3 \\ \hline 10 \end{array}$$

2. 1 + 9 = 10

$$\begin{array}{r} 1 \\ + 9 \\ \hline 10 \end{array}$$

Materials: Two-color counters, 10 per child

1. Have children put 7 red counters in the ten-frame and write 7. Have children finish filling the ten-frame with yellow counters. Ask: ***How many yellow counters did you use?*** Have children write 3. Say: ***So, 7 plus 3 equals 10.***
2. Have children put 1 red counter in the ten-frame and write 1. Have them finish filling the ten-frame with yellow counters. Have children complete the number sentences.

Intervention Lesson B10 83

Math Diagnosis and Intervention System
Intervention Lesson B10

Name ____________________

Parts of Ten (continued)

Write the addition sentence for each sum.
Use the ten-frame to help you.

3. 8 + 2 = 10

4. 9 + 1 = 10

5. 6 + 4 = 10

6. 5 + 5 = 10

Fill in the missing numbers to find each sum of 10.

7. $$\begin{array}{r} 2 \\ + 8 \\ \hline 10 \end{array}$$

8. $$\begin{array}{r} 3 \\ + 7 \\ \hline 10 \end{array}$$

9. $$\begin{array}{r} 4 \\ + 6 \\ \hline 10 \end{array}$$

10. $$\begin{array}{r} 5 \\ + 5 \\ \hline 10 \end{array}$$

84 Intervention Lesson B10

Teacher Notes

Ongoing Assessment

Ask: ***What is 8 plus 2?*** 10 ***What is 7 + 3?*** 10 and so on.

Error Intervention

If children have trouble writing the number sentences in vertical form,

then use B8: Adding Across and Down.

If You Have More Time

Ask children to make up joining stories with sums of 10.

Adding with 0, 1, 2

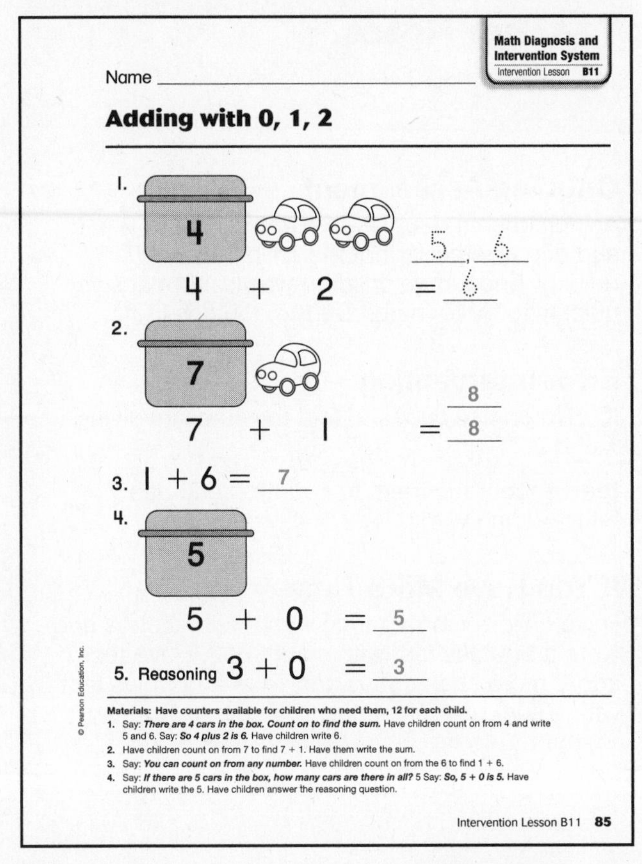

Math Diagnosis and Intervention System
Intervention Lesson B11

Name ____________

Adding with 0, 1, 2

1. 4 + 2 = 6 (5, 6)

2. 7 + 1 = 8 (8)

3. 1 + 6 = 7

4. 5 + 0 = 5

5. **Reasoning** 3 + 0 = 3

Materials: Have counters available for children who need them, 12 for each child.

1. Say: ***There are 4 cars in the box. Count on to find the sum.*** Have children count on from 4 and write 5 and 6. Say: ***So 4 plus 2 is 6.*** Have children write 6.
2. Have children count on from 7 to find 7 + 1. Have them write the sum.
3. Say: ***You can count on from any number.*** Have children count on from the 6 to find 1 + 6.
4. Say: ***If there are 5 cars in the box, how many cars are there in all?*** 5 Say: ***So, 5 + 0 is 5.*** Have children write the 5. Have children answer the reasoning question.

© Pearson Education, Inc.

Intervention Lesson B11 **85**

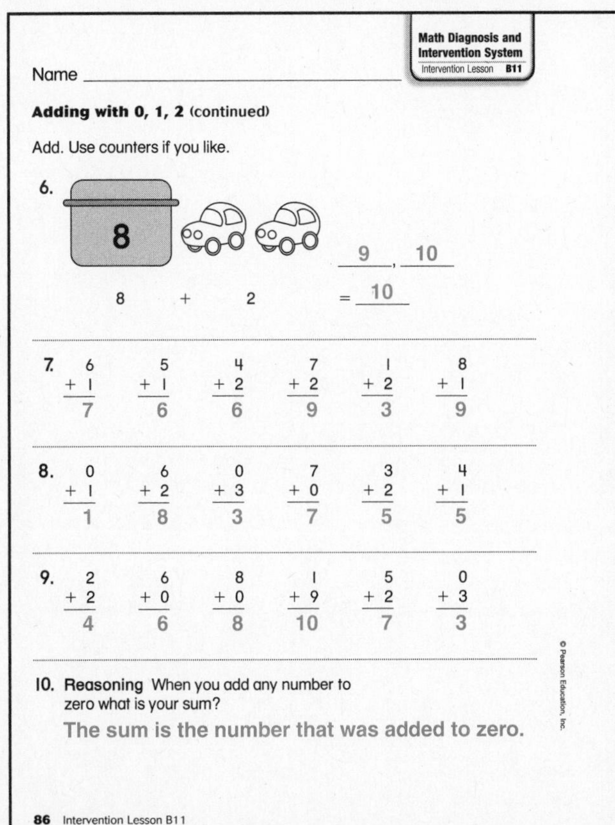

Math Diagnosis and Intervention System
Intervention Lesson B11

Name ____________

Adding with 0, 1, 2 (continued)

Add. Use counters if you like.

6. 8 + 2 = 10 (9, 10)

7. 6 + 1 = 7; 5 + 1 = 6; 4 + 2 = 6; 7 + 2 = 9; 1 + 2 = 3; 8 + 1 = 9

8. 0 + 1 = 1; 6 + 2 = 8; 0 + 3 = 3; 7 + 0 = 7; 3 + 2 = 5; 4 + 1 = 5

9. 2 + 2 = 4; 6 + 0 = 6; 8 + 0 = 8; 1 + 9 = 10; 5 + 2 = 7; 0 + 3 = 3

10. **Reasoning** When you add any number to zero what is your sum?
The sum is the number that was added to zero.

© Pearson Education, Inc.

86 Intervention Lesson B11

Teacher Notes

Ongoing Assessment

Observe which children need to use the counters and which ones can count on without them.

Error Intervention

If children have trouble counting on when the first number is 1 or 2,

then remind them that they can add in any order and have them rewrite 1 + 6 as 6 + 1. If necessary, use B9: Adding in Any Order.

If You Have More Time

Have children work in groups of 3 to write 30 addition sums on index cards, 10 facts with 0, 10 facts with 1, and 10 facts with 2. For example, write 8 + 1. Have them shuffle the cards and put them face down on the table. One child serves as referee and turns a card over so both children can see it at the same time. The other two children race to say the sum first. The one who says the correct sum first wins. Continue until all cards are used. Have the children change roles and repeat so the referee has a chance to play.

Adding Doubles

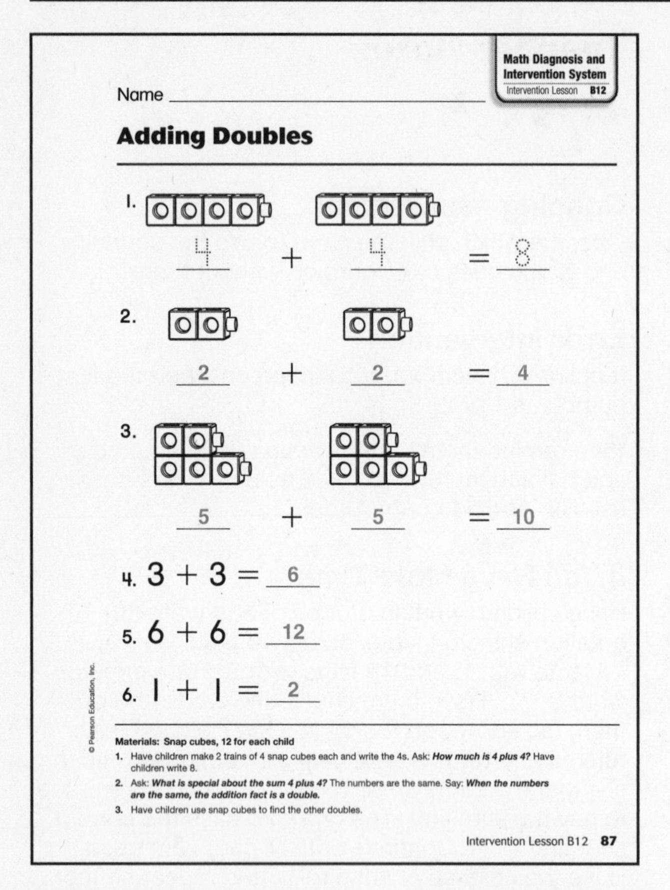

Math Diagnosis and Intervention System
Intervention Lesson B12

Name ______________________

Adding Doubles

1. 4 + 4 = 8

2. 2 + 2 = 4

3. 5 + 5 = 10

4. 3 + 3 = 6

5. 6 + 6 = 12

6. 1 + 1 = 2

Materials: Snap cubes, 12 for each child

1. Have children make 2 trains of 4 snap cubes each and write the 4s. Ask: ***How much is 4 plus 4?*** Have children write 8.
2. Ask: ***What is special about the sum 4 plus 4?*** The numbers are the same. Say: ***When the numbers are the same, the addition fact is a double.***
3. Have children use snap cubes to find the other doubles.

© Pearson Education, Inc.

Intervention Lesson B12 **87**

Math Diagnosis and Intervention System
Intervention Lesson B12

Name ______________________

Adding Doubles (continued)

Add to find the double.

7. 6 + 6 = 12

8. 3 + 3 = 6

9. 4 + 4 = 8

10. 1 + 1 = 2

Add. Circle the doubles facts.

11.

5	4	2	2	1	3
+ 2	+ 4	+ 2	+ 6	+ 8	+ 3
7	8	4	8	9	6

Reasoning Write the missing number that makes each sentence true.

12. 5 + 5 = 10

13. 3 + 3 = 6

© Pearson Education, Inc.

88 Intervention Lesson B12

Teacher Notes

Ongoing Assessment

Ask children a doubles fact from 1 + 1 to 6 + 6 and see whether or not the child can answer quickly. Encourage children who cannot answer quickly to try to memorize the doubles facts.

Error Intervention

If children use cubes to find the sums involving 1 and 2,

then encourage them to count on and use B11: Adding with 0, 1, 2.

If You Have More Time

Have children form a train with 2 snap cubes and write a doubles fact with a sum of 2. Have them add 2 more snap cubes and write a doubles fact with a sum of 4. Continue to a sum of 12.

Using Doubles to Add

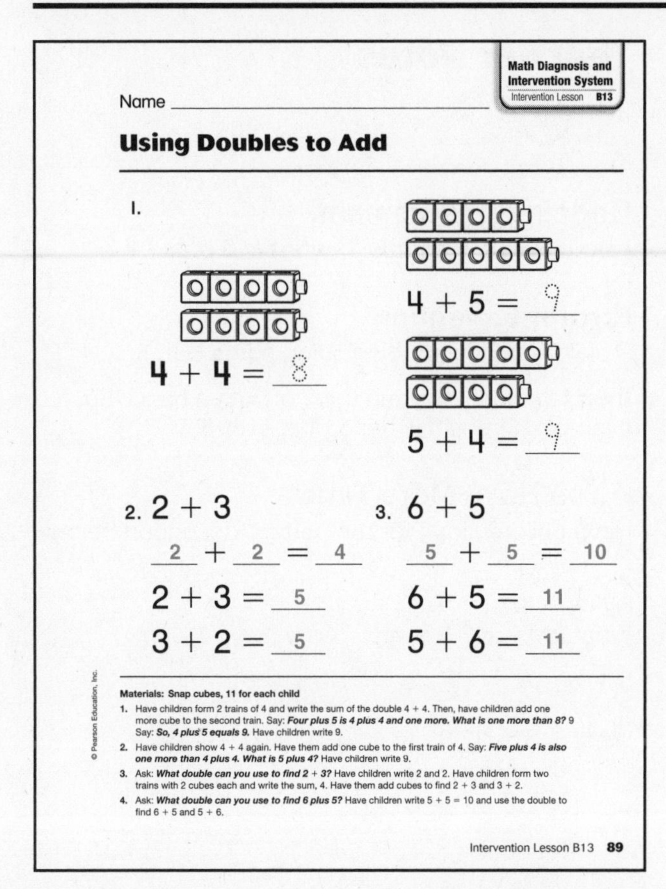

Math Diagnosis and Intervention System
Intervention Lesson B13

Name ______

Using Doubles to Add

1.

4 + 4 = 8

4 + 5 = 9

5 + 4 = 9

2. 2 + 3

2 + 2 = 4

2 + 3 = 5

3 + 2 = 5

3. 6 + 5

5 + 5 = 10

6 + 5 = 11

5 + 6 = 11

Materials: Snap cubes, 11 for each child

1. Have children form 2 trains of 4 and write the sum of the double 4 + 4. Then, have children add one more cube to the second train. Say: ***Four plus 5 is 4 plus 4 and one more. What is one more than 8?*** 9 Say: ***So, 4 plus 5 equals 9.*** Have children write 9.
2. Have children show 4 + 4 again. Have them add one cube to the first train of 4. Say: ***Five plus 4 is also one more than 4 plus 4. What is 5 plus 4?*** Have children write 9.
3. Ask: ***What double can you use to find 2 + 3?*** Have children write 2 and 2. Have children form two trains with 2 cubes each and write the sum, 4. Have them add cubes to find 2 + 3 and 3 + 2.
4. Ask: ***What double can you use to find 6 plus 5?*** Have children write 5 + 5 = 10 and use the double to find 6 + 5 and 5 + 6.

© Pearson Education, Inc.

Intervention Lesson B13 **89**

Math Diagnosis and Intervention System
Intervention Lesson B13

Name ______

Using Doubles to Add (continued)

Find each sum. Think of a double to help you.

4. 1 + 1 = 2 1 + 2 = 3	**5.** 3 + 3 = 6 3 + 4 = 7
6. 5 + 5 = 10 5 + 6 = 11	**7.** 4 + 4 = 8 4 + 5 = 9

8. 2 + 2 = 4   2 + 3 = 5   3 + 2 = 5

9. 3 + 3 = 6   3 + 4 = 7   4 + 3 = 7

10. 5 + 5 = 10   5 + 6 = 11   6 + 5 = 11

Solve.

11. Reasoning There are 4 birds in a tree. Double that many and one more are flying away. How many birds are flying away?

9 birds

© Pearson Education, Inc.

90 Intervention Lesson B13

Teacher Notes

Ongoing Assessment

Ask: ***What doubles fact can you use to find 3 + 4?*** 3 + 3 ***If 3 + 3 is 6, what is 3 + 4?*** 7

Error Intervention

If children do not know their doubles facts,

then use B12: Adding Doubles.

If children have trouble finding one more than the doubles,

then use B11: Adding 0, 1, 2.

If You Have More Time

Have children draw pictures to show doubles plus one facts. For example, they could draw two boxes with 2 toys in each and then one toy outside the box. Have them write the doubles fact and a doubles plus one fact to match the picture.

Facts with 5 on a Ten-Frame

Name ______________________

Facts with 5 on a Ten-Frame

1. 5 + 1 = 6
   6 + 4 = 10
2. 5 + 2 = 7
   7 + 3 = 10
3. 5 + 3 = 8
   8 + 2 = 10
4. 5 + 4 = 9
   9 + 1 = 10
5. 5 + 5 = 10

Materials: Two color counters, 10 for each child

1. Have children put 5 red counters in the first row of the ten-frame. Then have them put one yellow counter in the second row. Ask: ***What is 5 plus 1?*** Have children write 6.
2. Ask: ***How many counters would you need to fill the ten-frame?*** 4 Ask: ***So, 6 plus what number equals 10?*** Have children write 4.
3. Have children put 5 red counters in the first row of the ten-frame and two yellow counters in the second row. Ask questions like those above to have children find 5 + 2 and 7 + 3.
4. Do other problems similarly.

Name ______________________

Facts with 5 on a Ten-Frame (continued)

Write an addition fact with 5.
Then write an addition fact with 10.

6. 5 + 3 = 8
   8 + 2 = 10
7. 5 + 2 = 7
   7 + 3 = 10
8. 5 + 4 = 9
   9 + 1 = 10
9. 5 + 1 = 6
   6 + 4 = 10

Reasoning Write the missing numbers.

10. 5 + 5 = 10
11. 5 + 3 = 8   3 + 5 = 8

Teacher Notes

Ongoing Assessment

Ask: ***If 5 plus 2 equals 7, what is 2 plus 5?*** 7

Error Intervention

If children have trouble finding sums with 5,

then tell them they can think of 5 as a hand. So, for example, 5 plus 3 is hand plus 3, or 8.

If You Have More Time

Have children look for the pattern described below.

$5 + \underline{1} = 6$
$6 + \underline{4} = 10$
What is 1 + 4? 5

$5 + \underline{3} = 8$
$8 + \underline{2} = 10$
What is 3 + 2? 5

Making 10 on a Ten-Frame

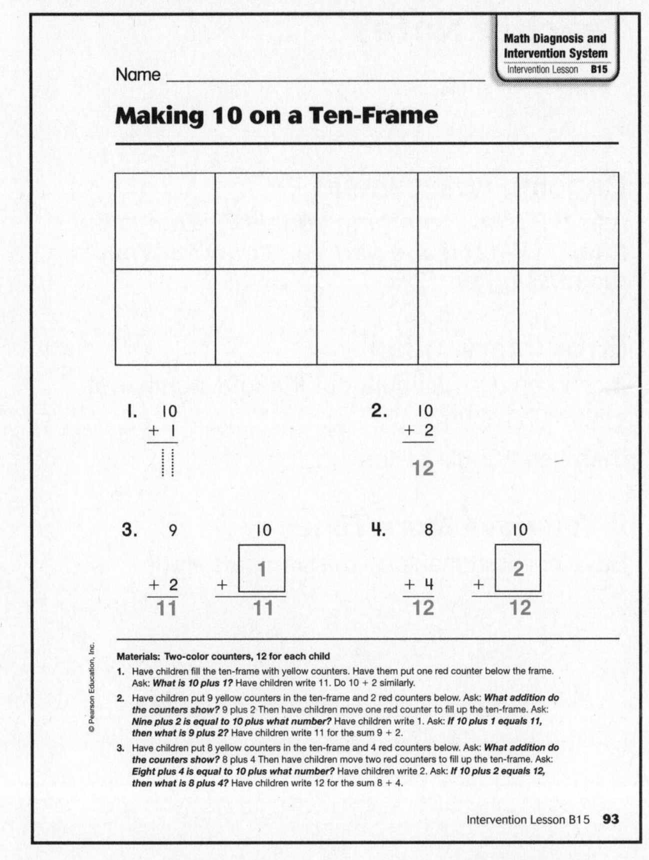

Math Diagnosis and Intervention System
Intervention Lesson B15

Name ______________________

Making 10 on a Ten-Frame

1. $10 + 1 = 11$
2. $10 + 2 = 12$
3. $9 + 2 = 11$; $10 + \boxed{1} = 11$
4. $8 + 4 = 12$; $10 + \boxed{2} = 12$

Materials: Two-color counters, 12 for each child

1. Have children fill the ten-frame with yellow counters. Have them put one red counter below the frame. Ask: ***What is 10 plus 1?*** Have children write 11. Do 10 + 2 similarly.
2. Have children put 9 yellow counters in the ten-frame and 2 red counters below. Ask: ***What addition do the counters show?*** 9 plus 2 Then have children move one red counter to fill up the ten-frame. Ask: ***Nine plus 2 is equal to 10 plus what number?*** Have children write 1. Ask: ***If 10 plus 1 equals 11, then what is 9 plus 2?*** Have children write 11 for the sum 9 + 2.
3. Have children put 8 yellow counters in the ten-frame and 4 red counters below. Ask: ***What addition do the counters show?*** 8 plus 4 Then have children move two red counters to fill up the ten-frame. Ask: ***Eight plus 4 is equal to 10 plus what number?*** Have children write 2. Ask: ***If 10 plus 2 equals 12, then what is 8 plus 4?*** Have children write 12 for the sum 8 + 4.

© Pearson Education, Inc.

Intervention Lesson B15 93

Math Diagnosis and Intervention System
Intervention Lesson B15

Name ______________________

Making 10 on a Ten-Frame (continued)

Write the missing numbers.
Find the sums.

5. $9 + 3 = 12$; $10 + \boxed{2} = 12$
6. $7 + 4 = 11$; $10 + \boxed{1} = 11$
7. $8 + 3 = 11$; $10 + \boxed{1} = 11$
8. $7 + 5 = 12$; $10 + \boxed{2} = 12$
9. $8 + 4 = 12$; $10 + \boxed{2} = 12$
10. $3 + 9 = 12$; $\boxed{2} + 10 = 12$

11. **Reasoning** Find 9 + 2.

9 + <u>1</u> = 10

1 less than 2 is <u>1</u>.

So, 9 + 2 = 10 + <u>1</u> = <u>11</u>.

94 Intervention Lesson B15

Teacher Notes

Ongoing Assessment

Ask: ***After you moved the counter into the ten-frame, how did you know 9 + 2 equals 10 + 1?*** Sample Answer: I didn't change the number of counters.

Error Intervention

If children have trouble with 10 + 1 and 10 + 2,

then use A9: Numbers to 12.

If children have trouble recognizing how much to add to make 10,

then use B10: Parts of Ten.

If You Have More Time

Have children draw a picture with 9 birds in a circle and 3 birds outside the circle. Below this, have them draw 10 birds in the circle and the same total number of birds. Have children write addition sentences for each picture.

Missing Parts

Math Diagnosis and Intervention System
Intervention Lesson B16

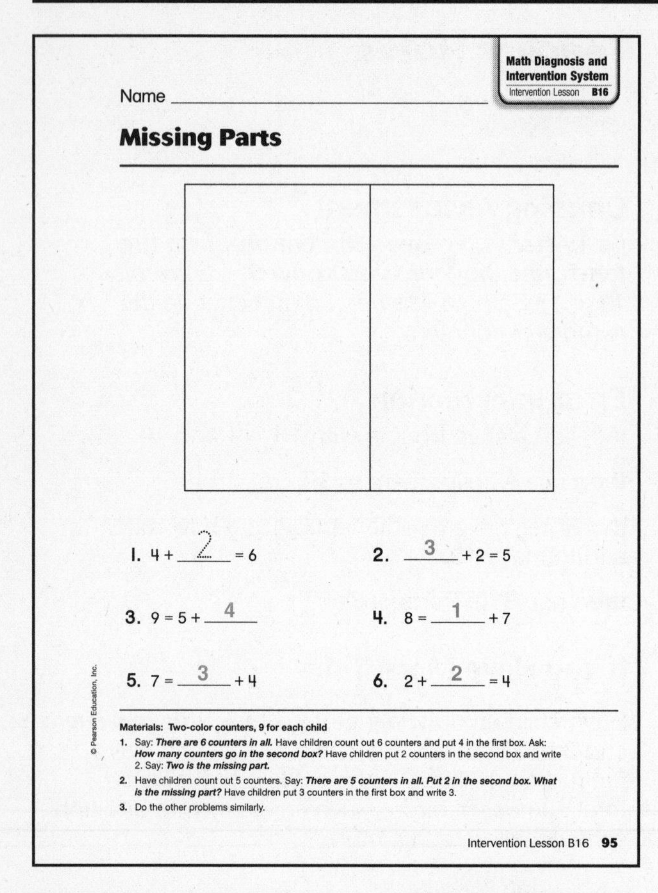

Math Diagnosis and Intervention System
Intervention Lesson B16

Name ____________________

Missing Parts

1. 4 + 2 = 6
2. 3 + 2 = 5
3. 9 = 5 + 4
4. 8 = 1 + 7
5. 7 = 3 + 4
6. 2 + 2 = 4

© Pearson Education, Inc.

Materials: Two-color counters, 9 for each child

1. Say: ***There are 6 counters in all.*** Have children count out 6 counters and put 4 in the first box. Ask: ***How many counters go in the second box?*** Have children put 2 counters in the second box and write 2. Say: ***Two is the missing part.***
2. Have children count out 5 counters. Say: ***There are 5 counters in all. Put 2 in the second box. What is the missing part?*** Have children put 3 counters in the first box and write 3.
3. Do the other problems similarly.

Intervention Lesson B16 **95**

Math Diagnosis and Intervention System
Intervention Lesson B16

Name ____________________

Missing Parts (continued)

Draw how many are missing.
Write the number.
Use counters if you like.

7. 7 in all
2 + 5 = 7

8. 4 in all
4 = 1 + 3

9. 8 in all
8 = 5 + 3

10. 6 in all
3 + 3 = 6

Write the missing numbers.
Use counters if you like.

11. 4 + 4 = 8

12. 1 + 6 = 7

Reasoning Write the number sentence.
Solve.

13. Fred bought 5 cookies.
His mother gave him some more.
Now Fred has 8 cookies.
How many more did she give him?

8 in all

5 + 3 = 8

© Pearson Education, Inc.

96 Intervention Lesson B16

Teacher Notes

Ongoing Assessment

Ask: ***If 3 plus something equals 8, What is the total?*** 8 ***What is the part you know?*** 3 ***What is the missing part?*** 5

Error Intervention

If children do not count out the total number of counters reliably,

then use A3: Six to Ten.

If You Have More Time

Have children make up missing part stories.

Separating Stories

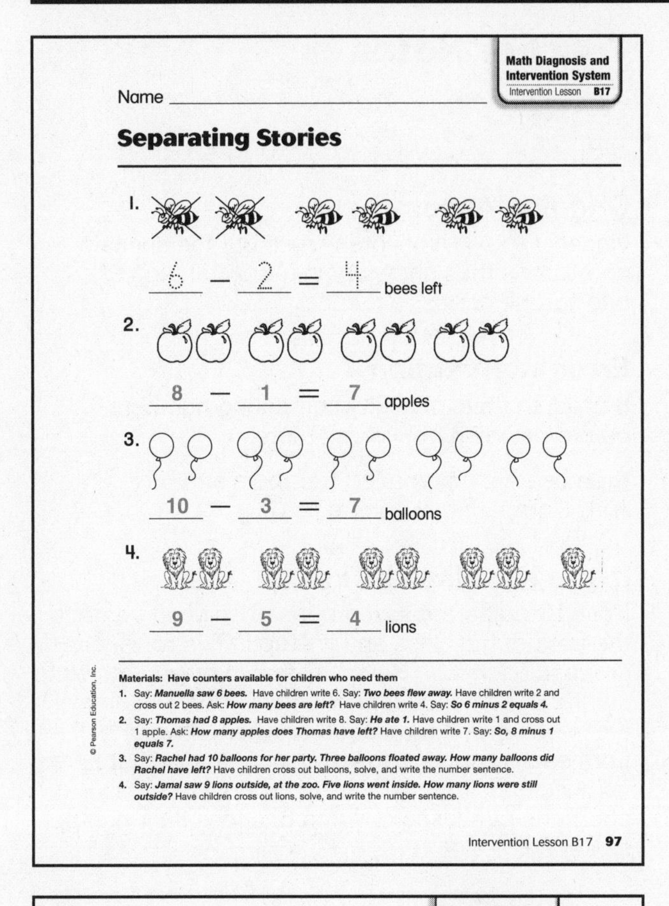

Math Diagnosis and Intervention System
Intervention Lesson B17

Name ______________________

Separating Stories

1. 6 – 2 = 4 bees left

2. 8 – 1 = 7 apples

3. 10 – 3 = 7 balloons

4. 9 – 5 = 4 lions

Materials: Have counters available for children who need them

1. Say: ***Manuella saw 6 bees.*** Have children write 6. Say: ***Two bees flew away.*** Have children write 2 and cross out 2 bees. Ask: ***How many bees are left?*** Have children write 4. Say: ***So 6 minus 2 equals 4.***
2. Say: ***Thomas had 8 apples.*** Have children write 8. Say: ***He ate 1.*** Have children write 1 and cross out 1 apple. Ask: ***How many apples does Thomas have left?*** Have children write 7. Say: ***So, 8 minus 1 equals 7.***
3. Say: ***Rachel had 10 balloons for her party. Three balloons floated away. How many balloons did Rachel have left?*** Have children cross out balloons, solve, and write the number sentence.
4. Say: ***Jamal saw 9 lions outside, at the zoo. Five lions went inside. How many lions were still outside?*** Have children cross out lions, solve, and write the number sentence.

© Pearson Education, Inc.

Intervention Lesson B17 **97**

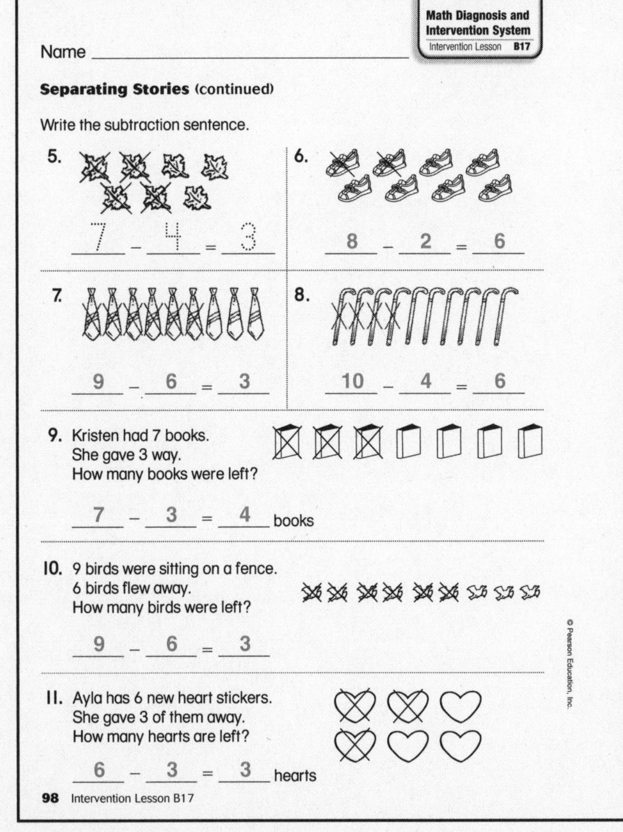

Math Diagnosis and Intervention System
Intervention Lesson B17

Name ______________________

Separating Stories (continued)

Write the subtraction sentence.

5. 7 – 4 = 3

6. 8 – 2 = 6

7. 9 – 6 = 3

8. 10 – 4 = 6

9. Kristen had 7 books.
She gave 3 way.
How many books were left?
7 – 3 = 4 books

10. 9 birds were sitting on a fence.
6 birds flew away.
How many birds were left?
9 – 6 = 3

11. Ayla has 6 new heart stickers.
She gave 3 of them away.
How many hearts are left?
6 – 3 = 3 hearts

© Pearson Education, Inc.

98 Intervention Lesson B17

Teacher Notes

Ongoing Assessment

Observe which children can solve the stories using the pictures and which need to use the counters.

Error Intervention

If children do not seem to understand the idea of separating,

then use B2: Subtraction.

If children have difficulty writing subtraction sentences,

then use B4: Finding Differences.

If You Have More Time

Have children tell stories about separating for another child to solve.

Comparing Stories

Name ______________________

Comparing Stories

1.

$\underline{7} - \underline{4} = \underline{3}$

2.

$\underline{6} - \underline{5} = \underline{1}$

3.

$\underline{4} - \underline{2} = \underline{2}$

1. Say: ***Victor saw 7 elephants and 4 giraffes.*** Have children write 7 and 4. Then have them cross out one elephant and one giraffe, then another elephant and another giraffe. Have them continue until all the giraffes are crossed out. Ask: ***How many more elephants than giraffes did Victor see?*** Have children write 3.
2. Say: ***Miranda saw 6 monkeys and 5 bears.*** Have children write 6 and 5. Then have them cross out one monkey and one bear, then another monkey and another bear. Have them continue until all the bears are crossed out. Ask: ***How many more bears than monkeys did she see?*** Have children write 1.
3. Say: ***Ahmed saw 4 tigers and 2 lions.*** How many more tigers than lions did he see? Have children cross out, solve, and write the number sentence.

Name ______________________

Comparing Stories (continued)

Write the subtraction sentence.

4. Pedro caught 8 butterflies. David caught 3 butterflies. How many more butterflies did Pedro catch?

   $\underline{8} - \underline{3} = \underline{5}$ butterflies

5. There are 2 ducks in the pond. There are 8 ducks out of the pond. How many more ducks are out of the pond?

   $\underline{8} - \underline{2} = \underline{6}$ ducks

6. There are 6 bees and 2 ants. How many more bees than ants are there?

   $\underline{6} - \underline{2} = \underline{4}$ more

7. **Reasoning** Draw 5 frogs on a log. Draw 3 frogs on the other log. How many more frogs are on one log than the other? Write a number sentence.

   $\underline{5} - \underline{3} = \underline{2}$ more

Teacher Notes

Ongoing Assessment

Observe to see if children cross out the animals one-to-one thus showing an understanding of one-to-one correspondence.

Error Intervention

If children have difficulty comparing numbers before deciding how much more,

then use A4: Comparing Numbers and A11: Comparing Numbers to 10.

If You Have More Time

Have two different size groups of children come to the front of the class and line up in two rows, one group in each row. Have children in their seats write a number sentence for how many more children are in one group than another. Then, have one child from each group sit down. Continue until there are no children left in the smaller group. Have children count the remaining children to check their number sentences.

Relating Addition and Subtraction

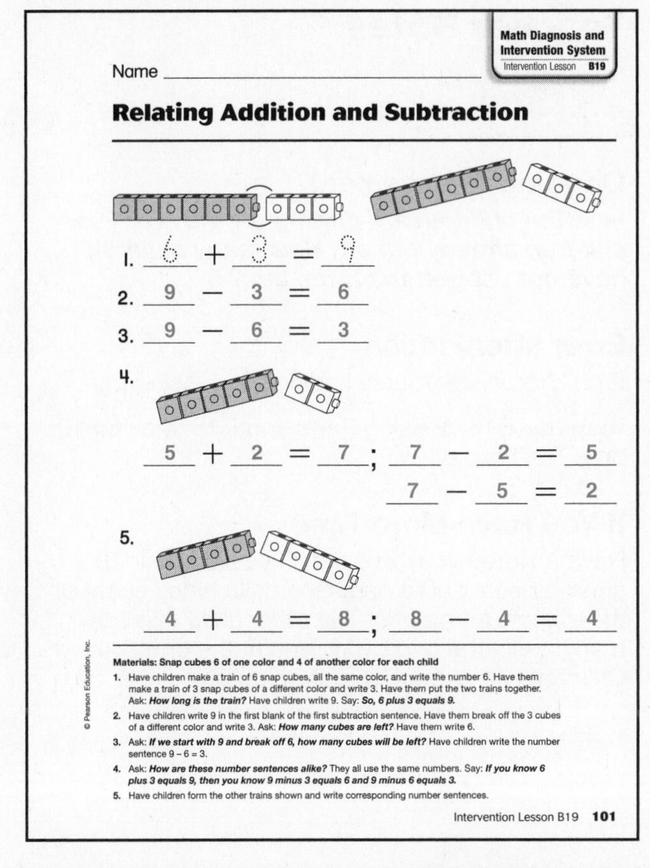
Math Diagnosis and Intervention System
Intervention Lesson B19

Name ____________

Relating Addition and Subtraction

1. 6 + 3 = 9
2. 9 − 3 = 6
3. 9 − 6 = 3
4. 5 + 2 = 7 ; 7 − 2 = 5
   7 − 5 = 2
5. 4 + 4 = 8 ; 8 − 4 = 4

Materials: Snap cubes 6 of one color and 4 of another color for each child

1. Have children make a train of 6 snap cubes, all the same color, and write the number 6. Have them make a train of 3 snap cubes of a different color and write 3. Have them put the two trains together. Ask: ***How long is the train?*** Have children write 9. Say: ***So, 6 plus 3 equals 9.***
2. Have children write 9 in the first blank of the first subtraction sentence. Have them break off the 3 cubes of a different color and write 3. Ask: ***How many cubes are left?*** Have them write 6.
3. Ask: ***If we start with 9 and break off 6, how many cubes will be left?*** Have children write the number sentence 9 – 6 = 3.
4. Ask: ***How are these number sentences alike?*** They all use the same numbers. Say: ***If you know 6 plus 3 equals 9, then you know 9 minus 3 equals 6 and 9 minus 6 equals 3.***
5. Have children form the other trains shown and write corresponding number sentences.

© Pearson Education, Inc.

Intervention Lesson B19 **101**

Math Diagnosis and Intervention System
Intervention Lesson B19

Name ____________

Relating Addition and Subtraction (continued)

Write two subtraction sentences for each addition sentence. Use cubes if you like.

6. 3 + 4 = 7
   7 − 4 = 3
   7 − 3 = 4

7. 1 + 7 = 8
   8 − 7 = 1
   8 − 1 = 7

8. 4 + 2 = 6
   6 − 2 = 4
   6 − 4 = 2

9. 4 + 5 = 9
   9 − 5 = 4
   9 − 4 = 5

10. 2 + 7 = 9
    9 − 7 = 2
    9 − 2 = 7

11. 6 + 1 = 7
    7 − 1 = 6
    7 − 6 = 1

Write a number sentence.

12. Tonya saw 8 butterflies. 3 flew away. How many butterflies are left?
    8 − 3 = 5

13. Jerome found 5 fossils. Kobe found 3 fossils. How many fossils did they find in all?
    5 + 3 = 8

© Pearson Education, Inc.

102 Intervention Lesson B19

Teacher Notes

Ongoing Assessment

Ask: ***If I have 4 snap cubes, and add 3, and then break off 3, how many do I have left?*** Children who can say 4 right away grasp the inverse relationship between addition and subtraction.

Error Intervention

If children have trouble writing addition or subtraction sentences,

then use B3: Finding Sums, B4: Finding Differences, B7: Joining Stories, and B17: Separating Stories.

If You Have More Time

Have children act out stories such as: *There are 5 children at the front of the room. Two children join them. Then, the 2 children leave. How many children are left at the front of the room?* Use different numbers until children realize the number left will always be the same as the number at the beginning, if you add and then subtract the same amount.

Missing Parts of 10

Math Diagnosis and Intervention System
Intervention Lesson **B20**

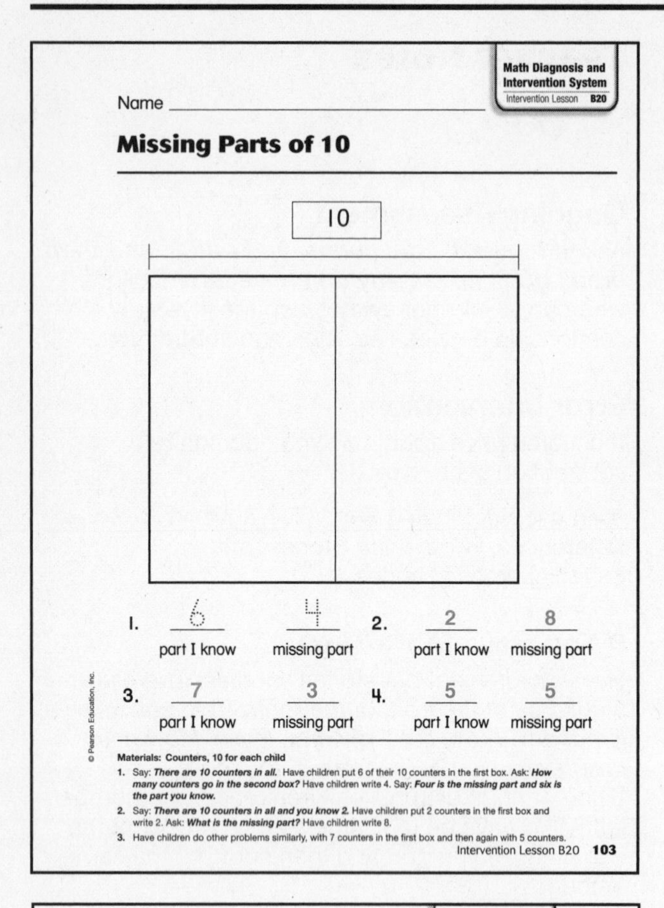

Math Diagnosis and Intervention System
Intervention Lesson B20

Name ______________________

Missing Parts of 10

10

1. 6 part I know 4 missing part
2. 2 part I know 8 missing part
3. 7 part I know 3 missing part
4. 5 part I know 5 missing part

Materials: Counters, 10 for each child

1. Say: ***There are 10 counters in all.*** Have children put 6 of their 10 counters in the first box. Ask: ***How many counters go in the second box?*** Have children write 4. Say: ***Four is the missing part and six is the part you know.***
2. Say: ***There are 10 counters in all and you know 2.*** Have children put 2 counters in the first box and write 2. Ask: ***What is the missing part?*** Have children write 8.
3. Have children do other problems similarly, with 7 counters in the first box and then again with 5 counters.

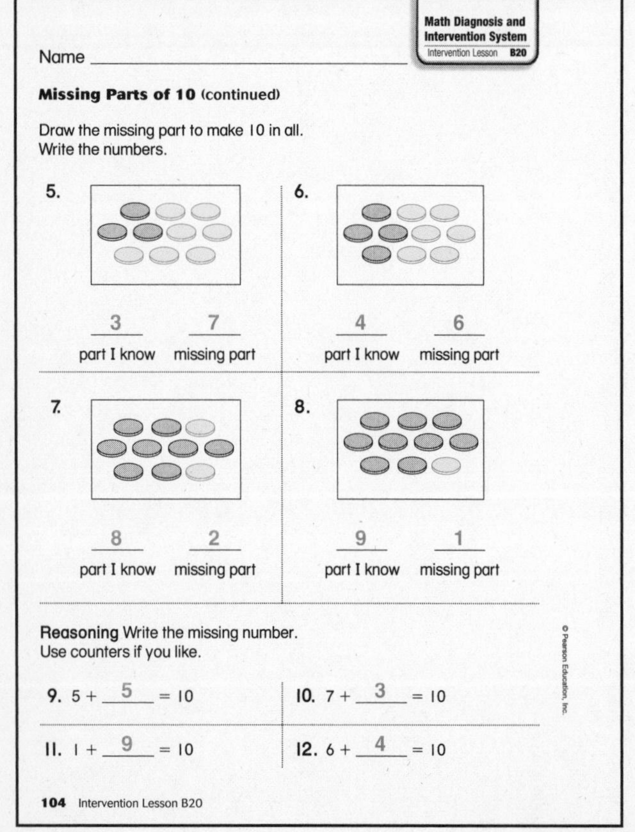

Math Diagnosis and Intervention System
Intervention Lesson B20

Name ______________________

Missing Parts of 10 (continued)

Draw the missing part to make 10 in all.
Write the numbers.

5. 3 part I know 7 missing part
6. 4 part I know 6 missing part
7. 8 part I know 2 missing part
8. 9 part I know 1 missing part

Reasoning Write the missing number.
Use counters if you like.

9. 5 + 5 = 10
10. 7 + 3 = 10
11. 1 + 9 = 10
12. 6 + 4 = 10

Teacher Notes

Ongoing Assessment

Ask: ***Ten children are getting off the bus. Four children already got off. How many children have not yet gotten off the bus?*** 6

Error Intervention

If children have trouble finding the missing part,

then use B16: Missing Parts and B15: Making 10 on a Ten-Frame.

If You Have More Time

Have children work in pairs. Give each pair 10 small objects and a bag. One child hides some of the objects in the bag. The other child tells how many are in the bag by looking at the ones outside. Children can change roles and repeat.

Subtracting Across and Down

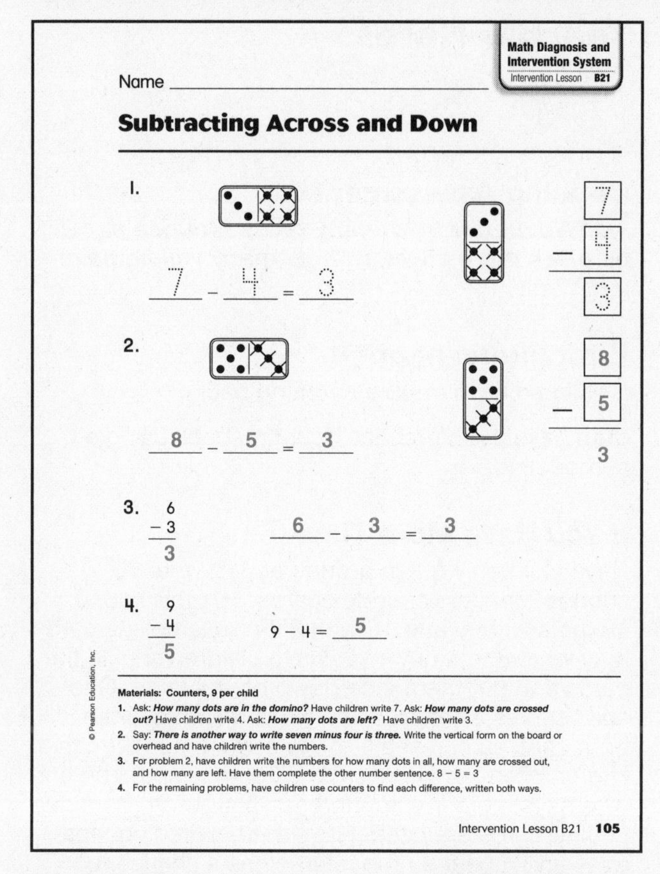

Math Diagnosis and Intervention System
Intervention Lesson B21

Name ____________________

Subtracting Across and Down

1. 7 – 4 = 3

$$\begin{array}{r} 7 \\ -\ 4 \\ \hline 3 \end{array}$$

2. 8 – 5 = 3

$$\begin{array}{r} 8 \\ -\ 5 \\ \hline 3 \end{array}$$

3. $\begin{array}{r} 6 \\ -\ 3 \\ \hline 3 \end{array}$ 6 – 3 = 3

4. $\begin{array}{r} 9 \\ -\ 4 \\ \hline 5 \end{array}$ 9 – 4 = 5

Materials: Counters, 9 per child

1. Ask: ***How many dots are in the domino?*** Have children write 7. Ask: ***How many dots are crossed out?*** Have children write 4. Ask: ***How many dots are left?*** Have children write 3.
2. Say: ***There is another way to write seven minus four is three.*** Write the vertical form on the board or overhead and have children write the numbers.
3. For problem 2, have children write the numbers for how many dots in all, how many are crossed out, and how many are left. Have them complete the other number sentence. 8 – 5 = 3
4. For the remaining problems, have children use counters to find each difference, written both ways.

Math Diagnosis and Intervention System
Intervention Lesson B21

Name ____________________

Subtracting Across and Down (continued)

Write the numbers. Subtract.

5. 6 – 4 = 2

$$\begin{array}{r} 6 \\ -\ 4 \\ \hline 2 \end{array}$$

6. 5 – 1 = 4

$$\begin{array}{r} 5 \\ -\ 1 \\ \hline 4 \end{array}$$

Find each difference.
Write the matching subtraction sentence.

7. $\begin{array}{r} 8 \\ -\ 3 \\ \hline 5 \end{array}$ 8 – 3 = 5

8. $\begin{array}{r} 4 \\ -\ 3 \\ \hline 1 \end{array}$ 4 – 3 = 1

9. **Reasoning** Write the missing number.

$\begin{array}{r} 9 \\ -\ 3 \\ \hline 6 \end{array}$ 9 – 3 = 6

Teacher Notes

Ongoing Assessment

Make sure children know the difference of a subtraction problem goes under the line when subtraction is written in vertical form.

Error Intervention

If children have difficulty finding differences from the pictures,

then have them show a counter for each dot, separate the ones crossed out, and find how many are left.

If You Have More Time

Ask a child to make up a separating story. Then, have the rest of the other children in the class write a number sentence vertically to match it. Continue with stories by other children.

Subtracting with 0, 1, and 2

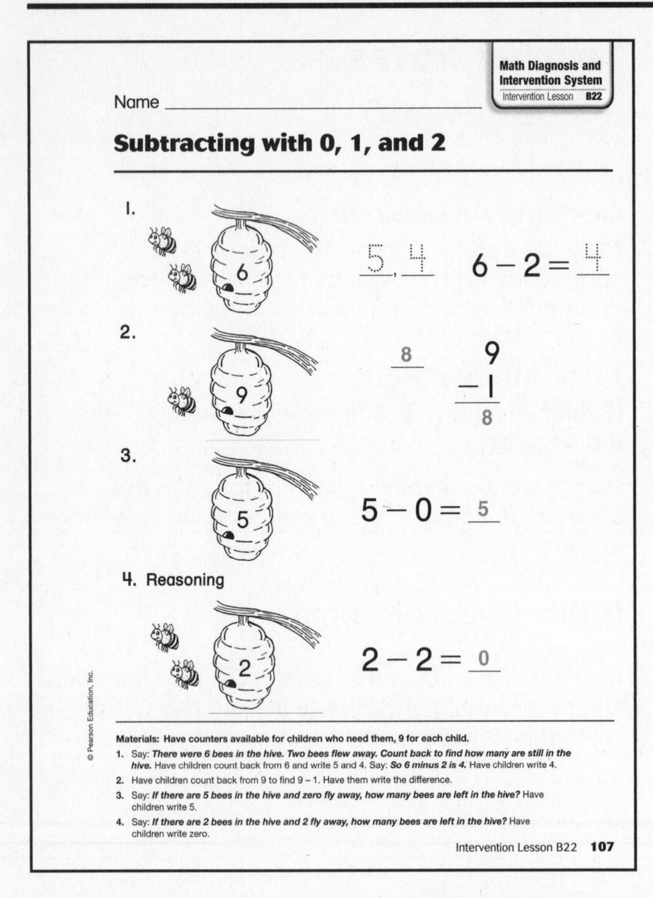

Math Diagnosis and Intervention System
Intervention Lesson B22

Name ______________________

Subtracting with 0, 1, and 2

1. 6   5, 4   6 − 2 = 4

2. 9   8   9 − 1 = 8

3. 5   5 − 0 = 5

4. **Reasoning** 2   2 − 2 = 0

Materials: Have counters available for children who need them, 9 for each child.

1. Say: ***There were 6 bees in the hive. Two bees flew away. Count back to find how many are still in the hive.*** Have children count back from 6 and write 5 and 4. Say: ***So 6 minus 2 is 4.*** Have children write 4.
2. Have children count back from 9 to find 9 – 1. Have them write the difference.
3. Say: ***If there are 5 bees in the hive and zero fly away, how many bees are left in the hive?*** Have children write 5.
4. Say: ***If there are 2 bees in the hive and 2 fly away, how many bees are left in the hive?*** Have children write zero.

© Pearson Education, Inc.

Intervention Lesson B22 **107**

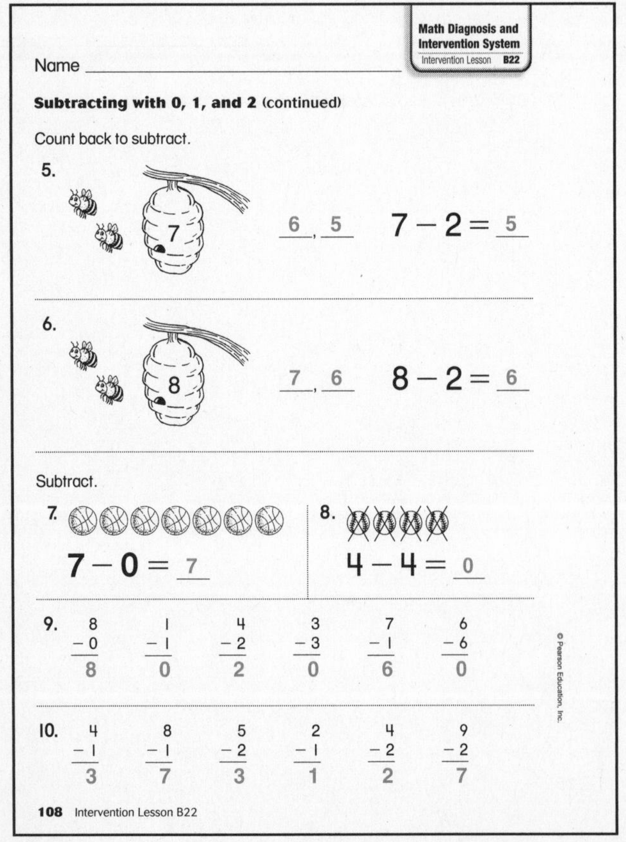

Math Diagnosis and Intervention System
Intervention Lesson B22

Name ______________________

Subtracting with 0, 1, and 2 (continued)

Count back to subtract.

5. 7   6, 5   7 − 2 = 5

6. 8   7, 6   8 − 2 = 6

Subtract.

7. 7 − 0 = 7

8. 4 − 4 = 0

9. 8 − 0 = 8; 1 − 1 = 0; 4 − 2 = 2; 3 − 3 = 0; 7 − 1 = 6; 6 − 6 = 0

10. 4 − 1 = 3; 8 − 1 = 7; 5 − 2 = 3; 2 − 1 = 1; 4 − 2 = 2; 9 − 2 = 7

© Pearson Education, Inc.

108 Intervention Lesson B22

Teacher Notes

Ongoing Assessment

Ask: ***No matter how many tacos Maurice has, if he gives them all away, how many will he have left?*** Zero

Error Intervention

If children have trouble counting back,

then have them practice counting back using a number line.

If You Have More Time

Have children work in groups of 3 to write 30 subtraction facts on index cards: 10 facts with 0, 10 facts with 1, and 10 with 2. For example, a card may write 8 − 1 or 7 − 2. Have children shuffle the cards and put them face down on the table. One child serves as referee and turns a card over so both children can see it at the same time. The other two children race to say the difference first. The one who says the correct difference first, wins. Continue until all cards are used. Have the children change roles and repeat so the referee has a chance to play.

Using Doubles to Subtract

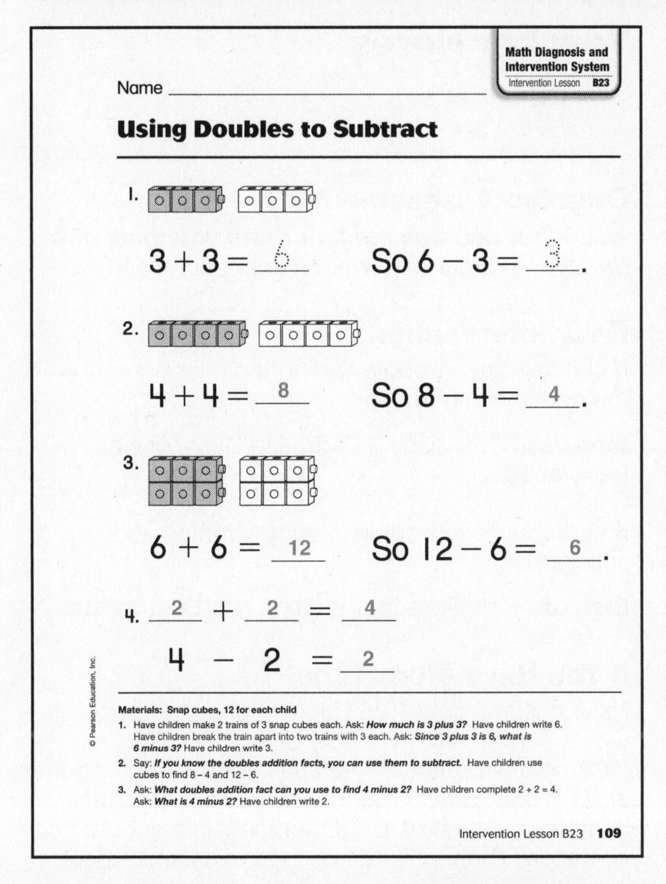

Math Diagnosis and Intervention System
Intervention Lesson B23

Name ________________

Using Doubles to Subtract

1. $3 + 3 =$ 6 So $6 - 3 =$ 3.

2. $4 + 4 =$ 8 So $8 - 4 =$ 4.

3. $6 + 6 =$ 12 So $12 - 6 =$ 6.

4. 2 + 2 = 4
$4 - 2 =$ 2

© Pearson Education, Inc.

Materials: Snap cubes, 12 for each child

1. Have children make 2 trains of 3 snap cubes each. Ask: ***How much is 3 plus 3?*** Have children write 6. Have children break the train apart into two trains with 3 each. Ask: ***Since 3 plus 3 is 6, what is 6 minus 3?*** Have children write 3.
2. Say: ***If you know the doubles addition facts, you can use them to subtract.*** Have children use cubes to find 8 – 4 and 12 – 6.
3. Ask: ***What doubles addition fact can you use to find 4 minus 2?*** Have children complete 2 + 2 = 4. Ask: ***What is 4 minus 2?*** Have children write 2.

Intervention Lesson B23 **109**

Teacher Notes

Ongoing Assessment

Ask: ***What double addition fact can help you find 4 – 2?*** 2 + 2 = 4

Error Intervention

If children do not know the double addition facts,

then use B12: Adding Doubles

If students have trouble relating addition and subtraction,

then use B19: Relating Addition and Subtraction.

If You Have More Time

Have children draw pictures to show double subtraction facts. Have them write a fact to match each picture.

Math Diagnosis and Intervention System
Intervention Lesson B23

Name ________________

Using Doubles to Subtract (continued)

Find the double. Then subtract.
Use cubes if you like.

5. $2 + 2 =$ 4
So $4 - 2 =$ 2.

6. $5 + 5 =$ 10
So $10 - 5 =$ 5.

Write an addition fact. Then subtract.

7. $1 + 1 =$ 2 So $2 - 1 =$ 1.

8. $3 + 3 =$ 6 So $6 - 3 =$ 3.

9. $4 + 4 =$ 8 So $8 - 4 =$ 4.

10. 6 + 6 = 12 So $12 - 6 =$ 6.

11. Carolyn has 6 apples and 3 oranges.
How many pieces of fruit does she have in all?

9 pieces of fruit

110 Intervention Lesson B23

Thinking Addition to 12 to Subtract

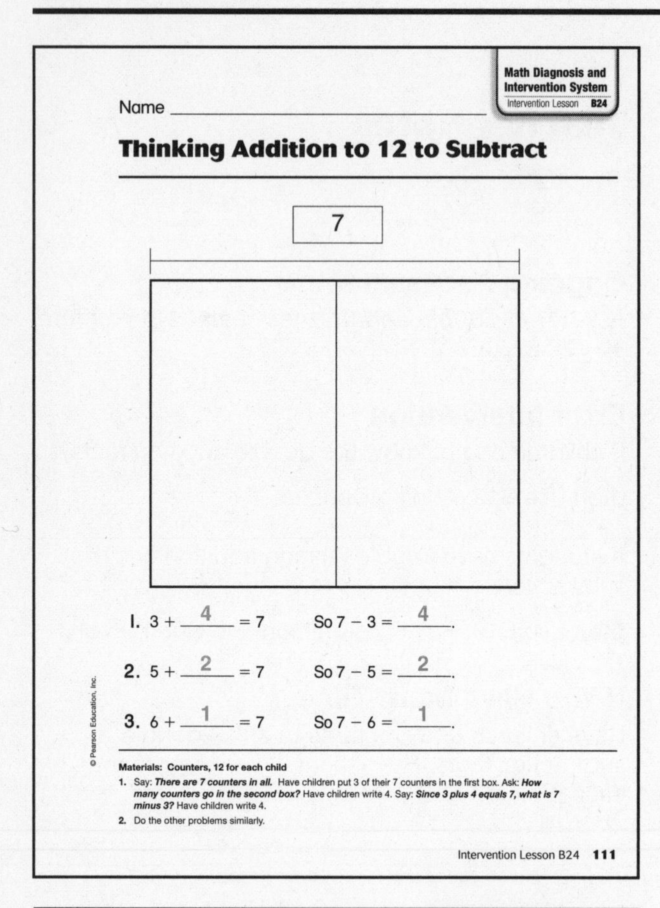
Math Diagnosis and Intervention System
Intervention Lesson B24

Name ____________________

Thinking Addition to 12 to Subtract

7

1. 3 + __4__ = 7   So 7 − 3 = __4__.
2. 5 + __2__ = 7   So 7 − 5 = __2__.
3. 6 + __1__ = 7   So 7 − 6 = __1__.

© Pearson Education, Inc.

Materials: Counters, 12 for each child

1. Say: ***There are 7 counters in all.*** Have children put 3 of their 7 counters in the first box. Ask: ***How many counters go in the second box?*** Have children write 4. Say: ***Since 3 plus 4 equals 7, what is 7 minus 3?*** Have children write 4.
2. Do the other problems similarly.

Intervention Lesson B24 **111**

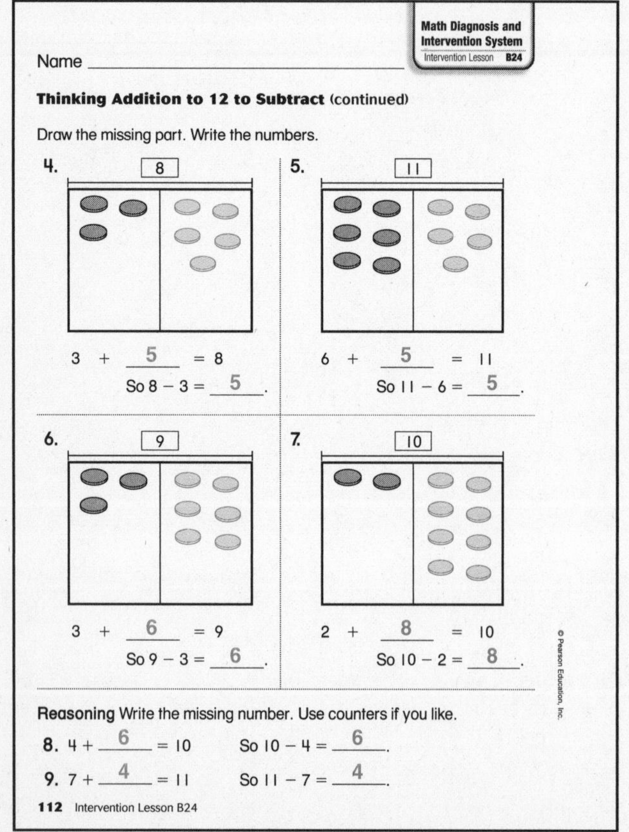
Math Diagnosis and Intervention System
Intervention Lesson B24

Name ____________________

Thinking Addition to 12 to Subtract (continued)

Draw the missing part. Write the numbers.

4. 8
3 + __5__ = 8
So 8 − 3 = __5__.

5. 11
6 + __5__ = 11
So 11 − 6 = __5__.

6. 9
3 + __6__ = 9
So 9 − 3 = __6__.

7. 10
2 + __8__ = 10
So 10 − 2 = __8__.

© Pearson Education, Inc.

Reasoning Write the missing number. Use counters if you like.

8. 4 + __6__ = 10   So 10 − 4 = __6__.
9. 7 + __4__ = 11   So 11 − 7 = __4__.

112 Intervention Lesson B24

Teacher Notes

Ongoing Assessment

Ask: ***What addition sentence can you think of to find 9 − 4?*** Four plus what number equals 9.

Error Intervention

If children have trouble finding the missing part in the addition sentences,

then use B16: Missing Parts and B20: Missing Parts of 10.

If students have trouble relating addition and subtraction,

then use B19: Relating Addition and Subtraction.

If You Have More Time

Have children play "I'm Thinking of a Number" with a partner. For instance, one child says, *I'm thinking of a number. When 4 is added to it the sum is 10. What is the number?* The partner says the number and then uses the numbers in a subtraction sentence. Then, children change roles and repeat.

Stories about Joining

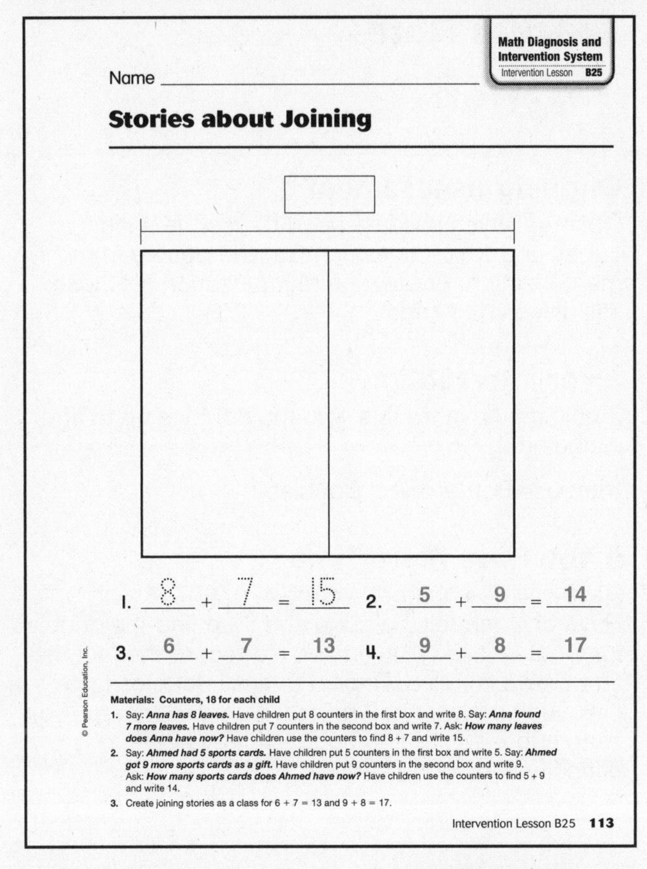
Math Diagnosis and Intervention System
Intervention Lesson B25

Name ______________________

Stories about Joining

1. 8 + 7 = 15
2. 5 + 9 = 14
3. 6 + 7 = 13
4. 9 + 8 = 17

Materials: Counters, 18 for each child

1. Say: ***Anna has 8 leaves.*** Have children put 8 counters in the first box and write 8. Say: ***Anna found 7 more leaves.*** Have children put 7 counters in the second box and write 7. Ask: ***How many leaves does Anna have now?*** Have children use the counters to find 8 + 7 and write 15.
2. Say: ***Ahmed had 5 sports cards.*** Have children put 5 counters in the first box and write 5. Say: ***Ahmed got 9 more sports cards as a gift.*** Have children put 9 counters in the second box and write 9. Ask: ***How many sports cards does Ahmed have now?*** Have children use the counters to find 5 + 9 and write 14.
3. Create joining stories as a class for 6 + 7 = 13 and 9 + 8 = 17.

Math Diagnosis and Intervention System
Intervention Lesson B25

Name ______________________

Stories about Joining (continued)

Draw a picture to find the sum.
Then write the numbers.

5. 9 turtles are by the pond.
7 more join them.
How many turtles are there in all?

9 + 7 = 16 (16)

6. 8 hens are in the yard.
6 more join them.
How many hens are there in all?

8 + 6 = 14 (14)

7. 9 cows are in the barn.
9 more join them.
How many cows are there in all?

9 + 9 = 18 (18)

Teacher Notes

Ongoing Assessment

Observe which children can solve the Exercises with pictures and which need to use counters.

Error Intervention

If children have trouble writing number sentences for the joining stories,

then use B1: Addition and B7: Joining Stories.

If You Have More Time

Have children work in pairs. One child tells a joining story. The other child writes a number sentence representing the story and then solves it. Then, children change roles and repeat.

Doubles to 18

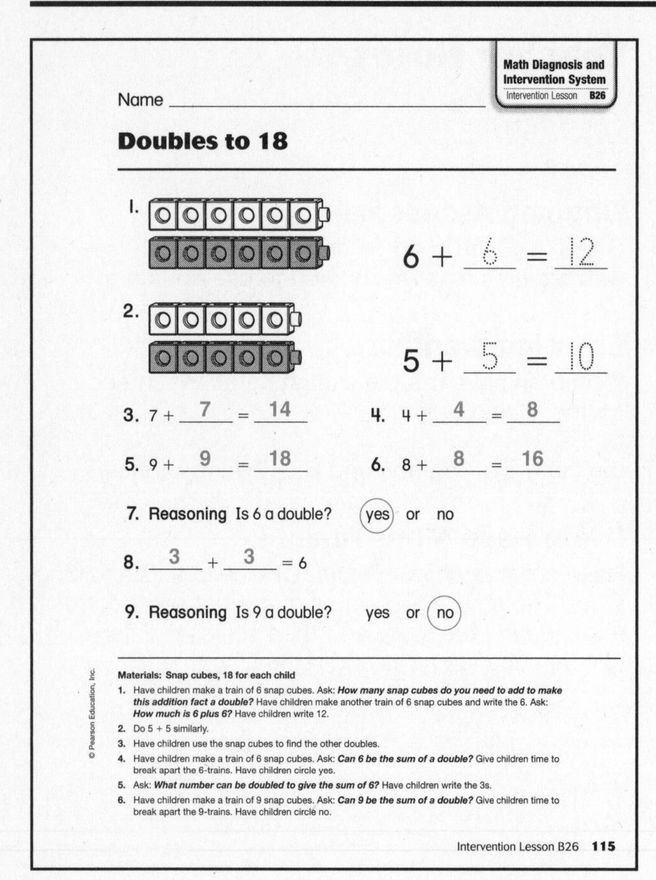

Math Diagnosis and Intervention System
Intervention Lesson B26

Name ______________________

Doubles to 18

1. 6 + 6 = 12
2. 5 + 5 = 10
3. 7 + 7 = 14
4. 4 + 4 = 8
5. 9 + 9 = 18
6. 8 + 8 = 16
7. **Reasoning** Is 6 a double? (yes) or no
8. 3 + 3 = 6
9. **Reasoning** Is 9 a double? yes or (no)

Materials: Snap cubes, 18 for each child

1. Have children make a train of 6 snap cubes. Ask: ***How many snap cubes do you need to add to make this addition fact a double?*** Have children make another train of 6 snap cubes and write the 6. Ask: ***How much is 6 plus 6?*** Have children write 12.
2. Do 5 + 5 similarly.
3. Have children use the snap cubes to find the other doubles.
4. Have children make a train of 6 snap cubes. Ask: ***Can 6 be the sum of a double?*** Give children time to break apart the 6-trains. Have children circle yes.
5. Ask: ***What number can be doubled to give the sum of 6?*** Have children write the 3s.
6. Have children make a train of 9 snap cubes. Ask: ***Can 9 be the sum of a double?*** Give children time to break apart the 9-trains. Have children circle no.

Intervention Lesson B26 **115**

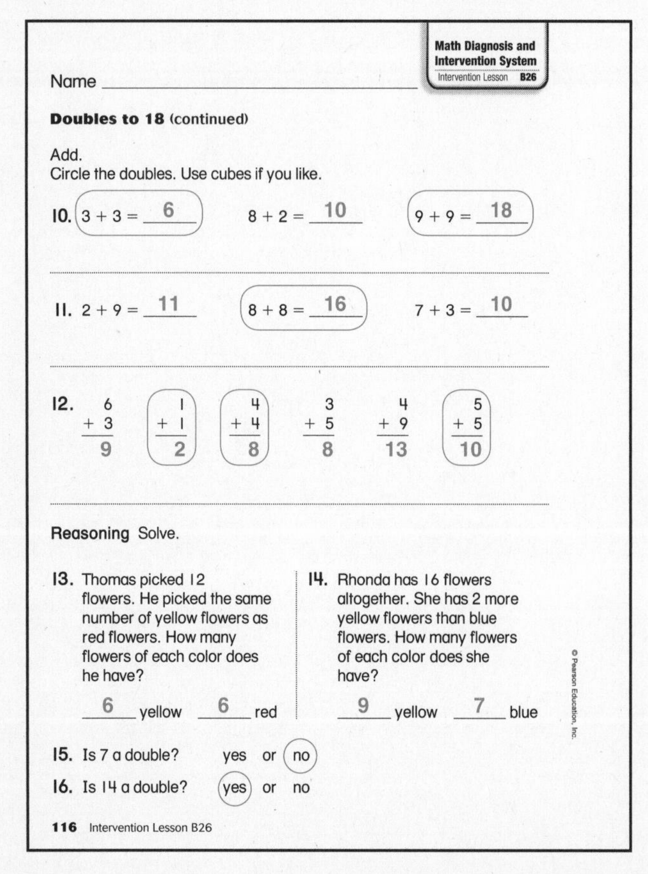

Math Diagnosis and Intervention System
Intervention Lesson B26

Name ______________________

Doubles to 18 (continued)

Add.
Circle the doubles. Use cubes if you like.

10. (3 + 3 = 6) 8 + 2 = 10 (9 + 9 = 18)

11. 2 + 9 = 11 (8 + 8 = 16) 7 + 3 = 10

12. 6 + 3 = 9 (1 + 1 = 2) (4 + 4 = 8) 3 + 5 = 8 4 + 9 = 13 (5 + 5 = 10)

Reasoning Solve.

13. Thomas picked 12 flowers. He picked the same number of yellow flowers as red flowers. How many flowers of each color does he have?
6 yellow 6 red

14. Rhonda has 16 flowers altogether. She has 2 more yellow flowers than blue flowers. How many flowers of each color does she have?
9 yellow 7 blue

15. Is 7 a double? yes or (no)
16. Is 14 a double? (yes) or no

116 Intervention Lesson B26

Teacher Notes

Ongoing Assessment

Observe which children need to use the snap cubes and which ones can find the double from memorization. Encourage memorization for those still using snap cubes.

Error Intervention

If children have trouble with the doubles up to and including 6 + 6,

then use B12: Adding Doubles.

If You Have More Time

Have children number a cube 4, 5, 6, 7, 8, and 9. Have children roll the cube and then find the double for what is rolled. Have the child record the fact the first time it is rolled. Repeat until all doubles facts 4 through 9 have been rolled. Allow children to use snap cubes to find the double if they are having difficulty finding the sum.

Using Doubles to Add

Name ____________________

Using Doubles to Add

1.

$6 + 6 =$ 12

$6 + 7 =$ 13

$7 + 6 =$ 13

2. $5 + 6$

$5 + 5 = 10$

$5 + 6 = 11$

$6 + 5 = 11$

3. $8 + 7$

$7 + 7 = 14$

$8 + 7 = 15$

$7 + 8 = 15$

Materials: Snap cubes, 15 for each child

1. Have children use snap cubes to form 2 trains of 6 and write the sum of the double 6 + 6. Then, have children add one more cube to the second train. Say: ***Six plus 7 is 6 plus 6 and one more. What is one more than 12?*** 13; Say: ***So, 6 plus 7 equals 13.*** Have children write 13.
2. Have children show 6 + 6 again. Have them add one cube to the first train of 6. Say: ***Seven plus 6 is also one more than 6 plus 6. What is 7 plus 6?*** Have children write 13.
3. Ask: ***What double can you use to find 5 + 6?*** Have children write 5 and 5. Have children form two trains with 5 cubes each and write the sum, 10. Have them add cubes to find 5 + 6 and 6 + 5.
4. Ask: ***What double can you use to find 8 plus 7?*** Have children write 7 + 7 = 14 and use the double to find 8 + 7 and 7 + 8.

Name ____________________

Using Doubles to Add (continued)

Find each sum. Think of a double to help you.

4. $2 + 2 =$ 4
   $2 + 3 =$ 5
5. $5 + 5 =$ 10
   $5 + 6 =$ 11
6. $8 + 8 =$ 16
   $8 + 9 =$ 17
7. $4 + 4 =$ 8
   $4 + 5 =$ 9
8. $7 + 7 =$ 14 $7 + 8 =$ 15 $8 + 7 =$ 15
9. $3 + 3 =$ 6 $3 + 4 =$ 7 $4 + 3 =$ 7
10. $1 + 1 =$ 2 $1 + 2 =$ 3 $2 + 1 =$ 3
11. $6 + 6 =$ 12 $6 + 7 =$ 13 $7 + 6 =$ 13
12. **Reasoning** There are 8 bees near a hive. There are double that many and one more in the hive. How many bees are in the hive? 17 bees

Teacher Notes

Ongoing Assessment

Ask: ***What doubles fact can you use to find 9 + 8?*** 8 + 8 ***If 8 + 8 is 16, what is 9 + 8?*** 17

Error Intervention

If children do not know their doubles facts,

then use B26: Doubles to 18 and B12: Adding Doubles.

If children have trouble with the doubles plus 1 up to and including 5 + 6,

then use B13: Using Doubles to Add.

If You Have More Time

Have children make up their own story problem involving doubles plus 1, like the story problem about bees in the exercises. Have a partner solve each story problem.

Adding 10

Math Diagnosis and Intervention System
Intervention Lesson B28

Name ____________________

Adding 10

1. 10 + 4 = 14
2. 10 + 5 = 15
3. 10 + 1 = 11
4. 10 + 2 = 12
5. 10 + 7 = 17
6. 10 + 10 = 20

Materials: Two-color counters, 20 for each child

1. Have children fill the ten-frame with yellow counters. Have them put four red counters below the frame. Have them count on from ten, 11, 12, 13, 14. Ask: ***What is 10 plus 4?*** Have children write 14.
2. Do 10 + 5 similarly.
3. Ask: ***How could you use tens and ones to find 10 + 5?*** Sample answer: The sum of 10 + 5 is 15, which is one ten and 5 ones.
4. Have children use the ten-frame or the pattern in tens and ones to find the other sums.

Intervention Lesson B28 119

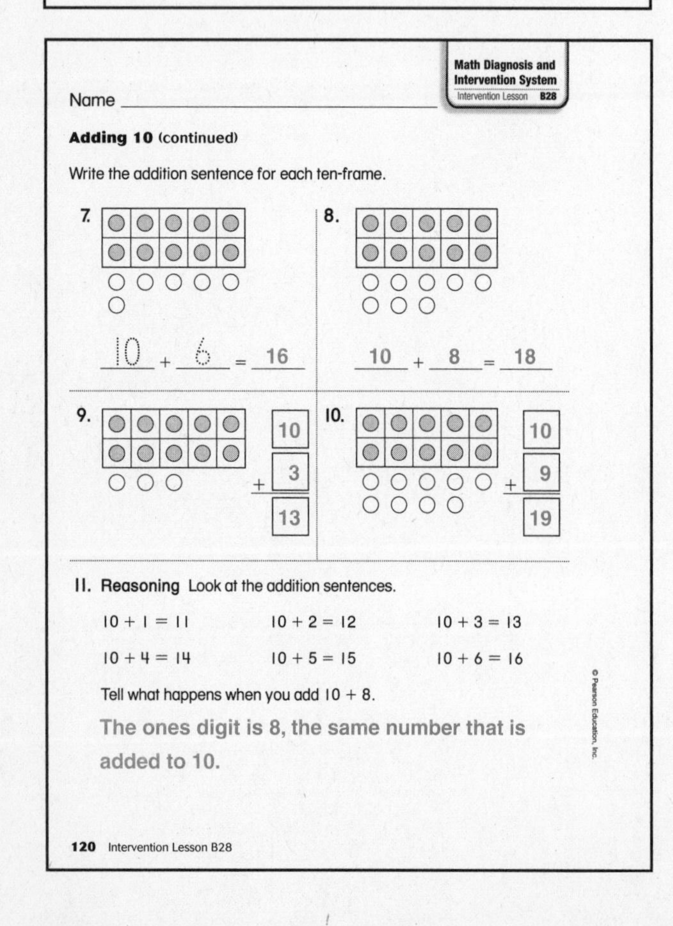

Math Diagnosis and Intervention System
Intervention Lesson B28

Name ____________________

Adding 10 (continued)

Write the addition sentence for each ten-frame.

7. 10 + 6 = 16
8. 10 + 8 = 18
9. 10 + 3 = 13
10. 10 + 9 = 19

11. **Reasoning** Look at the addition sentences.

10 + 1 = 11   10 + 2 = 12   10 + 3 = 13

10 + 4 = 14   10 + 5 = 15   10 + 6 = 16

Tell what happens when you add 10 + 8.

The ones digit is 8, the same number that is added to 10.

© Pearson Education, Inc.

120 Intervention Lesson B28

Teacher Notes

Ongoing Assessment

Observe which children can count on from 10 and which of those continue to count from 1. Reinforce the purpose of the ten-frame.

Error Intervention

If children have trouble with 10 + 1 through 10 + 9,

then use A14: Making Numbers 11 to 20.

If You Have More Time

Put children in pairs. Have partners take turns asking questions such as, *15 is 10 and how much more?* This activity allows children to reverse what they did in the lesson.

Making 10 to Add 9

Math Diagnosis and Intervention System
Intervention Lesson B29

Name ____________________

Making 10 to Add 9

1. $9 + 6 = 15$; $10 + \boxed{5} = 15$

2. $9 + 8 = 17$; $10 + \boxed{7} = 17$

Materials: Two-color counters, 17 for each child

1. Have children put 9 yellow counters in the ten-frame and 6 red counters below. Ask: ***What addition do the counters show?*** 9 plus 6; Then have children move one red counter to fill up the ten-frame. Ask: ***Nine plus 6 is equal to 10 plus what number?*** Have children write 5. Ask: ***What is 10 + 5?*** Have children write 15 for the sum of 10 + 5. Ask: ***If 10 plus 5 equals 15, then what is 9 plus 6?*** Have children write 15 for the sum of 9 + 6.
2. Do 9 + 8 similarly.

Intervention Lesson B29 **121**

Math Diagnosis and Intervention System
Intervention Lesson B29

Name ____________________

Making 10 to Add 9 (continued)

Draw more counters to add.
Write the missing numbers.
Find the sums.

3. $9 + 3 = 12$; $10 + \boxed{2} = 12$

4. $9 + 7 = 16$; $10 + \boxed{6} = 16$

5. $9 + 9 = 18$; $10 + \boxed{8} = 18$

6. $9 + 5 = 14$; $10 + \boxed{4} = 14$

122 Intervention Lesson B29

Teacher Notes

Ongoing Assessment

Ask: ***To add 9 + 6, how can you find what to add to 10, without using a ten-frame?*** Subtract 6 − 1 = 5. So, 9 + 6 = 10 + 5 = 15.

Error Intervention

If children have trouble with adding 10,

then use B28: Adding 10.

If You Have More Time

Have children number a cube 4, 5, 6, 7, 8, and 9. Have children roll the cube and then find the sum of 9 and what is rolled. Have the child record the fact the first time it is rolled. Repeat until all facts from 9 + 4 to 9 + 9 have been rolled. Allow children to use a ten-frame and counters if they are having difficulty finding the sum.

Making 10 to Add 8

Math Diagnosis and Intervention System
Intervention Lesson B30

Name ______________________

Making 10 to Add 8

1. $8 + 6 = 14$; $10 + \boxed{4} = 14$

2. $8 + 9 = 17$; $10 + \boxed{7} = 17$

3. Reasoning $8 + 5 = 10 +$ __3__ $=$ __13__

Materials: Two-color counters, 17 for each child

1. Have children put 8 yellow counters in the ten-frame and 6 red counters below. Ask: ***What addition do the counters show?*** 8 plus 6; Then have children move two red counters to fill up the ten-frame. Ask: ***Eight plus 6, is equal to 10 plus what number?*** Have children write 4. Ask: ***What is 10 + 4?*** Have children write 14 for the sum 10 + 4. Ask: ***If 10 plus 4 equals 14, then what is 8 plus 6?*** Have children write 14 for the sum 8 + 6.
2. Do 8 + 9 similarly.
3. Ask: ***Is 6, two less than 4?*** yes ***Is 7, two less than 9?*** yes; ***Is 8 + 5 equal to 10 plus 2 less than 5?*** yes ***What is 2 less than 5?*** Have children write 3 and find the sum.

Math Diagnosis and Intervention System
Intervention Lesson B30

Name ______________________

Making 10 to Add 8 (continued)

Draw more counters to add.
Write the missing numbers.
Find the sums.

4. $8 + 7 = 15$; $10 + \boxed{5} = 15$

5. $8 + 5 = 13$; $10 + \boxed{3} = 13$

6. $8 + 8 = 16$; $10 + \boxed{6} = 16$

7. $8 + 4 = 12$; $10 + \boxed{2} = 12$

8. Reasoning $8 + 9 = 10 +$ __7__ $=$ __17__

Teacher Notes

Ongoing Assessment

Ask: ***After we moved the two counters into the ten-frame, how did you know 8 + 6 equals 10 + 4?*** Sample Answer: I didn't change the number of counters.

Error Intervention

If children have trouble with adding 10,

then use B28: Adding 10.

If You Have More Time

Put children in pairs. Have one child number a cube 4, 5, 6, 7, 8, and 9. Have the other child number a cube 8, 8, 8, 9, 9, and 9. Each child rolls a cube. Have children write the sum of the numbers and a tens fact which could be used to find the sum. For example, if children roll 6 and 8, have them write 8 + 6 =14, 10 + 4 = 14.

Adding Three Numbers

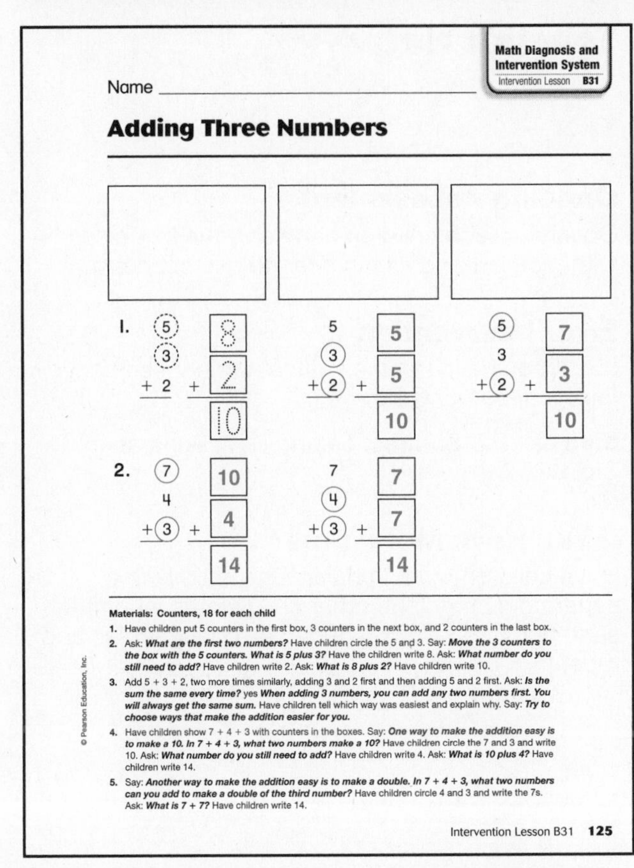
Math Diagnosis and Intervention System
Intervention Lesson B31

Name

Adding Three Numbers

1. 5 + 3 + 2: 8 + 2 = 10; 5 + 3 + 2: 5 + 5 = 10; 5 + 3 + 2: 7 + 3 = 10

2. 7 + 4 + 3: 10 + 4 = 14; 7 + 4 + 3: 7 + 7 = 14

Materials: Counters, 18 for each child

1. Have children put 5 counters in the first box, 3 counters in the next box, and 2 counters in the last box.
2. Ask: ***What are the first two numbers?*** Have children circle the 5 and 3. Say: ***Move the 3 counters to the box with the 5 counters. What is 5 plus 3?*** Have the children write 8. Ask: ***What number do you still need to add?*** Have children write 2. Ask: ***What is 8 plus 2?*** Have children write 10.
3. Add 5 + 3 + 2, two more times similarly, adding 3 and 2 first and then adding 5 and 2 first. Ask: ***Is the sum the same every time?*** yes ***When adding 3 numbers, you can add any two numbers first. You will always get the same sum.*** Have children tell which way was easiest and explain why. Say: ***Try to choose ways that make the addition easier for you.***
4. Have children show 7 + 4 + 3 with counters in the boxes. Say: ***One way to make the addition easy is to make a 10. In 7 + 4 + 3, what two numbers make a 10?*** Have children circle the 7 and 3 and write 10. Ask: ***What number do you still need to add?*** Have children write 4. Ask: ***What is 10 plus 4?*** Have children write 14.
5. Say: ***Another way to make the addition easy is to make a double. In 7 + 4 + 3, what two numbers can you add to make a double of the third number?*** Have children circle 4 and 3 and write the 7s. Ask: ***What is 7 + 7?*** Have children write 14.

© Pearson Education, Inc.

Intervention Lesson B31 **125**

Math Diagnosis and Intervention System
Intervention Lesson B31

Name

Adding Three Numbers (continued)

Find each sum.
Circle the numbers you added first.

Numbers circled and numbers in boxes will vary.

3. 9 + 6 + 4: ☐ + ☐ = 19

4. 2 + 6 + 4: ☐ + ☐ = 12

5. 2 + 9 + 1 = ____
☐ + ☐ = 12

6. 3 + 3 + 7 = ____
☐ + ☐ = 13

Find each sum.

7. 7 + 5 + 5 = 17; 2 + 8 + 6 = 16; 5 + 6 + 1 = 12; 5 + 2 + 5 = 12; 4 + 2 + 2 = 8; 8 + 3 + 5 = 16

8. 9 + 1 + 9 = 19

9. 2 + 5 + 7 = 14

10. **Reasoning** Find the missing number.

2 + 8 + 8 = 18

© Pearson Education, Inc.

126 Intervention Lesson B31

Teacher Notes

Ongoing Assessment

Observe if children are trying to make a ten or a double first, or if they are just adding in the order the numbers are given.

Error Intervention

If children have trouble making a ten,

then use B15: Making 10 on a Ten-Frame.

If children have trouble adding doubles,

then use B12: Adding Doubles and B26: Doubles to 18.

If You Have More Time

Have children work in groups of three. Have two children each number a cube 0 through 5. Have the third child number a cube 4 though 9. Have each child roll a cube. Then have them individually find the sum of the three numbers and take turns explaining how they found the sum. Repeat as time allows.

Stories about Separating

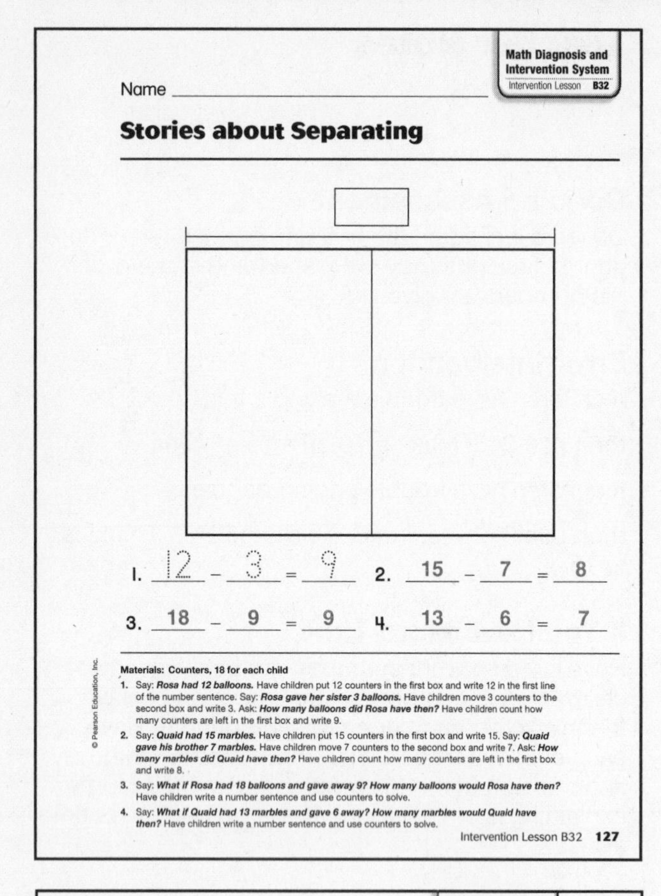
Math Diagnosis and Intervention System
Intervention Lesson B32

Name ____________________

Stories about Separating

1. 12 – 3 = 9
2. 15 – 7 = 8
3. 18 – 9 = 9
4. 13 – 6 = 7

Materials: Counters, 18 for each child

1. Say: ***Rosa had 12 balloons.*** Have children put 12 counters in the first box and write 12 in the first line of the number sentence. Say: ***Rosa gave her sister 3 balloons.*** Have children move 3 counters to the second box and write 3. Ask: ***How many balloons did Rosa have then?*** Have children count how many counters are left in the first box and write 9.
2. Say: ***Quaid had 15 marbles.*** Have children put 15 counters in the first box and write 15. Say: ***Quaid gave his brother 7 marbles.*** Have children move 7 counters to the second box and write 7. Ask: ***How many marbles did Quaid have then?*** Have children count how many counters are left in the first box and write 8.
3. Say: ***What if Rosa had 18 balloons and gave away 9? How many balloons would Rosa have then?*** Have children write a number sentence and use counters to solve.
4. Say: ***What if Quaid had 13 marbles and gave 6 away? How many marbles would Quaid have then?*** Have children write a number sentence and use counters to solve.

Math Diagnosis and Intervention System
Intervention Lesson B32

Name ____________________

Stories about Separating (continued)

Draw a picture to find the difference.
Then write the numbers.

5. 11 birds are sitting on the fence.
7 birds fly away.
How many birds are left?
11 – 7 = 4

11

6. 13 pigs are in the pen.
5 pigs run away.
How many pigs are still in the pen?
13 – 5 = 8

13

7. 16 ducks are in the pond.
9 ducks swim away.
How many ducks are left?
16 – 9 = 7

16

Teacher Notes

Ongoing Assessment

Observe which children can solve the Exercises with pictures and which need to use counters.

Error Intervention

If children have trouble writing number sentences for the separating stories,

then use B2: Subtraction and B17: Separating Stories.

If You Have More Time

Have children work in pairs. One child tells a separating story. The other child writes a number sentence and solves. Then, they change roles and repeat.

Stories about Comparing

Name ______________________

Stories about Comparing

1. 12 – 5 = 7 7 more crayons
2. 16 – 8 = 8 8 more grapes
3. 14 – 5 = 9 9 more apples
4. 15 – 6 = 9 9 more fish
5. 11 – 3 = 8 8 more hair bows

Materials: Counters, 18 for each child

1. Say: ***Alicia had 12 crayons.*** Have children show 12 counters in a row and write 12. Say: ***Max had 5 crayons.*** Have children show 5 counters in a row below Alicia's and write 5. Say: ***How many more crayons did Alicia have than Max?*** Have children remove 1 counter from each row at the same time. Have them continue removing pairs until all the counters in the top row are gone. Have children complete the number sentence by writing 7.
2. Say: ***Jaden had 16 grapes.*** Have children show 16 counters in a row and write 16. Say: ***Rafel had 8 grapes.*** Have children show 8 counters in a row below Jaden's and write 8. Say: ***How many more grapes did Jaden have than Max?*** Have children remove 1 counter from each row at the same time. Have them continue removing pairs until all the counters in the top row are gone. Have children complete the number sentence by writing 8.
3. Say: ***Vero had 14 apples and 5 oranges. How many more apples than oranges did she have?*** Have children use counters to write and solve the number sentence.
4. Say: ***Miles had 15 fish. Olivia had 6 fish. How many more fish did Miles have than Olivia?*** Have children use counters to write and solve the number sentence.
5. Say: ***Poppy had 11 hair bows. Lora had 3 hair bows. How many more hair bows did Poppy have than Lora?*** Have children use counters to write and solve the number sentence.

Name ______________________

Stories about Comparing (continued)

Draw a picture to find the differences.
Then write a subtraction sentence.

6. 11 dogs are in a pen. 5 dogs are chasing a cat. How many more dogs are in the pen?

   6 more dogs 11 – 5 = 6

7. Paul has 14 dimes. Sue has 6 dimes. How many more dimes does Paul have than Sue?

   8 more dimes 14 – 6 = 8

8. 17 apples are in a basket. 8 apples are on the ground. How many more apples are in the basket?

   9 more apples 17 – 8 = 9

Teacher Notes

Ongoing Assessment

Observe that children are taking away the counters in pairs, not all from one row. Make sure they understand that they are finding how many more counters are in one row than in the other.

Error Intervention

If children have trouble writing number sentences for the comparing stories,

then use B18: Comparing Stories.

If You Have More Time

Have two different size groups of children come to the front of the class and line up in two rows, one group in each row. Have children in their seats write a number sentence for how many more children are in one group than another. Then, have one child from each group sit down. Continue until there are no children left in the smaller group. Have children count the remaining children to check their number sentences.

Relating Addition and Subtraction to 18

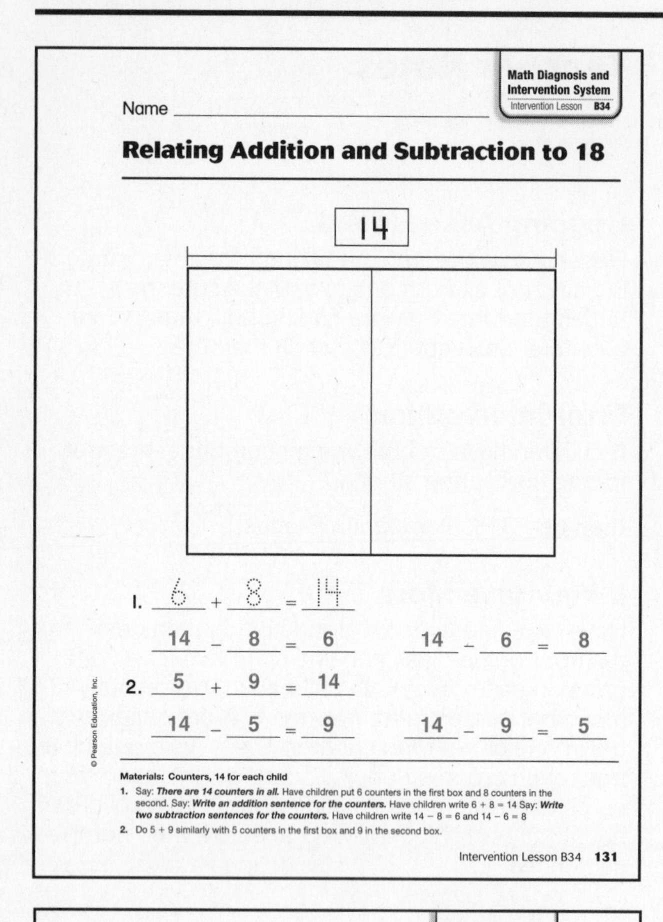

Math Diagnosis and Intervention System
Intervention Lesson B34

Name ______________________

Relating Addition and Subtraction to 18

14

1. 6 + 8 = 14
   14 − 8 = 6   14 − 6 = 8
2. 5 + 9 = 14
   14 − 5 = 9   14 − 9 = 5

Materials: Counters, 14 for each child

1. Say: ***There are 14 counters in all.*** Have children put 6 counters in the first box and 8 counters in the second. Say: ***Write an addition sentence for the counters.*** Have children write 6 + 8 = 14 Say: ***Write two subtraction sentences for the counters.*** Have children write 14 − 8 = 6 and 14 − 6 = 8
2. Do 5 + 9 similarly with 5 counters in the first box and 9 in the second box.

© Pearson Education, Inc.

Intervention Lesson B34 **131**

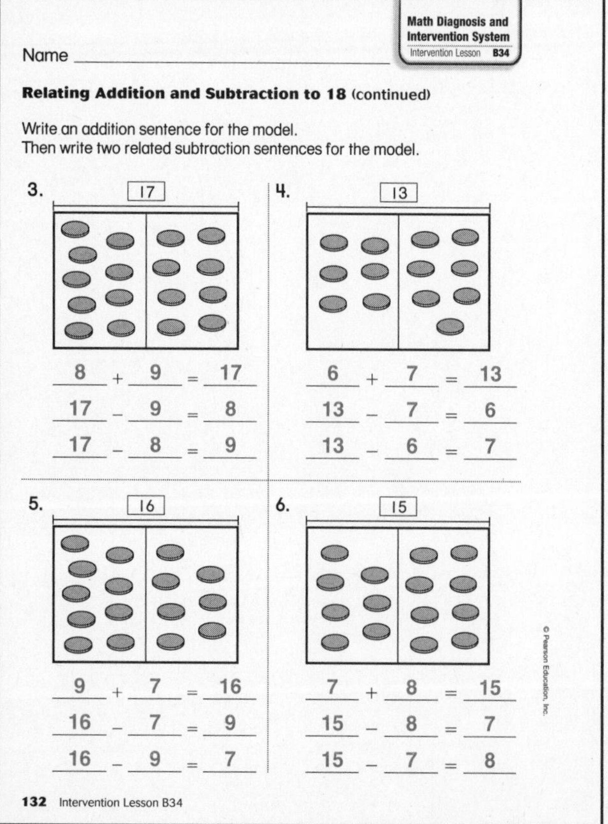

Math Diagnosis and Intervention System
Intervention Lesson B34

Name ______________________

Relating Addition and Subtraction to 18 (continued)

Write an addition sentence for the model.
Then write two related subtraction sentences for the model.

3. 17
   8 + 9 = 17
   17 − 9 = 8
   17 − 8 = 9
4. 13
   6 + 7 = 13
   13 − 7 = 6
   13 − 6 = 7
5. 16
   9 + 7 = 16
   16 − 7 = 9
   16 − 9 = 7
6. 15
   7 + 8 = 15
   15 − 8 = 7
   15 − 7 = 8

© Pearson Education, Inc.

132 Intervention Lesson B34

Teacher Notes

Ongoing Assessment

Ask: ***What are two subtraction sentences related to 4 + 9 = 13?*** 13 − 9 = 4 and 13 − 4 = 9

Error Intervention

If children have trouble writing addition or subtraction sentences,

then use B25: Stories about Joining, B32: Stories about Separating, and B33: Stories about Comparing.

If children have trouble relating addition to subtraction,

then use B19: Relating Addition and Subtraction, B23: Using Doubles to Subtract, and B24: Thinking Addition to 12 to Subtract.

If You Have More Time

Have children work in pairs. Have each child number a cube 4 through 9. Both children roll their cube, write an addition number sentence for the two numbers, then write the two related subtraction sentences. Repeat as time allows.

Fact Families

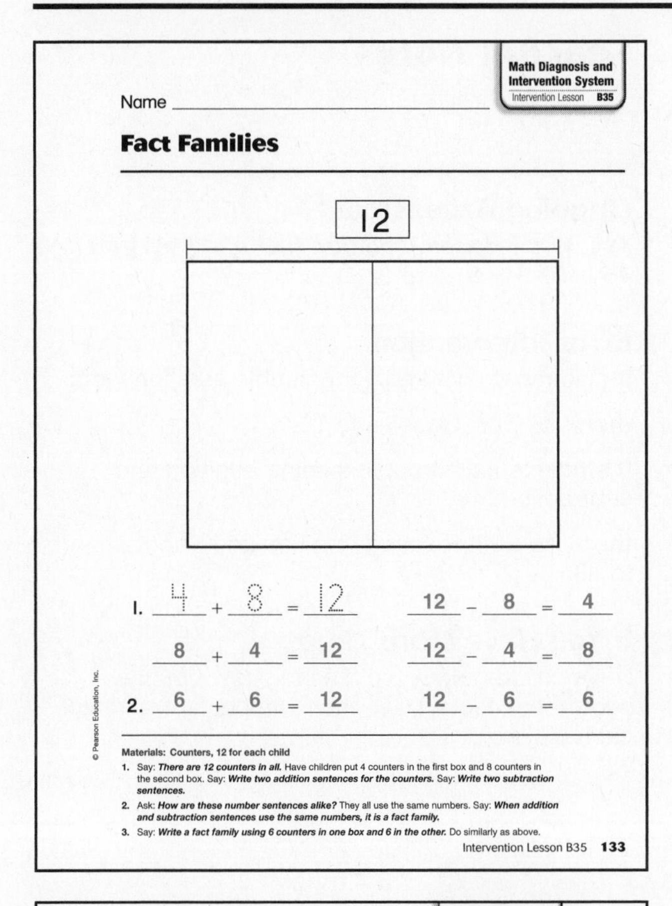

Math Diagnosis and Intervention System
Intervention Lesson B35

Name ____________________

Fact Families

12

1. 4 + 8 = 12   12 − 8 = 4
   8 + 4 = 12   12 − 4 = 8
2. 6 + 6 = 12   12 − 6 = 6

© Pearson Education, Inc.

Materials: Counters, 12 for each child

1. Say: ***There are 12 counters in all.*** Have children put 4 counters in the first box and 8 counters in the second box. Say: ***Write two addition sentences for the counters.*** Say: ***Write two subtraction sentences.***
2. Ask: ***How are these number sentences alike?*** They all use the same numbers. Say: ***When addition and subtraction sentences use the same numbers, it is a fact family.***
3. Say: ***Write a fact family using 6 counters in one box and 6 in the other.*** Do similarly as above.

Intervention Lesson B35 **133**

Math Diagnosis and Intervention System
Intervention Lesson B35

Name ____________________

Fact Families (continued)

Write the fact family for the model.

3. 13: 7 | 6
   7 + 6 = 13   13 − 7 = 6
   6 + 7 = 13   13 − 6 = 7

4. 16: 7 | 9
   7 + 9 = 16   16 − 7 = 9
   9 + 7 = 16   16 − 9 = 7

5. 12: 5 | 7
   5 + 7 = 12   12 − 5 = 7
   7 + 5 = 12   12 − 7 = 5

6. 18: 9 | 9
   9 + 9 = 18   18 − 9 = 9

7. 15: 7 | 8
   7 + 8 = 15   15 − 7 = 8
   8 + 7 = 15   15 − 8 = 7

134 Intervention Lesson B35

Teacher Notes

Ongoing Assessment

Ask: ***What is the fact family with 9, 4, and 13?***
9 + 4 = 13, 4 + 9 = 13, 13 − 4 = 9, and 13 − 9 = 4

Error Intervention

If children have trouble relating addition to subtraction,

then use B19: Relating Addition and Subtraction, B23: Using Doubles to Subtract, B24: Thinking Addition to 12 to Subtract, and B34: Relating Addition and Subtraction to 18.

If You Have More Time

Have children play "I'm Thinking of a Number" with a partner. For instance, one child says, *I'm thinking of a number. When 8 is added to it, the sum is 15. What is the number?* The partner says the number and then uses the numbers in a fact family. Children can change roles and repeat as time allows.

Thinking Addition to Subtract Doubles

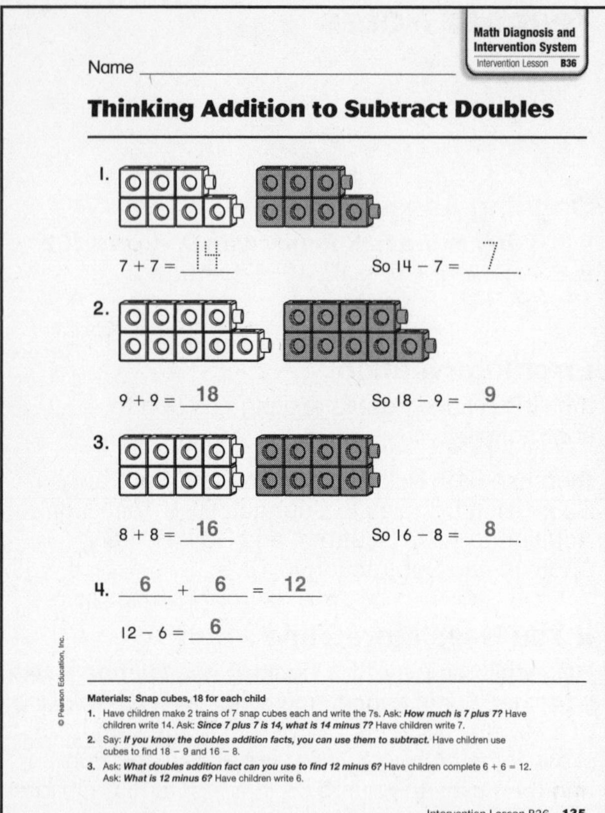
Math Diagnosis and Intervention System
Intervention Lesson B36

Name ____________________

Thinking Addition to Subtract Doubles

1. $7 + 7 =$ 14 So $14 - 7 =$ 7.

2. $9 + 9 =$ 18 So $18 - 9 =$ 9.

3. $8 + 8 =$ 16 So $16 - 8 =$ 8.

4. 6 + 6 = 12

$12 - 6 =$ 6

Materials: Snap cubes, 18 for each child

1. Have children make 2 trains of 7 snap cubes each and write the 7s. Ask: ***How much is 7 plus 7?*** Have children write 14. Ask: ***Since 7 plus 7 is 14, what is 14 minus 7?*** Have children write 7.
2. Say: ***If you know the doubles addition facts, you can use them to subtract.*** Have children use cubes to find 18 − 9 and 16 − 8.
3. Ask: ***What doubles addition fact can you use to find 12 minus 6?*** Have children complete 6 + 6 = 12. Ask: ***What is 12 minus 6?*** Have children write 6.

Intervention Lesson B36 135

Teacher Notes

Ongoing Assessment

Ask: ***What double addition fact can help you find 18 − 9?*** 9 + 9 = 18

Error Intervention

If children do not know the double addition facts,

then use B26: Doubles to 18.

If students have trouble relating addition and subtraction,

then use B34: Relating Addition and Subtraction to 18.

If You Have More Time

Have children draw pictures to show double subtraction facts. Have them write a fact to match each picture.

Math Diagnosis and Intervention System
Intervention Lesson B36

Name ____________________

Thinking Addition to Subtract Doubles (continued)

Subtract. Write the doubles fact that helped you.
Use cubes if needed.

5. $18 - 9 =$ 9
   9 + 9 = 18

6. $8 - 4 =$ 4
   4 + 4 = 8

7. $10 - 5 =$ 5
   5 + 5 = 10

8. $6 - 3 =$ 3
   3 + 3 = 6

9. $14 - 7 =$ 7; 7 + 7 = 14

10. $12 - 6 =$ 6; 6 + 6 = 12

Reasoning

11. Trent has 16 cars. He has the same number of red cars as blue cars. How many of each color does he have?

8 red 8 blue

136 Intervention Lesson B36

Using Addition to 18 to Subtract

Teacher Notes

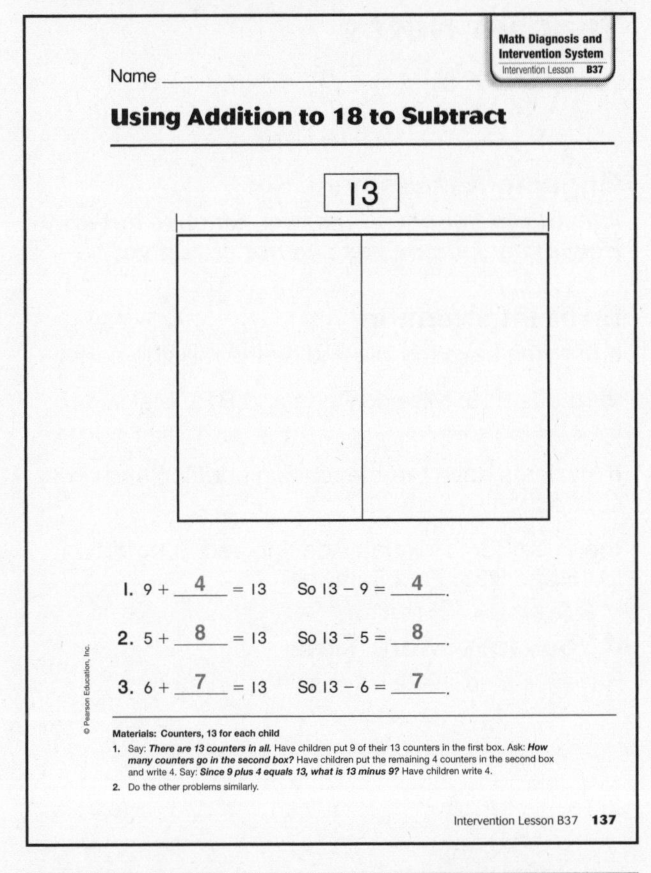

Math Diagnosis and Intervention System
Intervention Lesson B37

Name ______________

Using Addition to 18 to Subtract

13

1. 9 + 4 = 13 So 13 − 9 = 4.
2. 5 + 8 = 13 So 13 − 5 = 8.
3. 6 + 7 = 13 So 13 − 6 = 7.

Materials: Counters, 13 for each child

1. Say: ***There are 13 counters in all.*** Have children put 9 of their 13 counters in the first box. Ask: ***How many counters go in the second box?*** Have children put the remaining 4 counters in the second box and write 4. Say: ***Since 9 plus 4 equals 13, what is 13 minus 9?*** Have children write 4.
2. Do the other problems similarly.

Intervention Lesson B37 **137**

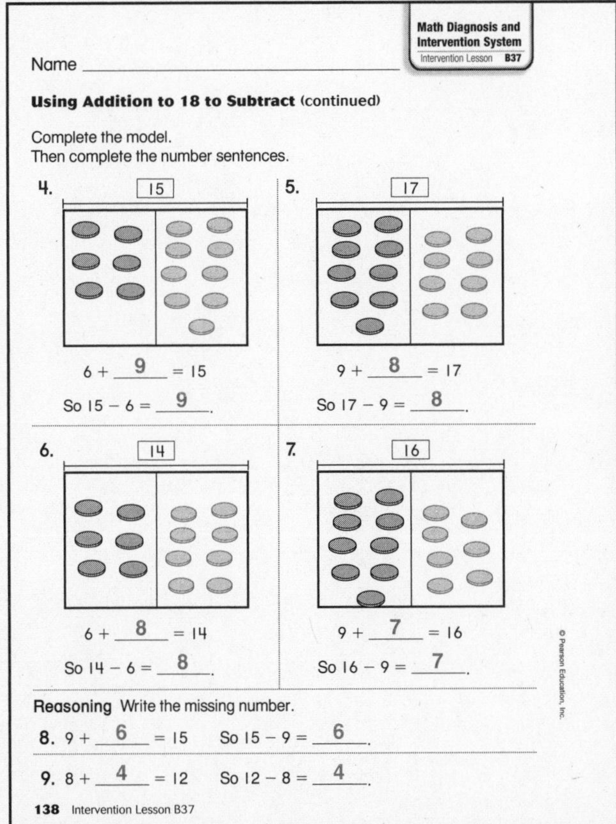

Math Diagnosis and Intervention System
Intervention Lesson B37

Name ______________

Using Addition to 18 to Subtract (continued)

Complete the model.
Then complete the number sentences.

4. 15
6 + 9 = 15
So 15 − 6 = 9.

5. 17
9 + 8 = 17
So 17 − 9 = 8.

6. 14
6 + 8 = 14
So 14 − 6 = 8.

7. 16
9 + 7 = 16
So 16 − 9 = 7.

Reasoning Write the missing number.

8. 9 + 6 = 15 So 15 − 9 = 6.
9. 8 + 4 = 12 So 12 − 8 = 4.

138 Intervention Lesson B37

Ongoing Assessment

Ask: ***What addition sentence can you use to help you find 16 − 7?*** Seven plus what number equals 16.

Error Intervention

If children have trouble finding the missing part in the addition sentences,

then use B16: Missing Parts and B20: Missing Parts of 10.

If students have trouble relating addition and subtraction,

then use B34: Relating Addition and Subtraction to 18, and B35: Fact Families.

If You Have More Time

Have children play "I'm Thinking of a Number" with a partner. For instance, one child says, *I'm thinking of a number. When 7 is added to it the sum is 13. What is the number?* The partner says the number and then uses the numbers in a subtraction sentence. Then, children change roles and repeat.

Finding the Missing Part

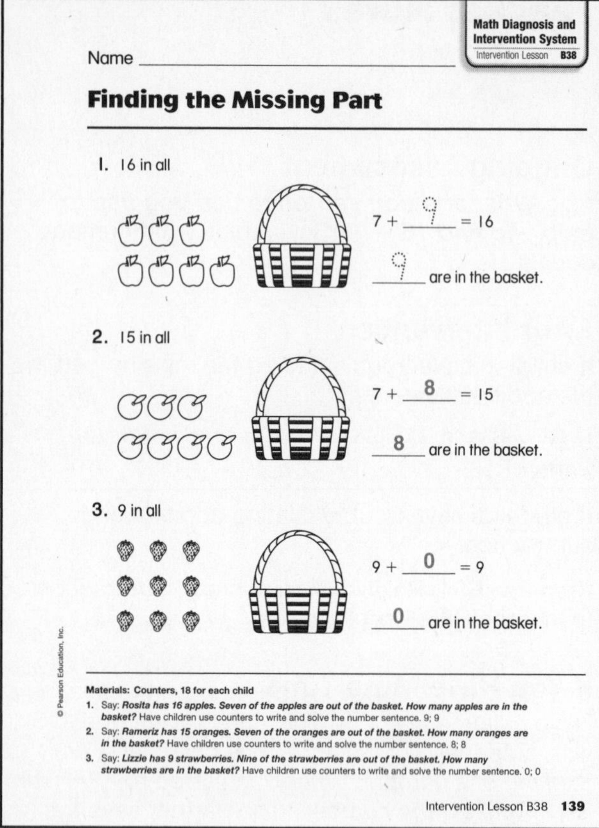
Math Diagnosis and Intervention System
Intervention Lesson B38

Name ______________________

Finding the Missing Part

1. 16 in all

7 + __9__ = 16

__9__ are in the basket.

2. 15 in all

7 + __8__ = 15

__8__ are in the basket.

3. 9 in all

9 + __0__ = 9

__0__ are in the basket.

© Pearson Education, Inc.

Materials: Counters, 18 for each child

1. Say: ***Rosita has 16 apples. Seven of the apples are out of the basket. How many apples are in the basket?*** Have children use counters to write and solve the number sentence. 9; 9
2. Say: ***Rameriz has 15 oranges. Seven of the oranges are out of the basket. How many oranges are in the basket?*** Have children use counters to write and solve the number sentence. 8; 8
3. Say: ***Lizzie has 9 strawberries. Nine of the strawberries are out of the basket. How many strawberries are in the basket?*** Have children use counters to write and solve the number sentence. 0; 0

Intervention Lesson B38 **139**

Teacher Notes

Ongoing Assessment

Ask: ***Gloria bought 17 lemons. She has cut up 9. How many lemons has she not cut up yet?*** 8

Error Intervention

If children have trouble finding the missing part,

then use B16: Missing Parts and B15: Making 10 on a Ten-Frame.

If students have trouble relating addition and subtraction,

then use B34: Relating Addition and Subtraction to 18 and B35: Fact Families.

If You Have More Time

Have children make up missing part stories.

Math Diagnosis and Intervention System
Intervention Lesson B38

Name ______________________

Finding the Missing Part (continued)

Find how many pieces of fruit are in each basket.

4. Martin has 14 pears.
7 are out of the basket.
How many are in the basket?

7 + __7__ = 14

__7__ are in the basket.

5. Pauline has 12 lemons.
8 are out of the basket.
How many are in the basket?

8 + __4__ = 12

__4__ are in the basket.

Reasoning

Find the missing numbers.

6.

4	4	4	4	4
+ 2	+ 4	+ 6	+ 8	+ 10
6	8	10	12	14

140 Intervention Lesson B38

Using Subtraction Strategies

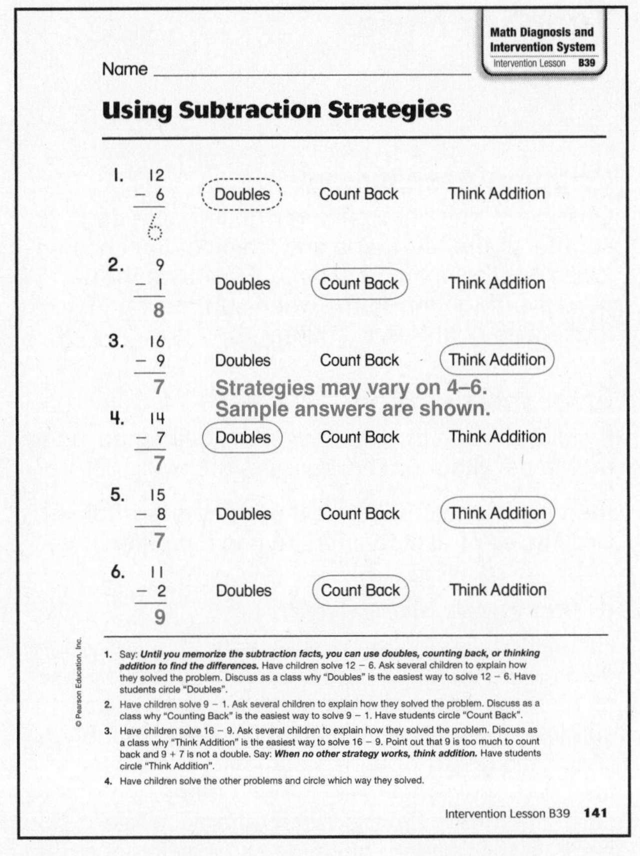

Math Diagnosis and Intervention System
Intervention Lesson B39

Name ____________________

Using Subtraction Strategies

1. 12 − 6 = 6 — **Doubles** (circled), Count Back, Think Addition
2. 9 − 1 = 8 — Doubles, **Count Back** (circled), Think Addition
3. 16 − 9 = 7 — Doubles, Count Back, **Think Addition** (circled)

Strategies may vary on 4–6.
Sample answers are shown.

4. 14 − 7 = 7 — **Doubles** (circled), Count Back, Think Addition
5. 15 − 8 = 7 — Doubles, Count Back, **Think Addition** (circled)
6. 11 − 2 = 9 — Doubles, **Count Back** (circled), Think Addition

1. Say: ***Until you memorize the subtraction facts, you can use doubles, counting back, or thinking addition to find the differences.*** Have children solve 12 − 6. Ask several children to explain how they solved the problem. Discuss as a class why "Doubles" is the easiest way to solve 12 − 6. Have students circle "Doubles".
2. Have children solve 9 − 1. Ask several children to explain how they solved the problem. Discuss as a class why "Counting Back" is the easiest way to solve 9 − 1. Have students circle "Count Back".
3. Have children solve 16 − 9. Ask several children to explain how they solved the problem. Discuss as a class why "Think Addition" is the easiest way to solve 16 − 9. Point out that 9 is too much to count back and 9 + 7 is not a double. Say: ***When no other strategy works, think addition.*** Have students circle "Think Addition".
4. Have children solve the other problems and circle which way they solved.

Math Diagnosis and Intervention System
Intervention Lesson B39

Name ____________________

Using Subtraction Strategies (continued)

Subtract.
Circle the easiest way to find the difference.
Strategies used may vary.

7. 10 − 2 = 8 — Doubles, **Count Back** (circled), Think Addition
8. 18 − 9 = 9 — **Doubles** (circled), Count Back, Think Addition
9. 15 − 9 = 6 — Doubles, Count Back, **Think Addition** (circled)
10. 14 − 8 = 6 — Doubles, Count Back, **Think Addition** (circled)
11. 10 − 5 = 5 — **Doubles** (circled), Count Back, Think Addition
12. 8 − 1 = 7 — Doubles, **Count Back** (circled), Think Addition

Subtract.

13. 9 − 2 = 7; 10 − 1 = 9; 15 − 6 = 9; 12 − 4 = 8; 13 − 9 = 4; 12 − 8 = 4

14. 16 − 8 = 8; 17 − 9 = 8; 12 − 5 = 7; 11 − 3 = 8; 15 − 7 = 8; 6 − 1 = 5

Teacher Notes

Ongoing Assessment

Ask: ***Explain why you and your friend might solve 11 − 3 differently.*** Sample answer: I thought counting back was easiest. My friend thought addition was easiest.

Error Intervention

If children have trouble identifying subtraction using counting back,

then use B22: Subtracting with 0, 1, and 2.

If children have trouble identifying subtraction using doubles,

then use B23: Using Doubles to Subtract and B36: Thinking Addition to Subtract Doubles.

If children have trouble identifying subtraction using addition,

then use B24: Thinking Addition to 12 to Subtract and B37: Using Addition to 18 to Subtract.

If You Have More Time

Have children work in groups of three. Write on the board: 12 − 9 = ____, 16 − 8 = ____, 17 − 8 = ____, Doubles, Count Back, and Think Addition. Have each child find the difference of the first problem. Then, in their groups, have children take turns explaining which method they thought was the easiest to use to find the difference. Repeat with the last two subtraction problems.

Subtraction Facts with 10

Name ____________________

Subtraction Facts with 10

1. 16 − 10 = 6
2. 20 − 10 = 10
3. 18 − 8 = 10
4. 19 − 9 = 10
5. 12 − 10 = 2
6. 15 − 10 = 5

Materials: Counters, 20 for each child

1. Have children fill the ten-frame with yellow counters. Have them put six red counters below the frame. Ask: ***What is an easy way to find 16 minus 10?*** Take away all the counters in the ten-frame. Have children remove all 10 counters from the ten-frame and count how many are left. Have children write 6. Do 20 − 10 similarly.
2. Have children show 18 with 10 counters in the ten-frame and 8 counters below it. Ask: ***What is an easy way to find 18 minus 8?*** Have children remove all the counters below the ten-frame. Ask: ***How many counters are left?*** Have children write 10. Do 19 − 9 similarly.
3. Have children use the ten-frame to find the other differences.
4. Ask: ***How could you find 14 − 10 without counters?*** Since 14 is one ten and 4 ones, when you take away 10, the 4 ones are left. ***How could you find 15 − 5 without counters?*** Since 15 is one ten and 5 ones, when you take away the 5 ones, only the ten is left.

Name ____________________

Subtraction Facts with 10 (continued)

Cross out to subtract.

7. 14 − 10 = 4
8. 12 − 10 = 2
9. 13 − 10 = 3
10. 16 − 10 = 6

Subtract.

11. 17 − 10 = 7; 15 − 10 = 5; 20 − 10 = 10; 18 − 10 = 8; 19 − 10 = 9

12. **Reasoning** Look at the subtraction sentences.

11 − 10 = 1　　12 − 10 = 2　　13 − 10 = 3
14 − 10 = 4　　15 − 10 = 5　　16 − 10 = 6

Tell what happens when you subtract 19 − 10.

You are left with 9. Since 19 is one ten and 9 ones, when you take away 10, the 9 ones are left.

Teacher Notes

Ongoing Assessment

Observe which children continue to count each counter in the ten-frame and which of the children cross out the entire ten-frame. Reinforce the purpose of the ten-frame when subtracting 10 to those who count each counter.

Error Intervention

If children have trouble finding the difference in the problems without a ten-frame,

then encourage them to either draw a ten-frame and circles or use counters to find the difference.

If You Have More Time

Have children work in pairs to write 20 subtraction differences on index cards. Each child makes a set of 10 cards, "11 − 10" through "20 − 10". Have children combine sets and shuffle the cards. Each child then gets 10 cards. Each child turns over their first card. They calculate the difference of their card. The child with the larger difference keeps both cards. If the children have the same difference, they each keep their own card. Continue until all cards are used.

Addition Properties

Math Diagnosis and Intervention System
Intervention Lesson B41

Name ____________________

Addition Properties

Materials 4 half sheets of paper, 24 color tiles (8 each of 3 colors) per pair

1. Show 2 + 5 and 5 + 2 by placing the tiles on the paper.

2. Add. 2 + 5 = 7 and 5 + 2 = 7

3. The Commutative Property says that you can change the order of the addends and the sum will be the same.

   So, 2 + 5 = 5 + 2.

4. Use the tiles to show (4 + 3) + 1. Use 3 different colors of tiles.

5. Add. Remember the parentheses show which numbers to add first.

   (4 + 3) + 1 = 7 + 1 = 8

6. Move the paper with 3 tiles closer to the paper with 1 tile to show 4 + (3 + 1).

7. Add. 4 + (3 + 1) = 4 + 4 = 8

8. The Associative Property says that you can group addends in any way and the sum will be the same.

   So, (4 + 3) + 1 = 4 + (3 + 1).

Intervention Lesson B41 145

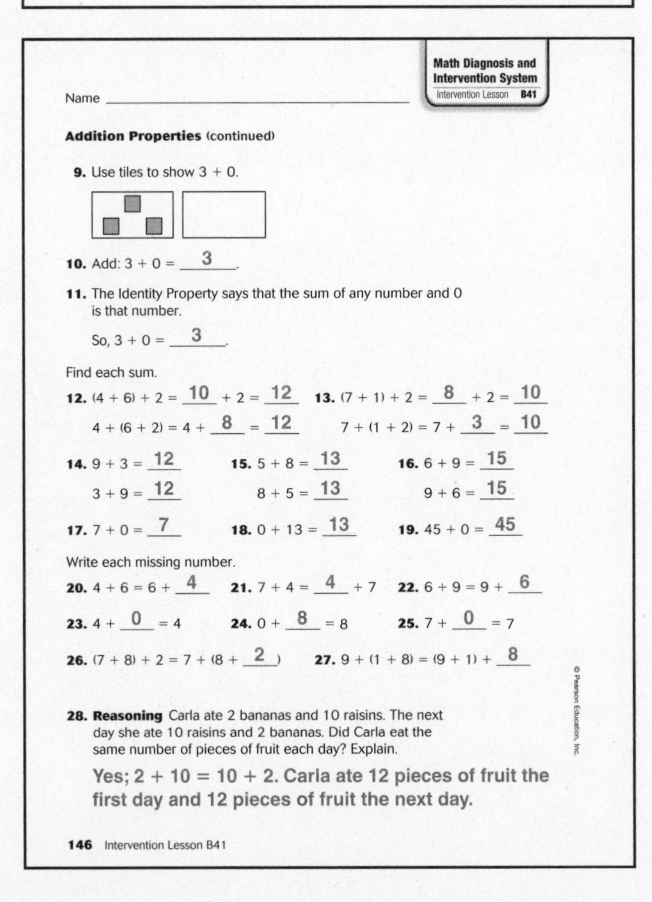

Math Diagnosis and Intervention System
Intervention Lesson B41

Name ____________________

Addition Properties (continued)

9. Use tiles to show 3 + 0.

10. Add: 3 + 0 = 3.

11. The Identity Property says that the sum of any number and 0 is that number.

    So, 3 + 0 = 3.

Find each sum.

12. (4 + 6) + 2 = 10 + 2 = 12
    4 + (6 + 2) = 4 + 8 = 12

13. (7 + 1) + 2 = 8 + 2 = 10
    7 + (1 + 2) = 7 + 3 = 10

14. 9 + 3 = 12
    3 + 9 = 12

15. 5 + 8 = 13
    8 + 5 = 13

16. 6 + 9 = 15
    9 + 6 = 15

17. 7 + 0 = 7

18. 0 + 13 = 13

19. 45 + 0 = 45

Write each missing number.

20. 4 + 6 = 6 + 4

21. 7 + 4 = 4 + 7

22. 6 + 9 = 9 + 6

23. 4 + 0 = 4

24. 0 + 8 = 8

25. 7 + 0 = 7

26. (7 + 8) + 2 = 7 + (8 + 2)

27. 9 + (1 + 8) = (9 + 1) + 8

28. **Reasoning** Carla ate 2 bananas and 10 raisins. The next day she ate 10 raisins and 2 bananas. Did Carla eat the same number of pieces of fruit each day? Explain.

    Yes; 2 + 10 = 10 + 2. Carla ate 12 pieces of fruit the first day and 12 pieces of fruit the next day.

© Pearson Education, Inc.

146 Intervention Lesson B41

Teacher Notes

Ongoing Assessment

Ask: ***Why does (3 + 2) + 6 = 5 + 6?*** You need to add what is in parentheses first. (3 + 2) = 5

Error Intervention

If students are having trouble remembering the meanings of the Commutative and Associative Properties,

then explain to them that when you commute you move from one place to another, so the Commutative Property means you move the numbers around. When you talk to different groups of people you associate with the different groups, so the Associative Property means you can make different groups with your numbers.

If You Have More Time

Have students write their own examples of each of the three properties.

Relating Addition and Subtraction

Name ____________________

Relating Addition and Subtraction

Materials 16 counters per student

1. Use counters to show each number sentence in the table. Find the missing number. Draw the counters you used in the table.

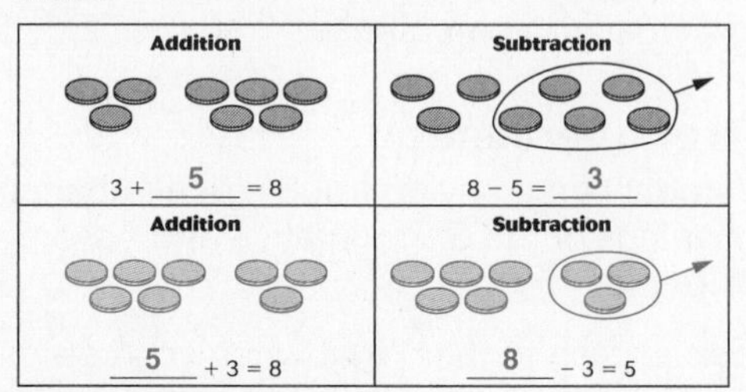

Addition	Subtraction
3 + 5 = 8	8 − 5 = 3
Addition	**Subtraction**
5 + 3 = 8	8 − 3 = 5

2. Related addition and subtraction facts have the same numbers. These same numbers are called a fact family. What three numbers were used in the fact family above? **3, 5, and 8**

3. Fill in the blanks to complete the fact family.

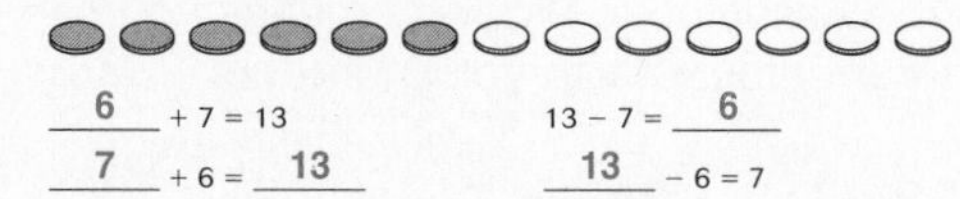

6 + 7 = 13　　13 − 7 = 6

7 + 6 = 13　　13 − 6 = 7

4. What three numbers were used in the fact family in Question 3? **6, 7, and 13**

Name ____________________

Relating Addition and Subtraction (continued)

Complete the related addition and subtraction facts.

5. 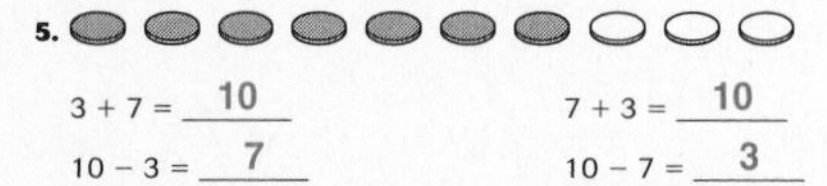

3 + 7 = 10　　7 + 3 = 10

10 − 3 = 7　　10 − 7 = 3

6.

5 + 7 = 12　　7 + 5 = 12

12 − 7 = 5　　12 − 5 = 7

Complete each fact family. You may use counters to help.

7. 4 + 8 = 12　12 − 4 = 8
8 + 4 = 12　12 − 8 = 4

8. 5 + 9 = 14　14 − 5 = 9
9 + 5 = 14　14 − 9 = 5

9. 8 + 3 = 11　11 − 8 = 3
3 + 8 = 11　11 − 3 = 8

10. 6 + 7 = 13　13 − 6 = 7
7 + 6 = 13　13 − 7 = 6

11. Reasoning John has 14 pencils. He gives some to Sonja. He has 8 left. How many pencils did John give to Sonja? **6 pencils**

12. Write two facts that are related to the subtraction fact 14 − 8 = 6.
Possible answers: 6 + 8 = 14; 8 + 6 = 14; 14 − 6 = 8; 14 − 8 = 6

Teacher Notes

Ongoing Assessment

Ask: ***Why does 8 − 4 = 4 have only 1 other fact in its family?*** It is a doubles fact. Since the 4 is used twice, 4 + 4 = 8 can not be written another way. The same is true for 8 − 4 = 4.

Error Intervention

If students have trouble finding a missing number,

then remind them that a fact family uses the same 3 numbers. So the facts have to be an arrangement of only those 3 numbers.

If You Have More Time

Have students write the fact family for 2, 4, and 6.

Multiplication as Repeated Addition

Name ______________________

Multiplication as Repeated Addition

Materials 24 counters and 4 half-sheets of paper per student or pair

Freyja has 4 plates. Each plate has 5 cherries. Answer 1 to 6 to find how many cherries she has in all.

You can use multiplication to find how many in all when you have equal groups.

1. Show 4 plates with 5 cherries on each using counters.

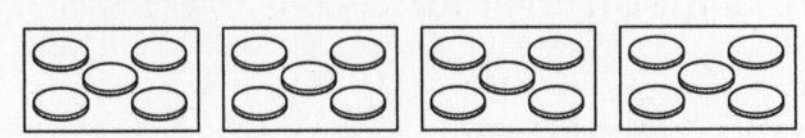

2. Use addition to find how many cherries Freyja has.

5 + 5 + 5 + 5 = 20

3. How many plates? 4

4. How many cherries on each plate? 5

5. Use multiplication to find how many cherries Freyja has in all.

4 × 5 = 20

Number of Plates; Number of Cherries on Each Plate

6. How many cherries does Freyja have in all? 20

7. Use counters and repeated addition to find 3 × 8.

3 × 8 = 8 + 8 + 8

= 24

Name ______________________

Multiplication as Repeated Addition (continued)

Add. Then multiply. Use counters if you like.

8. ♡♡♡ ♡♡♡

3 + 3 = 6

2 × 3 = 6

9.

2 + 2 + 2 + 2 = 8

4 × 2 = 8

Use the pictures to fill in the blanks.

10. **11.**

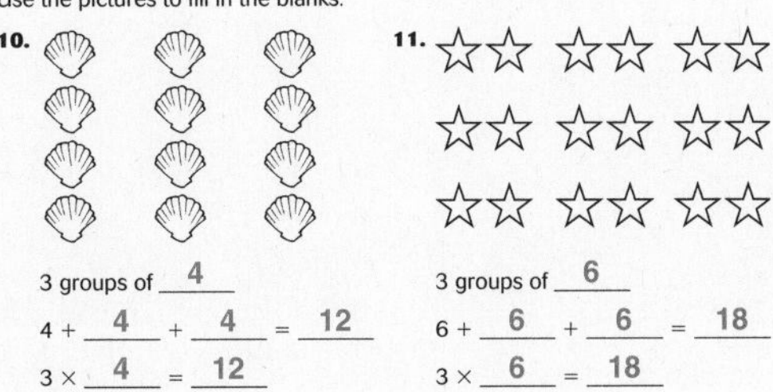

3 groups of 4

4 + 4 + 4 = 12

3 × 4 = 12

3 groups of 6

6 + 6 + 6 = 18

3 × 6 = 18

Fill in the blanks to make each number sentence true.

12. 8 + 8 + 8 + 8 + 8 + 8 = 6 × 8

13. 9 + 9 + 9 + 9 = 4 × 9

14. Reasoning Melissa says that 5 + 5 + 5 + 3 is the same thing as 4 × 5. Explain why Melissa is wrong.

The only way an addition problem can be written as a multiplication problem is if there are equal groups. There are three 5s and one 3, so there are not equal groups.

Teacher Notes

Ongoing Assessment

Ask: ***What repeated addition sentence can you write for the number of legs on 5 dogs?*** 4 + 4 + 4 + 4 + 4 = 20 ***What multiplication sentence can you write for the number of legs on 5 dogs?*** 5 × 4 = 20

Error Intervention

If students have difficulty finding the total in groups of 2, 5 or 10,

then use A16: Using Skip Counting.

If You Have More Time

Have students work in pairs and take turns naming something that comes in packages of 2 to 9. One partner writes a number sentence for how much would be in 3 packages and the other partner does the same for 4 packages.

Arrays and Multiplication

Math Diagnosis and Intervention System
Intervention Lesson **B44**

Name ______________________

Math Diagnosis and Intervention System
Intervention Lesson B44

Arrays and Multiplication

Materials 16 counters per student

1. Show an array of 4 rows with 2 counters in each row.
2. Write a multiplication sentence for the array.

   4 × 2 = 8
   Number of Rows × Number of Counters in Each Row = Total Number of Counters

3. How many counters are in the array? 8

4. Show an array of 2 rows with 4 counters in each row.
5. Write a multiplication sentence for this array.

   2 × 4 = 8
   Number of Rows × Number of Counters in Each Row = Total Number of Counters

6. How many counters are in this array? 8
7. Both arrays have 8 counters.
   So, 4 × 2 = 2 × 4
8. Since both arrays have 8 counters then you can say,
   4 × 2 = 8, and 2 × 4 = 8

Knowing one multiplication fact means you know another.

9. If you know 3 × 8 = 24, then you know 8 × 3 = 24.

Name ______________________

Math Diagnosis and Intervention System
Intervention Lesson B44

Arrays and Multiplication (continued)

Write a multiplication sentence for each array.

10. 6 × 5 = 30

11. 5 × 7 = 35

Draw an array to find each multiplication fact. Write the product.

12. 3 × 5 = 15
    The array should show 3 rows of 5.

13. 2 × 6 = 12
    The array should show 2 rows of 6.

Fill in the blanks.

14. 4 × 8 = 32, so 8 × 4 = 32
15. 9 × 2 = 18, so 2 × 9 = 18
16. 5 × 7 = 35, so 7 × 5 = 35
17. 3 × 6 = 18, so 6 × 3 = 18
18. 2 × 4 = 8, so 4 × 2 = 8
19. 1 × 6 = 6, so 6 × 1 = 6
20. **Reasoning** How does an array show equal groups?
    Each row has the same number of objects.

Teacher Notes

Ongoing Assessment

Ask: ***If you know 9 × 4 = 36, why can you say you know that 4 × 9 = 36?*** Sample answer: The arrays are made with the same number of counters, one array is just the other one turned sideways.

Error Intervention

If students get confused on the correct fact for a given array or have difficulty drawing the right number of rows with the right number in each for a given fact,

then encourage the students to read the multiplication fact as "6 rows of 4" instead of "6 times 4".

If You Have More Time

Have students in pairs. Have one partner draw an array, or make it if counters are available, and write the multiplication sentence. Then have the other partner draw or make the corresponding fact, like 5 × 7 for 7 × 5, and write the multiplication sentence for it.

Using Multiplication to Compare

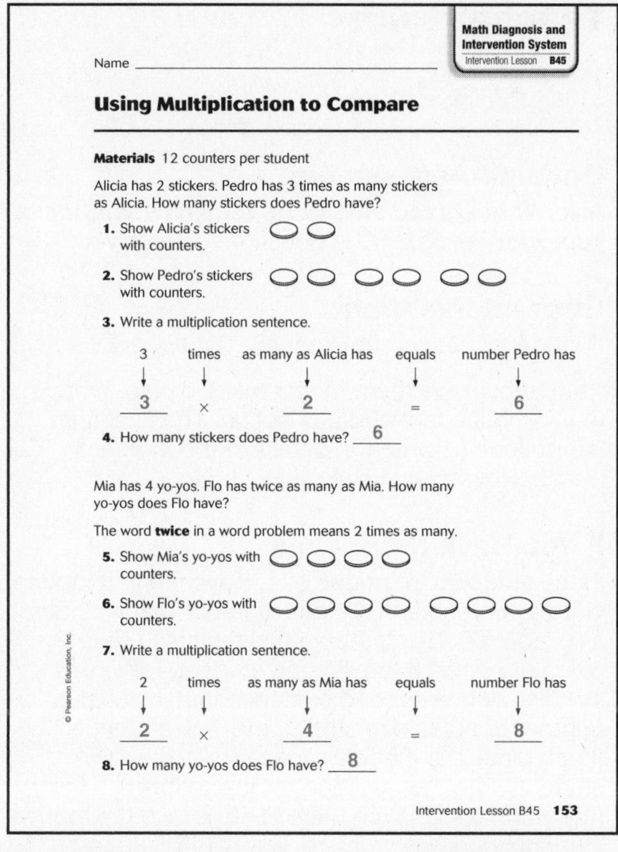

Math Diagnosis and Intervention System
Intervention Lesson B45

Name ________________

Using Multiplication to Compare

Materials 12 counters per student

Alicia has 2 stickers. Pedro has 3 times as many stickers as Alicia. How many stickers does Pedro have?

1. Show Alicia's stickers with counters.

2. Show Pedro's stickers with counters.

3. Write a multiplication sentence.

3	times	as many as Alicia has	equals	number Pedro has
↓	↓	↓	↓	↓
3	×	2	=	6

4. How many stickers does Pedro have? 6

Mia has 4 yo-yos. Flo has twice as many as Mia. How many yo-yos does Flo have?

The word **twice** in a word problem means 2 times as many.

5. Show Mia's yo-yos with counters.

6. Show Flo's yo-yos with counters.

7. Write a multiplication sentence.

2	times	as many as Mia has	equals	number Flo has
↓	↓	↓	↓	↓
2	×	4	=	8

8. How many yo-yos does Flo have? 8

© Pearson Education, Inc.

Intervention Lesson B45 **153**

Math Diagnosis and Intervention System
Intervention Lesson B45

Name ________________

Using Multiplication to Compare (continued)

Solve. You may use drawings or counters to help.

9. Janos has 3 stickers. Lucy has twice as many stickers as Janos. How many stickers does Lucy have?

6 stickers

10. Rob has 4 model airplanes. Julio has 3 times as many model airplanes as Rob. How many model airplanes does Julio have?

12 model airplanes

11. Mr. King has 5 apples left in his store. Ruth needs twice as many apples to bake apple pies. How many apples does Ruth need?

10 apples

Use the recipe to answer Exercises 12–15.

Fruit Smoothie
3 large bananas
2 cups strawberries
1 cup orange juice
1 cup cranberry juice
1 cup ice cubes
Blend until smooth.
Makes 5 servings.

12. The recipe serves 5 people. Joan wants to make the recipe for 15 people. How many times more is this?

3 times more

13. How many bananas will Joan need to make the recipe for 15 people?

$3 \times 3 = 9$ bananas

14. How many cups of strawberries will Joan need to make the recipe for 15 people?

6 cups

15. **Reasoning** If Joan wants to make twice as much as the recipe in the chart, what will she need to do to all of the ingredients?

double them

© Pearson Education, Inc.

154 Intervention Lesson B45

Teacher Notes

Ongoing Assessment

Ask: ***12 is twice as many as what number?*** 6

Error Intervention

If students have trouble figuring out how to draw the unknown amount,

then encourage students to show the first group *n* times. For example, since Wayne has 3 times as many as Alicia, show what Alicia has 3 times.

If You Have More Time

Have students cut out 9 small squares and label them 1 through 9. Have one partner pick a square. The other partner calculates 3 times the number picked. Do not return the number to the pile. Continue until all squares have been picked. Repeat the activity by having students calculate 5 times each number picked.

Writing Multiplication Stories

Math Diagnosis and Intervention System
Intervention Lesson B46

Name ______________________

Writing Multiplication Stories

Follow 1 to 5 below to write a multiplication story for 5 × 4 that is about hamburgers and pickle slices.

1. 5 × 4 means __5__ groups of __4__.

2. So, 5 × 4 might mean __5__ hamburgers with __4__ pickle slices each.

3. Write a story about 5 hamburgers with 4 pickle slices each.

Mrs. __any last name__ went through a drive thru and bought __5__ hamburgers. Each hamburger had __4__ pickle slices. How many __pickle slices__ were there in all?

4. Draw a picture to find how many pickle slices there were in all. **Drawing should show 5 groups of 4.**

5 × 4 = __20__

5. How many pickle slices were there in all? __20__

6. Write a multiplication story for 6 × 3 about nests and eggs.

Mr. __any last name__ found __6__ nests. Each nest had __3__ eggs. How many __eggs__ did he find in all?

7. Draw a picture to find how many eggs he found in all. **Drawing should show 6 groups of 3.**

6 × 3 = __18__

8. How many eggs did he find in all? __18__

Math Diagnosis and Intervention System
Intervention Lesson B46

Name ______________________

Writing Multiplication Stories (continued)

Write a multiplication story. Then find the product.

9.

2 × 5 = __10__

Check students' stories.

Write a multiplication story for Exercises 10 and 11. Draw a picture to find each product.

10. 6 × 6 = __36__

Check students' stories and pictures.

11. 4 × 5 = __20__

Check students' stories and pictures.

12. There are 4 houses on Oak Street. Four people live in each house. How many people live on Oak Street?

4 × 4 = 16 people

Teacher Notes

Ongoing Assessment

Ask: ***What should always be the last sentence of your story problem?*** A question to be solved.

Error Intervention

If students have trouble completing a story,

then encourage them to first make a plan. Write a multiplication fact and a question. Then use that information to write the details of the problem. (3 × 2; How many fish in all?)

If You Have More Time

Place students in groups of 4. Have the first student write a sentence on a piece of paper that includes a number of objects. (Seth has 6 plates.) Give the piece of paper to the second student. Have this student write a second sentence that includes a number of objects related to the first sentence. (Each plate has 4 apple slices.) Have the third student write the question for the problem. (How many apple slices are there in all?) Have the fourth student solve the problem. Repeat the process 3 more times so that each student does a different part of the problem.

Multiplying by 2 and 5

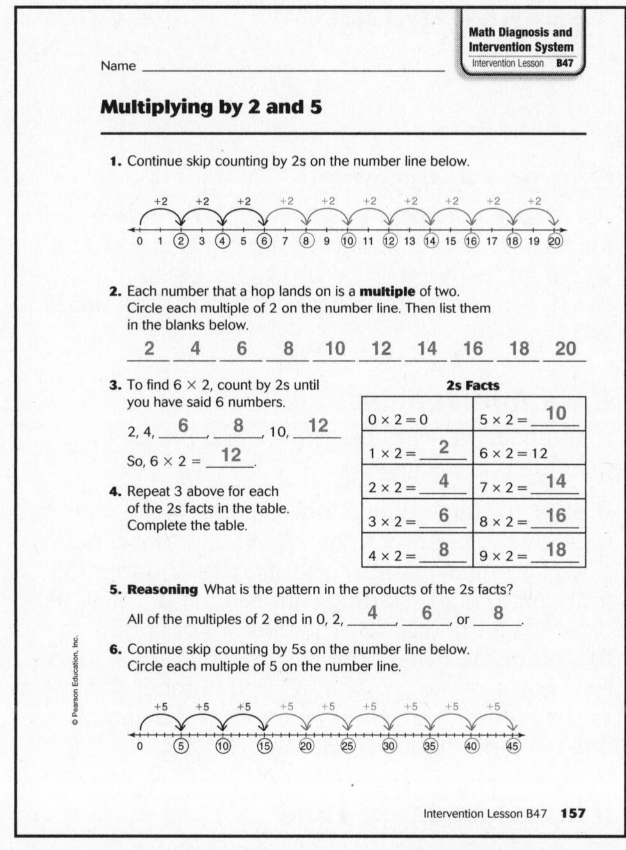

Name ____________________

Multiplying by 2 and 5

1. Continue skip counting by 2s on the number line below.

2. Each number that a hop lands on is a **multiple** of two. Circle each multiple of 2 on the number line. Then list them in the blanks below.

2, 4, 6, 8, 10, 12, 14, 16, 18, 20

3. To find 6 × 2, count by 2s until you have said 6 numbers.

2, 4, 6, 8, 10, 12

So, 6 × 2 = 12.

4. Repeat 3 above for each of the 2s facts in the table. Complete the table.

2s Facts

0 × 2 = 0	5 × 2 = 10
1 × 2 = 2	6 × 2 = 12
2 × 2 = 4	7 × 2 = 14
3 × 2 = 6	8 × 2 = 16
4 × 2 = 8	9 × 2 = 18

5. Reasoning What is the pattern in the products of the 2s facts?

All of the multiples of 2 end in 0, 2, 4, 6, or 8.

6. Continue skip counting by 5s on the number line below. Circle each multiple of 5 on the number line.

Teacher Notes

Ongoing Assessment

Ask: ***Since all the multiples of 2 end in either 0, 2, 4, 6, or 8, are multiples of 2 odd or even?*** Even

Error Intervention

If students are having trouble with problems like 2 × 8,

then have the students think about the doubles addition facts. 2 × 8 is 2 groups of 8, or 8 + 8. Since 8 + 8 = 16, then 2 × 8 = 16.

If You Have More Time

Have 2 students each take 9 index cards and label their cards 1 through 9. Shuffle the cards. The first round is 2s facts. Each student takes a turn drawing a card and finding the product of that number times 2. If correct, the student keeps the card, otherwise it goes back into the pile. After all cards from the pile are used, shuffle and repeat with the 5s facts.

Name ____________________

Multiplying by 2 and 5 (continued)

7. Circle each multiple of 5 on the number line. Then list them in the blanks below.

5, 10, 15, 20, 25, 30, 35, 40, 45

8. To find 7 × 5, count by 5s until you have said 7 numbers.

5, 10, 15, 20, 25, 30, 35

So, 7 × 5 = 35.

9. Repeat 8 above for each of the 5s facts in the table.

5s Facts

0 × 5 = 0	5 × 5 = 25
1 × 5 = 5	6 × 5 = 30
2 × 5 = 10	7 × 5 = 35
3 × 5 = 15	8 × 5 = 40
4 × 5 = 20	9 × 5 = 45

10. Reasoning What is the pattern in the products of the 5s facts?

All of the multiples of 5 end in 0 or 5.

Complete each multiplication problem.

11. 2 × 3 = 6 **12.** 2 × 6 = 12 **13.** 2 × 2 = 4 **14.** 2 × 1 = 2

15. 7 × 2 = 14 **16.** 7 × 5 = 35 **17.** 5 × 3 = 15 **18.** 8 × 5 = 40

19. 5 × 4 = 20 **20.** 1 × 5 = 5 **21.** 2 × 4 = 8 **22.** 5 × 2 = 10

23. Reasoning Movie tickets are on sale for $5 each. Ross, Emily, and John want to see the movie. Is $18 enough for all of their tickets? Explain.

Yes; 3 × 5 = 15 and $15 < $18.

Multiplying by 9

Math Diagnosis and Intervention System
Intervention Lesson **B48**

Name ______________________

Math Diagnosis and Intervention System
Intervention Lesson B48

Multiplying by 9

Learn how to multiply by 9 by answering 1 to 5.

1. Complete the table.

Fact	Product	Two Digits in the Product	Sum of the Two Digits in the Product
0 × 9 =	0	0 and 0	0 + 0 = 0
1 × 9 =	9	0 and 9	0 + 9 = 9
2 × 9 =	18	1 and 8	1 + 8 = 9
3 × 9 =	27	2 and 7	2 + 7 = 9
4 × 9 =	36	3 and 6	3 + 6 = 9
5 × 9 =	45	4 and 5	4 + 5 = 9
6 × 9 =	54	5 and 4	5 + 4 = 9
7 × 9 =	63	6 and 3	6 + 3 = 9
8 × 9 =	72	7 and 2	7 + 2 = 9
9 × 9 =	81	8 and 1	8 + 1 = 9

2. Reasoning Besides the product of 0 × 9, what pattern do you see in the sums of the digits of each product?

The sum of the digits is always 9.

3. Look at the number being multiplied by 9 in each product and the tens digit of that product.

When 3 is multiplied by 9, what is the tens digit of the product? 2.

When 6 is multiplied by 9, what is the tens digit of the product? 5.

Name ______________________

Math Diagnosis and Intervention System
Intervention Lesson B48

Multiplying by 9 (continued)

4. Reasoning Complete to describe the pattern you see in the tens digits of the products when a factor is multiplied by 9.

The tens digit of the product is 1 less than the other factor.

5. Complete the following to find 7 × 9.

The tens digit is 7 − 1 = 6.

The ones digit is 9 − 6 = 3.

So, 7 × 9 = 63 and 9 × 7 = 63.

Find each product.

6. 1 × 9 = 9 **7.** 9 × 2 = 18 **8.** 9 × 4 = 36 **9.** 9 × 0 = 0

10. 6 × 9 = 54 **11.** 9 × 9 = 81 **12.** 8 × 9 = 72 **13.** 5 × 9 = 45

14. 9 × 7 = 63 **15.** 3 × 9 = 27 **16.** 2 × 9 = 18 **17.** 9 × 6 = 54

18. Reasoning Joshua and his sister have each saved $9. They wish to buy a new game that costs $20. If they put their savings together, do they have enough money to buy the game?

No, they only have $18; they are $2 short.

19. Reasoning Jane said that 7 × 9 = 62. Explain how you know this is incorrect.

The sum of the digits in the product does not equal 9.

Teacher Notes

Ongoing Assessment

Ask: ***Larry said that 6 × 9 = 45. Why is this incorrect?*** The tens digit of the product must be 1 less than the number by which 9 is being multiplied. 6 − 1 = 5, so the tens digit must be 5. The product is 54, not 45.

Error Intervention

If students have trouble while using the method described in the lesson,

then show the students how to use their fingers to multiply by 9. Put both hands on your desk, palms down. Mentally number your fingers and thumbs from left to right, starting with 1. To find 3 × 9, bend down finger number 3. The number of fingers to the left of the bent finger shows the number in the tens place of the product. (2) The number of fingers to the right of the bent finger shows the number of ones in the product. (7) So, 3 × 9 = 27.

If You Have More Time

Have pairs play I'm Thinking of a Number. One partner writes down a number from 0 to 9, such as 7, and says: I'm thinking of a number. When it is multiplied by 9, the product is 63. What is the number? The other partner says the number. Then, students change roles and repeat.

Multiplying by 1 or 0

Math Diagnosis and Intervention System
Intervention Lesson B49

Name ________________

Multiplying by 1 or 0

Materials 9 counters and 9 half sheets of paper per student

Complete 1 to 6 to discover that when you multiply any number by 1, the product is the other number.

Use the paper to show groups and the counters to show the number in each.

1. Show 5 × 1.

2. How many counters in all? 5 5 × 1 = 5

3. Show 4 × 1.

4. How many counters in all? 4 4 × 1 = 4

5. Use the paper and counters to complete the table on the right.

6. Reasoning What pattern do you see in the table?

Sample answer: The product is the same as the number being multiplied by 1.

1s Facts

0 × 1 = 0	5 × 1 = 5
1 × 1 = 1	6 × 1 = 6
2 × 1 = 2	7 × 1 = 7
3 × 1 = 3	8 × 1 = 8
4 × 1 = 4	9 × 1 = 9

Complete 7 to 12 to discover that when you multiply any number by 0, the product is 0.

7. Show 3 × 0.

8. How many counters in all? 0

9. Show 6 × 0.

10. How many counters in all? 0

Math Diagnosis and Intervention System
Intervention Lesson B49

Name ________________

Multiplying by 1 or 0 (continued)

11. Use the paper and counters to complete the table on the right.

12. Reasoning What pattern do you see in the table?

Sample answer: The product is always 0.

0s Facts

0 × 0 = 0	5 × 0 = 0
1 × 0 = 0	6 × 0 = 0
2 × 0 = 0	7 × 0 = 0
3 × 0 = 0	8 × 0 = 0
4 × 0 = 0	9 × 0 = 0

Find each product.

13. 2 × 1 = 2 **14.** 4 × 0 = 0 **15.** 6 × 1 = 6

16. 1 × 9 = 9 **17.** 1 × 2 = 2 **18.** 4 × 1 = 4

19. 3 × 0 = 0 **20.** 0 × 9 = 0 **21.** 8 × 1 = 8 **22.** 1 × 8 = 8 **23.** 9 × 1 = 9

24. 5 × 1 = 5 **25.** 5 × 0 = 0 **26.** 1 × 1 = 1 **27.** 1 × 0 = 0 **28.** 7 × 1 = 7

29. Reasoning Explain why 1 × 0 = 0.

Possible Answer: Because when you multiply any number by zero, the answer is always zero. Also, when you multiply any number by one, the answer is always the other number.

Teacher Notes

Ongoing Assessment

Ask: ***What is 3,234 × 1? How do you know?***
3,234; I know because any number multiplied by 1 is that number.

Error Intervention

If students write the products of 0 facts as the other number instead of 0,

then they might be confusing the Zero Property of Multiplication with the Zero Property of Addition. Remind students that 0 × 3 is "no groups of 3" and that 3 × 0 is "3 groups of nothing", which both result in 0. Point out that this is not the same thing as "3 added to nothing" or "nothing added to 3".

If You Have More Time

Have students write their own multiplication stories for 8 × 1 and 8 × 0.

Multiplying by 3

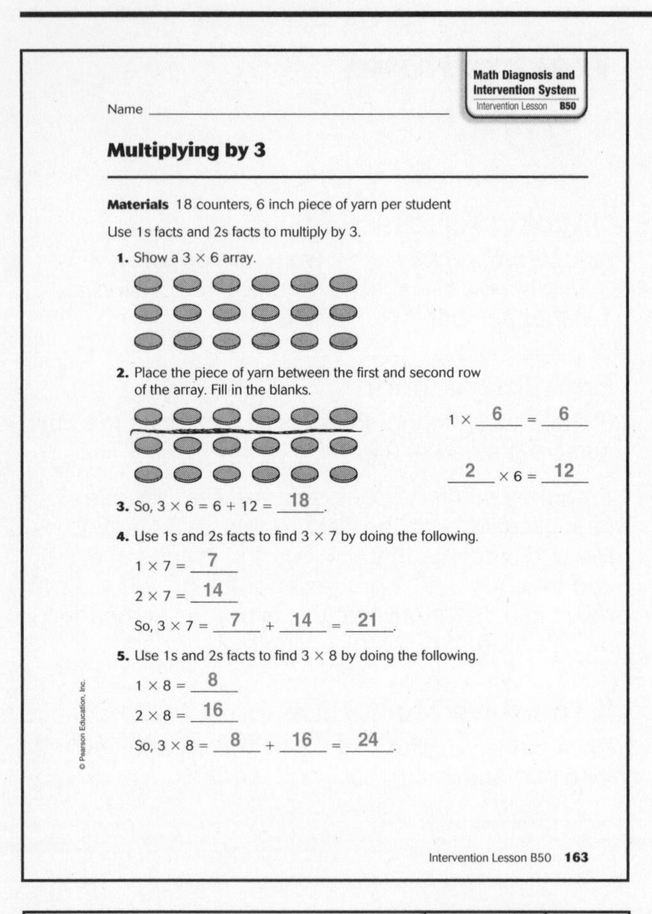

Math Diagnosis and Intervention System
Intervention Lesson B50

Name ____________________

Multiplying by 3

Materials 18 counters, 6 inch piece of yarn per student

Use 1s facts and 2s facts to multiply by 3.

1. Show a 3 × 6 array.

2. Place the piece of yarn between the first and second row of the array. Fill in the blanks.

1 × 6 = 6

2 × 6 = 12

3. So, 3 × 6 = 6 + 12 = 18.

4. Use 1s and 2s facts to find 3 × 7 by doing the following.

1 × 7 = 7

2 × 7 = 14

So, 3 × 7 = 7 + 14 = 21.

5. Use 1s and 2s facts to find 3 × 8 by doing the following.

1 × 8 = 8

2 × 8 = 16

So, 3 × 8 = 8 + 16 = 24.

© Pearson Education, Inc.

Intervention Lesson B50 **163**

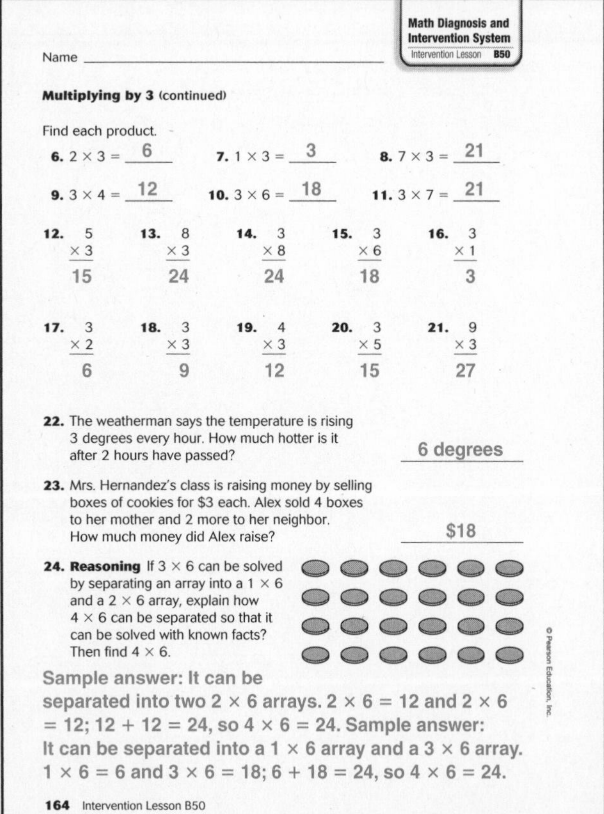

Math Diagnosis and Intervention System
Intervention Lesson B50

Name ____________________

Multiplying by 3 (continued)

Find each product.

6. 2 × 3 = 6
7. 1 × 3 = 3
8. 7 × 3 = 21
9. 3 × 4 = 12
10. 3 × 6 = 18
11. 3 × 7 = 21
12. 5 × 3 = 15
13. 8 × 3 = 24
14. 3 × 8 = 24
15. 3 × 6 = 18
16. 3 × 1 = 3
17. 3 × 2 = 6
18. 3 × 3 = 9
19. 4 × 3 = 12
20. 3 × 5 = 15
21. 9 × 3 = 27

22. The weatherman says the temperature is rising 3 degrees every hour. How much hotter is it after 2 hours have passed? 6 degrees

23. Mrs. Hernandez's class is raising money by selling boxes of cookies for $3 each. Alex sold 4 boxes to her mother and 2 more to her neighbor. How much money did Alex raise? $18

24. **Reasoning** If 3 × 6 can be solved by separating an array into a 1 × 6 and a 2 × 6 array, explain how 4 × 6 can be separated so that it can be solved with known facts? Then find 4 × 6.

Sample answer: It can be separated into two 2 × 6 arrays. 2 × 6 = 12 and 2 × 6 = 12; 12 + 12 = 24, so 4 × 6 = 24. Sample answer: It can be separated into a 1 × 6 array and a 3 × 6 array. 1 × 6 = 6 and 3 × 6 = 18; 6 + 18 = 24, so 4 × 6 = 24.

© Pearson Education, Inc.

164 Intervention Lesson B50

Teacher Notes

Ongoing Assessment

Ask: ***Which multiplication fact can be found using 1 × 4 plus 2 × 4?*** 3 × 4

Error Intervention

If students have problems using known facts to find the 3s facts,

then have them draw a number line and skip count by 3s. Then have students circle all the multiples of 3. Explain that the number of hops represents the number that is being multiplied by 3. So if they hop 5 times, the number they land on is 5 × 3 = 15.

If You Have More Time

Group students in pairs. Give each pair of students 20 index cards and at least 100 counters. Have each partner label 10 index cards (for a total of 20 index cards) with the 3s facts expressions (3 × 0 through 3 × 9). Have students shuffle the cards. Partners take turns drawing a card. The student finds the product and then takes that number of counters and stacks them in one tall column. The students take turns drawing a card, solving the expression, and stacking counters on their own tall column. When a student's column topples, he or she counts the number of counters successfully stacked. The other partner continues until his or her column topples. The student with the most counters successfully stacked wins. If all 20 cards are used without either tower toppling, the person with the most counters wins.

Multiplying by 4

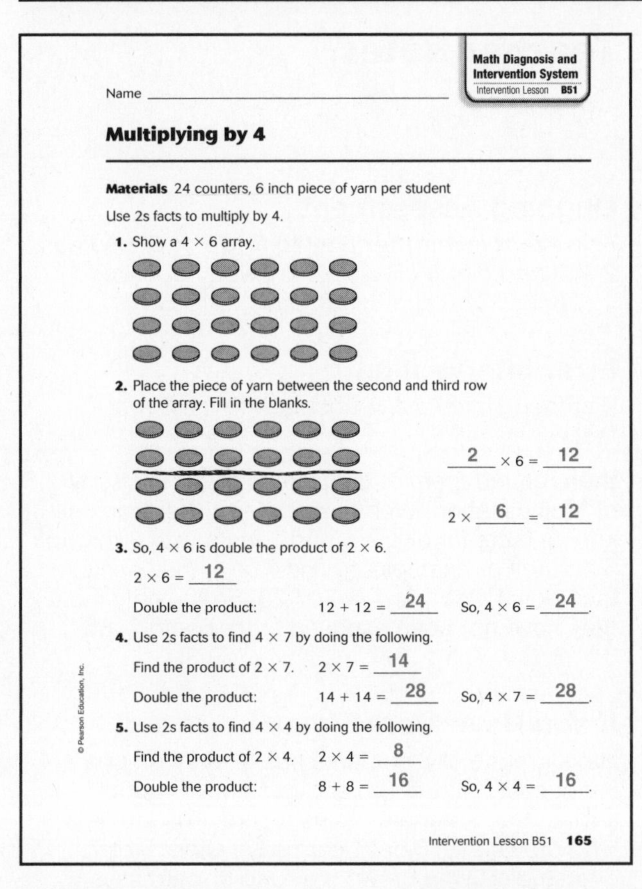

Math Diagnosis and Intervention System
Intervention Lesson B51

Name ______________________

Multiplying by 4

Materials 24 counters, 6 inch piece of yarn per student

Use 2s facts to multiply by 4.

1. Show a 4 × 6 array.

2. Place the piece of yarn between the second and third row of the array. Fill in the blanks.

2 × 6 = 12

2 × 6 = 12

3. So, 4 × 6 is double the product of 2 × 6.

2 × 6 = 12

Double the product: 12 + 12 = 24 So, 4 × 6 = 24.

4. Use 2s facts to find 4 × 7 by doing the following.

Find the product of 2 × 7. 2 × 7 = 14

Double the product: 14 + 14 = 28 So, 4 × 7 = 28.

5. Use 2s facts to find 4 × 4 by doing the following.

Find the product of 2 × 4. 2 × 4 = 8

Double the product: 8 + 8 = 16 So, 4 × 4 = 16.

© Pearson Education, Inc.

Intervention Lesson B51 **165**

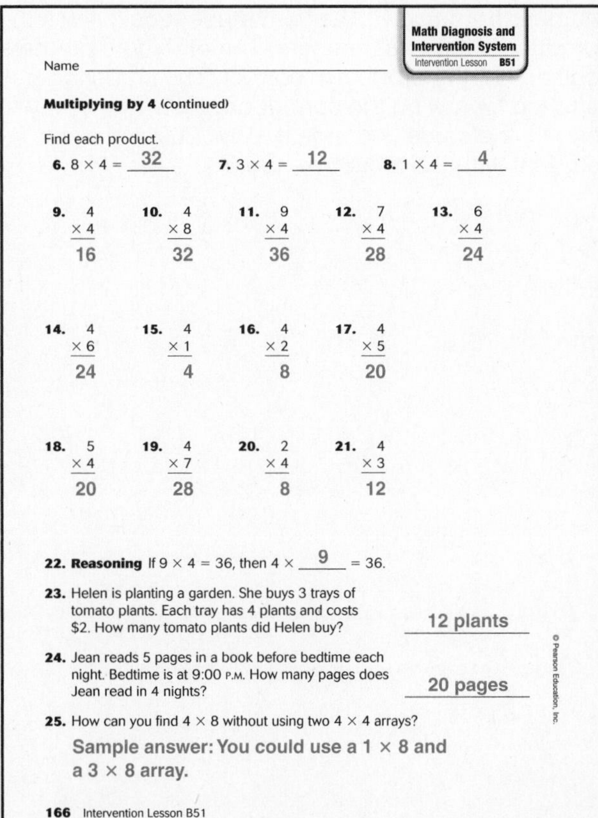

Math Diagnosis and Intervention System
Intervention Lesson B51

Name ______________________

Multiplying by 4 (continued)

Find each product.

6. 8 × 4 = 32 **7.** 3 × 4 = 12 **8.** 1 × 4 = 4

9. 4 × 4 = 16 **10.** 4 × 8 = 32 **11.** 9 × 4 = 36 **12.** 7 × 4 = 28 **13.** 6 × 4 = 24

14. 4 × 6 = 24 **15.** 4 × 1 = 4 **16.** 4 × 2 = 8 **17.** 4 × 5 = 20

18. 5 × 4 = 20 **19.** 4 × 7 = 28 **20.** 2 × 4 = 8 **21.** 4 × 3 = 12

22. Reasoning If 9 × 4 = 36, then 4 × 9 = 36.

23. Helen is planting a garden. She buys 3 trays of tomato plants. Each tray has 4 plants and costs $2. How many tomato plants did Helen buy? 12 plants

24. Jean reads 5 pages in a book before bedtime each night. Bedtime is at 9:00 P.M. How many pages does Jean read in 4 nights? 20 pages

25. How can you find 4 × 8 without using two 4 × 4 arrays?

Sample answer: You could use a 1 × 8 and a 3 × 8 array.

© Pearson Education, Inc.

166 Intervention Lesson B51

Teacher Notes

Ongoing Assessment

Ask: ***Which 4 multiplication fact can be found using 18 + 18?*** 4 × 9

Error Intervention

If students understand how to use the 2s facts to find the 4s facts, but are having trouble remembering the 2s facts,

then use G25: Multiplying by 2 and 5.

If You Have More Time

Group students in pairs. Give each pair of students 20 index cards. Have partners label the cards. One card will have the expression (4 × 8). The other card will have the product (32). Do this for 4 × 0 through 4 × 9. (10 cards should be expressions, 10 cards should be products). Have students play a "Go Fish" game. Shuffle all the cards. Deal out 5 cards each. Put the rest in a "draw" pile. A student who has 32 would need to ask for "4 × 8". A student who has 4 × 8 would need to ask for 32. If the other person does not have the card asked for, the asker must draw a card. When a match is made the student puts the pair to the side and goes again. Once a player has no cards left, the students count how many complete facts they have matched. The player with the most complete facts wins.

Multiplying by 6 or 7

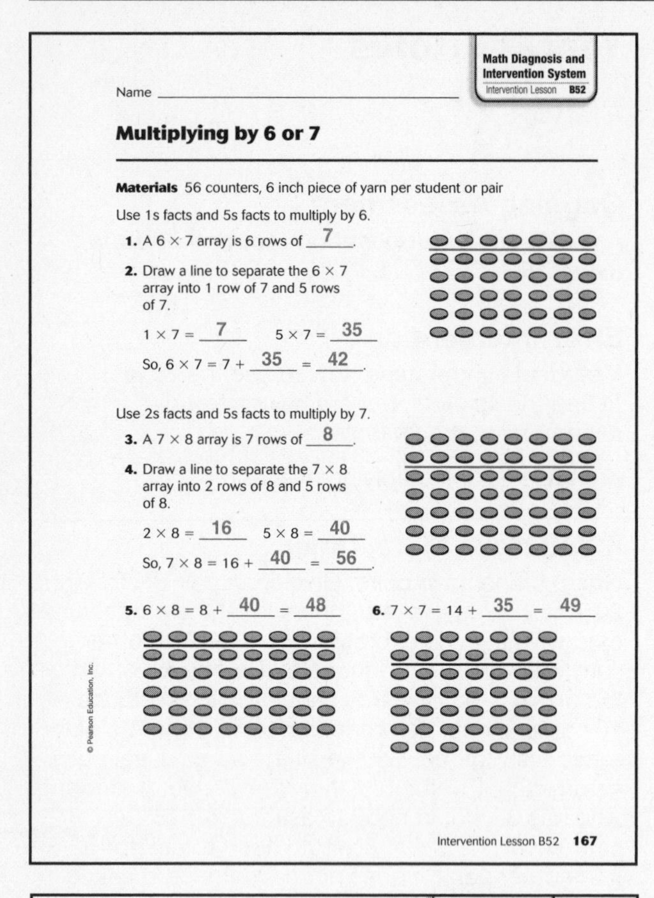

Math Diagnosis and Intervention System
Intervention Lesson B52

Name ______________________

Multiplying by 6 or 7

Materials 56 counters, 6 inch piece of yarn per student or pair

Use 1s facts and 5s facts to multiply by 6.

1. A 6 × 7 array is 6 rows of 7.

2. Draw a line to separate the 6 × 7 array into 1 row of 7 and 5 rows of 7.

1 × 7 = 7   5 × 7 = 35

So, 6 × 7 = 7 + 35 = 42.

Use 2s facts and 5s facts to multiply by 7.

3. A 7 × 8 array is 7 rows of 8.

4. Draw a line to separate the 7 × 8 array into 2 rows of 8 and 5 rows of 8.

2 × 8 = 16   5 × 8 = 40

So, 7 × 8 = 16 + 40 = 56.

5. 6 × 8 = 8 + 40 = 48   **6.** 7 × 7 = 14 + 35 = 49

© Pearson Education, Inc.

Intervention Lesson B52 **167**

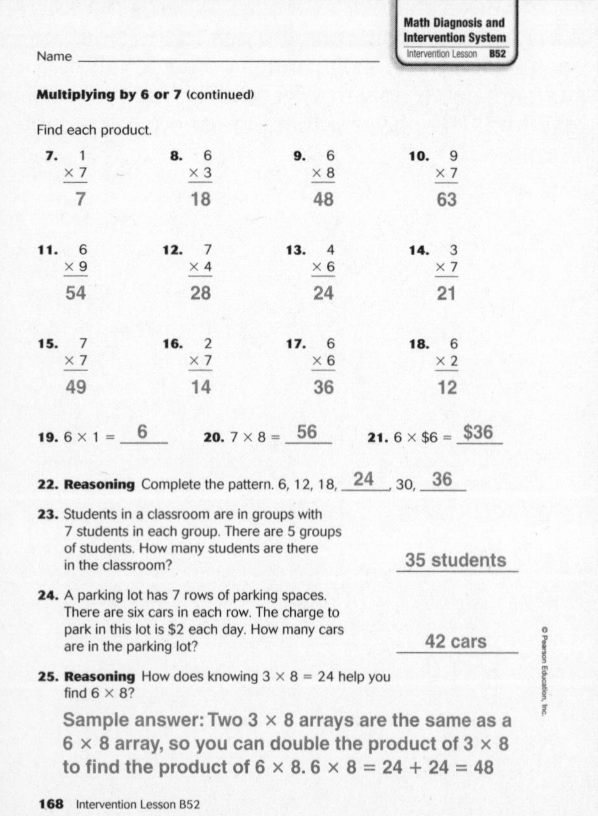

Math Diagnosis and Intervention System
Intervention Lesson B52

Name ______________________

Multiplying by 6 or 7 (continued)

Find each product.

7. 1 × 7 = 7   **8.** 6 × 3 = 18   **9.** 6 × 8 = 48   **10.** 9 × 7 = 63

11. 6 × 9 = 54   **12.** 7 × 4 = 28   **13.** 4 × 6 = 24   **14.** 3 × 7 = 21

15. 7 × 7 = 49   **16.** 2 × 7 = 14   **17.** 6 × 6 = 36   **18.** 6 × 2 = 12

19. 6 × 1 = 6   **20.** 7 × 8 = 56   **21.** 6 × $6 = $36

22. Reasoning Complete the pattern. 6, 12, 18, 24, 30, 36

23. Students in a classroom are in groups with 7 students in each group. There are 5 groups of students. How many students are there in the classroom? 35 students

24. A parking lot has 7 rows of parking spaces. There are six cars in each row. The charge to park in this lot is $2 each day. How many cars are in the parking lot? 42 cars

25. Reasoning How does knowing 3 × 8 = 24 help you find 6 × 8?

Sample answer: Two 3 × 8 arrays are the same as a 6 × 8 array, so you can double the product of 3 × 8 to find the product of 6 × 8. 6 × 8 = 24 + 24 = 48

© Pearson Education, Inc.

168 Intervention Lesson B52

Teacher Notes

Ongoing Assessment

Ask: ***What is another way to find 7 × 8, besides 2 × 8 and 5 × 8?*** Possible answers: 3 × 8 and 4 × 8; or 1 × 8 and 6 × 8; or 7 × 4 and 7 × 4.

Error Intervention

If students are having trouble with the 6 and 7 facts,

then remind them of the Commutative Property of Multiplication. With this property, they can use known facts for all the 6 and 7 facts with 0 through 5 and 9. For example, to find 7 × 4, they can use the known fact that 4 × 7 = 28. So the only facts they have not been exposed to for 6 and 7 are: 6 × 6, 6 × 7, 6 × 8, 7 × 7, and 7 × 8.

If You Have More Time

Have groups of 3 students put “6 or 7” on one index card, “0 to 9” on another, and “Product” on a third. Each student draws a card. The student who draws the “6 or 7” card says either 6 or 7. The student who draws the “0 to 9” card says a number from 0 to 9. The third student calculates the product of the two numbers. The other two partners check that the product is correct. The student gets a token for saying the correct product. Then, they shuffle the cards and repeat. After 20 rounds, the student with the most tokens wins.

Math Diagnosis and Intervention System
Intervention Lesson **B53**

Multiplying by 8

Math Diagnosis and Intervention System
Intervention Lesson B53

Name ______________________

Multiplying by 8

Use 4s facts to multiply by 8.

1. An 8×7 array is 8 rows of 7.
2. Draw a line to separate the 8×7 array into two arrays with 4 rows of 7.
3. Since the 8×7 array is the same thing as two 4×7 arrays, you can find the product of 4×7 and then double it.

   $4 \times 7 =$ 28

   Double the product: 28 + 28 = 56

   So, $8 \times 7 =$ 56.

You can also use 3s facts and 5s facts to multiply by 8.

4. Draw a line to separate the 8×7 array into a 3×7 array and a 5×7.

   $3 \times 7 =$ 21

   $5 \times 7 =$ 35
5. Since the 8×7 array is the same thing as a 3×7 array plus a 5×7 array, add the products.

   $8 \times 7 = 21 +$ 35

   $=$ 56

   So, $8 \times 7 =$ 56.
6. **Reasoning** Explain two ways to find 8×6.

   $4 \times 6 = 24$ and $24 + 24 = 48$. So $8 \times 6 = 48$.
   $3 \times 6 = 18$, $5 \times 6 = 30$, and $18 + 30 = 48$.
   So $8 \times 6 = 48$.

Math Diagnosis and Intervention System
Intervention Lesson B53

Name ______________________

Multiplying by 8 (continued)

In Exercises 7–10, use 3s facts, 4s facts and 5s facts to fill in the blanks and find the product.

7. $8 \times 8 = 24 +$ 40 $=$ 64
8. $8 \times 8 = 32 +$ 32 $=$ 64
9. $8 \times 9 = 27 +$ 45 $=$ 72
10. $8 \times 9 = 36 +$ 36 $=$ 72

Find each product.

11. $8 \times 1 =$ 8
12. $2 \times 8 =$ 16
13. $6 \times 8 =$ 48
14. $0 \times 8 =$ 0
15. $8 \times 2 =$ 16
16. $8 \times 4 =$ 32
17. $1 \times 8 =$ 8
18. $8 \times 3 =$ 24
19. $8 \times 6 =$ 48
20. $9 \times 8 =$ 72
21. $7 \times 8 =$ 56
22. $8 \times 5 =$ 40
23. $8 \times 8 =$ 64
24. $4 \times 8 =$ 32
25. There are 8 ounces in each cup of water. A recipe calls for 3 cups of water. How many ounces of water are needed for the recipe? 24 ounces
26. Each chapter in a book has 8 pages and 3 pictures. There are 6 chapters in the book. How many pages are there in the book? 48 pages
27. **Reasoning** If $9 \times 8 = 72$, then $8 \times 9 =$ 72.
28. **Reasoning** Find 8×5. Tell how you found it.

   $8 \times 5 = 40$. Strategies will vary.

Teacher Notes

Ongoing Assessment

Ask: ***What are 4 different ways you can find 8×8, using other known facts?*** 1×8 and 7×8; 2×8 and 6×8; 3×8 and 5×8; 4×8 and 4×8

Error Intervention

If students are having trouble solving the 8s facts because they have trouble with the 4s facts,

then use G29: Multiplying by 4.

If You Have More Time

Group students in pairs. Have partners number a cube 0 through 5, then number a second cube 0, 1, 2, 3, 3, and 4. One student rolls both die and then finds the sum. The second student then multiplies that sum by 8. Have students take turns rolling and computing.

Multiplying by 10

Name ______________________

Multiplying by 10

Answer 1 to 5 to learn how to multiply by 10.

1. Continue skip counting by 10s on the number line below.

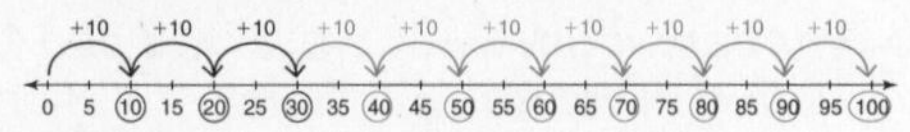

2. Each number a hop lands on is a **multiple** of ten. Circle each multiple of 10 on the number line. Then list them in the blanks below.

10 20 30 40 50 60 70 80 90 100

3. To find 6 × 10, count by 10s until you have said 6 numbers.

10, 20, 30, 40, 50, 60

So, 6 × 10 = 60.

4. Do this for each of the 10s facts. Complete the table.

5. Reasoning Complete to describe the patterns in the products of the 10s facts.

10s Facts

0 × 10 = 0	6 × 10 = 60
1 × 10 = 10	7 × 10 = 70
2 × 10 = 20	8 × 10 = 80
3 × 10 = 30	9 × 10 = 90
4 × 10 = 40	10 × 10 = 100
5 × 10 = 50	

All the multiples of 10 end in what number? 0

So, when you multiply a number by 10,

you just write the number and a 0.

6. Reasoning What is 10 × 7? Explain how you know.

10 × 7 = 7 × 10 and 7 × 10 = 70. So, 10 × 7 = 70.

Name ______________________

Multiplying by 10 (continued)

Find each product.

7. 2 × 10 = 20 **8.** 4 × 10 = 40 **9.** 6 × 10 = 60

10. 10 × 6 = 60 **11.** 10 × 2 = 20 **12.** 10 × 5 = 50

13. 3 × 10 = 30 **14.** 10 × 9 = 90 **15.** 8 × 10 = 80 **16.** 10 × 8 = 80 **17.** 9 × 10 = 90

18. 5 × 10 = 50 **19.** 10 × 3 = 30 **20.** 10 × 1 = 10 **21.** 1 × 10 = 10 **22.** 7 × 10 = 70

23. There are 8 markers in one box. How many markers are in 10 boxes? 80 markers

24. Reasoning Complete the pattern. 10, 20, 30, 40, 50, 60, 70

25. Reasoning Seven friends get together to play a marble game. Sixty marbles are needed to play this game. Each friend brings ten marbles. Are there enough marbles to play the game?

Yes, they have 70 marbles and only 60 are needed.

26. Reasoning Jake said that 10 × 4 is 100. Is Jake correct? Explain.

No. 4 × 10 is 40.

Teacher Notes

Ongoing Assessment

Ask: ***Explain why 76 cannot be a product to a multiplication problem with 10 as a factor.*** When 10 is a factor, the product must have a 0 in the ones place; 76 does not.

Error Intervention

If students have trouble with the 10s facts,

then use A16: Using Skip Counting.

If You Have More Time

Have students explain why counting the value of 6 dimes is the same as multiplying 6 × 10.

Multiplying by 11 and 12

Math Diagnosis and Intervention System
Intervention Lesson B55

Name ____________________

Multiplying by 11 and 12

When multiplying by 11, multiply the factor that is not 11 by 10. Then add that factor to the product.

Find 4 × 11 by answering 1 to 4.

1. What is the factor that is not 11? 4

2. Multiply the factor that is not 11 by 10. 4 × 10 = 40

3. Add the factor that is not 11 to the product. 40 + 4 = 44

4. So, 4 × 11 = 44

When multiplying by 12, break the 12 into 10 + 2. Multiply the factor that is not 12 by 10 and by 2. Then, add the two products.

Find 8 × 12 by answering 5 to 9.

5. What is the factor that is not 12? 8

6. Multiply the factor that is not 12 by 10. 8 × 10 = 80

7. Multiply the factor that is not 12 by 2. 8 × 2 = 16

8. Add the products together. 80 + 16 = 96

9. So, 8 × 12 = 96.

10. Find 11 × 12.

10 × 12 = 120 1 × 12 = 12 120 + 12 = 132

So, 11 × 12 = 132.

11. To find 12 × 12, add 10 × 12 and 2 × 12, so 120 + 24.

So, 12 × 12 = 144.

Math Diagnosis and Intervention System
Intervention Lesson B55

Name ____________________

Multiplying by 11 and 12 (continued)

Find each product.

12. 7 × 11
7 × 10 = 70
7 × 1 = 7
7 × 11 = 77

13. 5 × 12
5 × 10 = 50
5 × 2 = 10
5 × 12 = 60

14. 3 × 12 = 36 **15.** 5 × 11 = 55 **16.** 7 × 12 = 84

17. 10 × 11 = 110 **18.** 12 × 4 = 48 **19.** 11 × 12 = 132

20. 11 × 6 = 66 **21.** 3 × 11 = 33 **22.** 12 × 6 = 72

23. 9 × 11 = 99 **24.** 12 × 9 = 108 **25.** 5 × 11 = 55

26. 11 × 12 = 132 **27.** 8 × 11 = 88 **28.** 10 × 12 = 120

29. There are 2 baseball teams with 12 players on each team. How many players are playing baseball? 24 players

30. Twelve eggs are in a carton. Twelve cartons are in a case. How many eggs are in one case? 144 eggs

31. Reasoning Complete the pattern using multiples of 11, up to 9 × 11.

11, 22, 33, 44, 55, 66, 77, 88, 99

32. Reasoning Explain how to find 9 × 12.

9 × 10 = 90, 9 × 2 = 18, 90 + 18 = 108. So 9 × 12 = 108.

Teacher Notes

Ongoing Assessment

Ask: ***Why is it easier to break a 12s fact into 10 and 2 instead of 8 and 4?*** Adding a number to a multiple of 10 is much easier than adding two other numbers.

Error Intervention

If students have trouble with the multiplication facts for 10 and 2,

then use G32: Multiplying by 10 and G25: Multiplying by 2 and 5.

If You Have More Time

Group students in pairs. Give each pair of students 26 index cards. Have partners each label 13 cards, 0 through 12, and shuffle the cards. Each student draws a card. Then, at the same time they place the cards face up on the desk. The first student who says the correct product earns both cards. If they say the product at the same time, one card is awarded to each player. Continue until all cards are used. The partner with the most cards wins the round. Shuffle all cards and play as many rounds as time permits.

Multiplying Three Numbers

Math Diagnosis and Intervention System
Intervention Lesson B56

Name ______________________

Multiplying Three Numbers

Does it matter how you multiply 5 × 2 × 3? Answer 1–8 to find out.

To show the factors you are multiplying first, use parentheses as grouping symbols.

1. Group the first two factors together. (5 × 2) × 3
2. Multiply what is in the parentheses first. 5 × 2 = 10
3. Then, multiply the product of what is in parentheses by the third factor. 10 × 3 = 30
4. So, (5 × 2) × 3 = 30.
5. Start again and group the last two factors together. 5 × (2 × 3)
6. Multiply what is in the parentheses first. 2 × 3 = 6
7. Then, multiply 5 by the product of what is in parentheses. 5 × 6 = 30
8. So, 5 × (2 × 3) = 30.

It does not matter how the factors are grouped; the product will be the same.

9. 5 × (2 × 3) = (5 × 2) × 3

Find 3 × 2 × 4 two different ways.

10. Do the 3 × 2 first.
3 × 2 = 6   6 × 4 = 24   So, (3 × 2) × 4 = 24.
11. Do the 2 × 4 first.
2 × 4 = 8   3 × 8 = 24   So, 3 × (2 × 4) = 24.

Math Diagnosis and Intervention System
Intervention Lesson B56

Name ______________________

Multiplying Three Numbers (continued)

Find each product two different ways.

12. (1 × 3) × 6 = 18
1 × (3 × 6) = 18
13. (5 × 2) × 4 = 40
5 × (2 × 4) = 40
14. (2 × 4) × 1 = 8
2 × (4 × 1) = 8
15. (2 × 2) × 5 = 20
2 × (2 × 5) = 20

Find each product.

16. 2 × 4 × 3 = 24
17. 7 × 1 × 3 = 21
18. 3 × 3 × 2 = 18
19. 3 × 2 × 6 = 36
20. (4 × 2) × 2 = 16
21. 3 × (0 × 7) = 0
22. 1 × 7 × 9 = 63
23. 8 × (2 × 3) = 48
24. (2 × 5) × 6 = 60
25. 9 × 0 × 3 = 0
26. 4 × 5 × 1 = 20
27. (3 × 6) × 1 = 18

28. **Reasoning** When multiplying three numbers, if one of the factors is zero, what will the answer be? Zero

29. A classroom of students is getting ready to take a test. There are 5 rows of desks in the room and 4 students are in each row. Each student is required to have 2 pencils. How many pencils are needed? 40 pencils

Teacher Notes

Ongoing Assessment

Ask: ***What are three ways to find 1 × 2 × 3?***
(1 × 2) × 3; 1 × (2 × 3); and (1 × 3) × 2

Error Intervention

If students forget to multiply the third factor,

then encourage them to write either "______ × 4" or "4 × ______". Where the blank shows the product of the first two factors and the number is the third factor.

If You Have More Time

Have students write problems involving products with 3 factors, for a partner to solve.

Meanings for Division

Math Diagnosis and Intervention System
Intervention Lesson B57

Name ______________________

Meanings for Division

Materials 15 counters and 3 half sheets of paper, per pair

Martina has 15 dolls. She put them into 3 equal groups. Answer 1 to 3 to find how many dolls were in each group.

1. Count out 15 counters. Place the counters on the sheets of paper to form 3 equal groups.

2. Write a number sentence to show division as sharing.

15 (Total) ÷ 3 (Number of equal groups) = 5 (Number in each group)

3. How many dolls were in each group? 5

Mrs. Gentry had only 6 tokens. As the students left her room, she gave each student 2 tokens. Answer 4 to 6 to find how many students got tokens.

4. Show 6 tokens.

5. Find the number of times 2 can be subtracted from 6 until nothing is left.

$6 - 2 = 4$ 1 time
$4 - 2 = 2$ 2 times
$2 - 2 = 0$ 3 times

6. Write a number sentence to show division as repeated subtraction.

6 (Total) ÷ 2 (Number subtracted each time) = 3 (Number of times 2 was subtracted)

7. How many students got tokens? 3

Teacher Notes

Ongoing Assessment

Ask: ***Can 13 erasers be shared equally between 6 students? Explain.*** No, each student would get 2 erasers, but there would be 1 eraser left over.

Error Intervention

If students get confused when drawing division as sharing,

then encourage the student to draw circles to represent equal groups. For example, if a number is being divided by 4, draw 4 circles. Tell students to imagine placing one item at a time in each circle, until the total number is reached. The number of items in each circle is the quotient.

If You Have More Time

Have students explain which type of division they like best, division as sharing or division as repeated subtraction.

Math Diagnosis and Intervention System
Intervention Lesson B57

Name ______________________

Meanings for Division (continued)

Draw pictures to solve each problem. **Check students' drawings.**

8. Put 20 counters into 5 equal groups. How many counters are in each group? **4 counters**

9. Put 12 counters in a row. How many times can you subtract 4 counters? **3 times**

10. You put 24 cards into 4 equal piles. How many cards are in each pile? **6 cards**

11. You put 21 chairs into rows of 7. How many rows do you make? **3 rows**

12. You have 30 oranges. If you need 6 oranges to fill a bag, how many bags can you fill? **5 bags**

13. You put 10 marbles into equal groups of 5. How many groups are there? **2 groups**

14. Eight people went to the museum in two cars. The same number of people went in each car. How many people went in each car? **4 people**

15. **Reasoning** How can you use repeated subtraction to find 30 ÷ 5?
Subtract 5 repeatedly from 30 until reaching zero, and then count the number of times 5 was subtracted, which is 6.

Writing Division Stories

Name ______________________________

Writing Division Stories

Materials counters, 18 per student or pair of students

To write a division story for 18 ÷ 3 that is about 18 grapes and 3 sisters, fill in the blanks below.

1. Mrs. __any last name__ put __18__ grapes into a bowl. Mrs. __any last name__'s daughters, __any girl's name__, __any girl's name__, and __any girl's name__ shared the grapes equally. How many __grapes__ did each sister get?

3. Use counters to show how many grapes there were in all.

4. Divide the 18 counters into 3 equal groups.

5. How many grapes did each sister get? __6__ grapes

6. Write a division story for 10 ÷ 5 about apples and bags.

Mr. __any last name__ bought __10__ apples. He put __5__ apples into each bag. How many __bags__ did he use?

7. Use counters to show how many apples he bought.

8. Divide the 10 counters into groups with 5 in each group.

9. How many bags did he use? __2__ bags

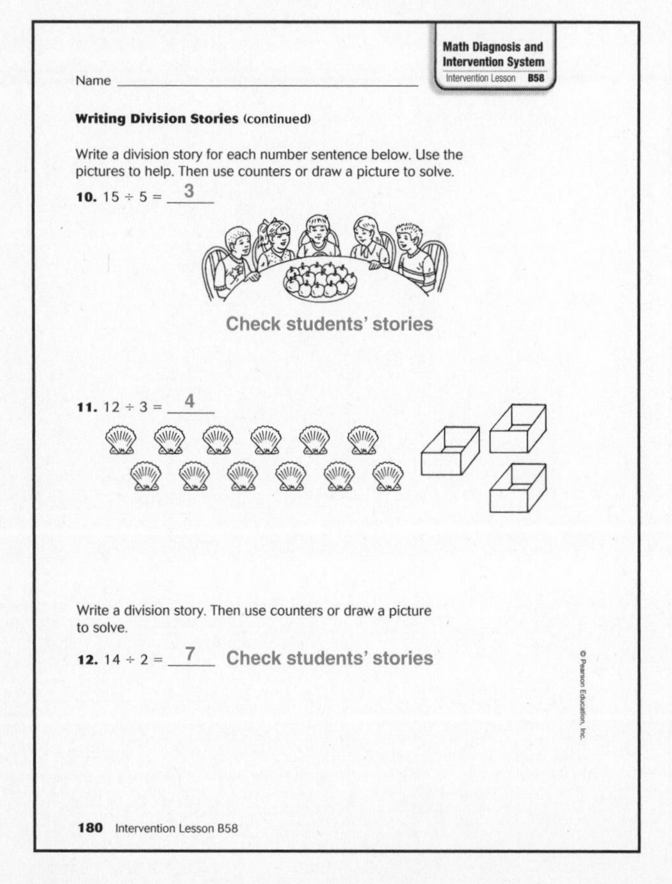
Math Diagnosis and Intervention System
Intervention Lesson B58

Name ______________________________

Writing Division Stories (continued)

Write a division story for each number sentence below. Use the pictures to help. Then use counters or draw a picture to solve.

10. 15 ÷ 5 = __3__

Check students' stories

11. 12 ÷ 3 = __4__

Write a division story. Then use counters or draw a picture to solve.

12. 14 ÷ 2 = __7__ Check students' stories

© Pearson Education, Inc.

180 Intervention Lesson B58

Teacher Notes

Ongoing Assessment

Ask: ***What should always be the last sentence of your story problem?*** A question to be solved.

Error Intervention

If students have trouble completing a story,

then encourage them to first make a plan. Write a division fact and a question. Then use that information to write the details of the problem. For example, 14 ÷ 7; 14 stickers; 7 pages; Stella has 14 stickers to put on 7 pages. How many stickers can Stella put on each page if she wants the same number on each page?

If You Have More Time

Place students in groups of 4. Have the first student write a sentence on a piece of paper that includes a number of objects. (Trent had 16 carrots.) Give the piece of paper to the second student. Have this student write a second sentence that includes a number of groups for the objects in the first sentence. (Each day he ate 2 carrots.) Have the third student write the question for the problem. (How many days will Trent be able to eat carrots before he runs out?) Have the fourth student solve the problem. Repeat this process three more times so that each student does a different part of the problem.

Relating Multiplication and Division

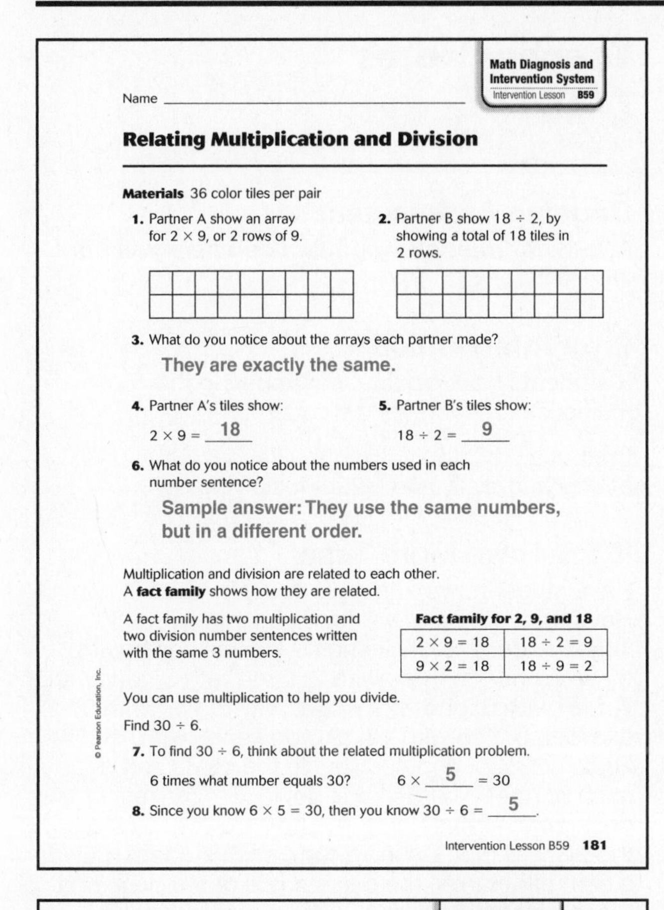

Math Diagnosis and Intervention System
Intervention Lesson B59

Name ____________________

Relating Multiplication and Division

Materials 36 color tiles per pair

1. Partner A show an array for 2 × 9, or 2 rows of 9.
2. Partner B show 18 ÷ 2, by showing a total of 18 tiles in 2 rows.
3. What do you notice about the arrays each partner made?
   They are exactly the same.
4. Partner A's tiles show: 2 × 9 = 18
5. Partner B's tiles show: 18 ÷ 2 = 9
6. What do you notice about the numbers used in each number sentence?
   Sample answer: They use the same numbers, but in a different order.

Multiplication and division are related to each other. A **fact family** shows how they are related.

A fact family has two multiplication and two division number sentences written with the same 3 numbers.

Fact family for 2, 9, and 18	
2 × 9 = 18	18 ÷ 2 = 9
9 × 2 = 18	18 ÷ 9 = 2

You can use multiplication to help you divide.

Find 30 ÷ 6.

7. To find 30 ÷ 6, think about the related multiplication problem.
   6 times what number equals 30? 6 × 5 = 30
8. Since you know 6 × 5 = 30, then you know 30 ÷ 6 = 5.

© Pearson Education, Inc.

Intervention Lesson B59 181

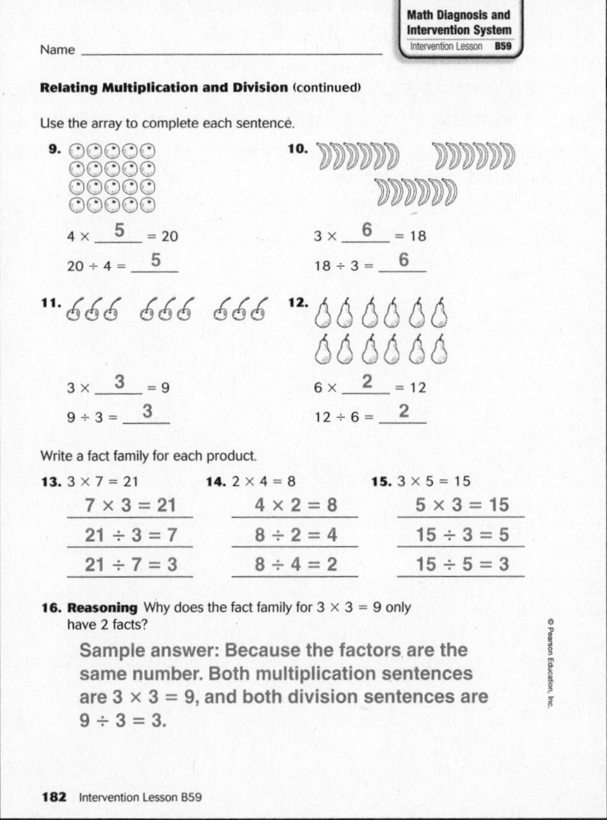

Math Diagnosis and Intervention System
Intervention Lesson B59

Name ____________________

Relating Multiplication and Division (continued)

Use the array to complete each sentence.

9. 4 × 5 = 20
   20 ÷ 4 = 5
10. 3 × 6 = 18
    18 ÷ 3 = 6
11. 3 × 3 = 9
    9 ÷ 3 = 3
12. 6 × 2 = 12
    12 ÷ 6 = 2

Write a fact family for each product.

13. 3 × 7 = 21
    7 × 3 = 21
    21 ÷ 3 = 7
    21 ÷ 7 = 3
14. 2 × 4 = 8
    4 × 2 = 8
    8 ÷ 2 = 4
    8 ÷ 4 = 2
15. 3 × 5 = 15
    5 × 3 = 15
    15 ÷ 3 = 5
    15 ÷ 5 = 3
16. **Reasoning** Why does the fact family for 3 × 3 = 9 only have 2 facts?
    Sample answer: Because the factors are the same number. Both multiplication sentences are 3 × 3 = 9, and both division sentences are 9 ÷ 3 = 3.

© Pearson Education, Inc.

182 Intervention Lesson B59

Teacher Notes

Ongoing Assessment

Ask: ***What multiplication facts are part of the fact family for 10 ÷ 5 = 2?*** 5 × 2 = 10 and 2 × 5 = 10

Error Intervention

If students have trouble understanding how two different operations can be related,

then use G2: Relating Addition and Subtraction.

If You Have More Time

Have student work in pairs. Give each pair 24 counters. Have them make an array and write the fact family for the array. Then have them make a different array and write a different fact family.

Dividing by 2 Through 5

Math Diagnosis and Intervention System
Intervention Lesson B60

Name ______________________

Dividing by 2 Through 5

Materials Have counters available for students to use.

You can use multiplication facts to help you divide.

Anna Maria has 24 leaves in her collection. She puts 4 leaves on each page in her scrap book. How many pages does she need for all her leaves?

Find 24 ÷ 4.

1. To find 24 ÷ 4, think about the related multiplication problem.

4 times what number equals 24? 4 × 6 = 24

2. Since you know 4 × 6 = 24, then you know 24 ÷ 4 = 6.

3. How many pages does Anna Maria need for all her leaves? 6

Find 45 ÷ 5.

4. 5 times what number equals 45? 5 × 9 = 45

5. Since you know 5 × 9 = 45, then you know 45 ÷ 5 = 9.

A division problem can be written two different ways.

30 ÷ 5 = 6 $\quad 5\overline{)30}$ with quotient 6

Both problems are read "30 divided by 5 equals 6."

6. Think: 3 × 5 = 15 So, $3\overline{)15}$ = 5.

7. Think: 4 × 4 = 16 So 16 ÷ 4 = 4.

8. Think: 2 × 9 = 18 So 18 ÷ 2 = 9.

Math Diagnosis and Intervention System
Intervention Lesson B60

Name ______________________

Dividing by 2 Through 5 (continued)

Use the multiplication fact to find each quotient.

9. 4 × 6 = 24 **10.** 6 × 5 = 30 **11.** 2 × 6 = 12

24 ÷ 4 = 6 30 ÷ 6 = 5 12 ÷ 2 = 6

12. 5 × 5 = 25 **13.** 3 × 9 = 27 **14.** 4 × 7 = 28

25 ÷ 5 = 5 27 ÷ 3 = 9 28 ÷ 4 = 7

Find each quotient.

15. 25 ÷ 5 = 5 **16.** 20 ÷ 4 = 5 **17.** 12 ÷ 3 = 4

18. $5\overline{)35}$ 7 **19.** $4\overline{)36}$ 9 **20.** $3\overline{)21}$ 7

21. Mario has 15 eggs. He wants to share them equally with 3 friends. How many eggs will each friend get?

Think: 3 × 5 = 15. So, 15 ÷ 3 = 5 eggs.

22. Todd has 40 whistles. He wants to divide them evenly between his 5 friends. How many whistles will each friend get? 8 whistles

23. Reasoning What multiplication fact can you use to find 27 ÷ 3? Explain how to find 27 ÷ 3.

3 × 9 = 27, so 27 ÷ 3 = 9

24. If 4 × 10 = 40, then what is 40 ÷ 4? 10

Teacher Notes

Ongoing Assessment

Ask: ***What multiplication fact can help you find 18 ÷ 3?*** 3 × 6 = 18

Error Intervention

If students have trouble remembering the multiplication facts for 2 through 5,

then use G25: Multiplying by 2 and 5, G28: Multiplying by 3, and G29: Multiplying by 4.

If You Have More Time

Have students work in pairs and play Fact Rummy. Have partners create a deck of cards out of 30 index cards. The deck should include cards with these numbers: three with 2, three with 3, four with 4, four with 5, one with 6, two with 7, two with 8, two with 9, two with 12, and one each with 15, 18, 20, 27, 28, 35, and 40. Shuffle the cards and deal each partner 7 cards, face down. Set the rest of the deck on the table and turn one card over to start the discard pile. During a turn, each student draws a card either from the discard pile or the deck and tries to match 3 cards that form a multiplication or division fact, such as 4, 5, and 20. The student discards a card face up. The game is over when one student has no cards left. Add the numbers on all the matched cards for each student and subtract any cards still in a student's hand. The student with the highest score wins.

Dividing by 6 and 7

Math Diagnosis and Intervention System
Intervention Lesson B61

Name ____________________

Dividing by 6 and 7

Materials Have counters available for students to use.

You can use multiplication facts to help you divide.

Ahmed has 24 bugs to put on 6 boards. He wants the same number of bugs on each board. How many bugs should he put on each board?

Find 24 ÷ 6.

1. To find 24 ÷ 6, think about the related multiplication problem.
   6 times what number equals 24? 6 × __4__ = 24
2. Since you know 6 × 4 = 24, then you know 24 ÷ 6 = __4__.
3. How many bugs should Ahmed put on each board? __4__

Find 21 ÷ 7.

4. To find 21 ÷ 7, think about the related multiplication problem.
   7 times what number equals 21? 7 × __3__ = 21
5. Since you know 7 × 3 = 21, then you know 21 ÷ 7 = __3__.
6. Think: 6 × __5__ = 30 So, 6)30 = __5__.
7. Think: 7 × __7__ = 49 So 49 ÷ 7 = __7__.
8. Think: 6 × __8__ = 48 So 48 ÷ 6 = __8__.
9. **Reasoning** Explain how to find 63 ÷ 7.
   Think: 7 times what number equals 63. Since 7 × 9 = 63, 63 ÷ 7 = 9.

Intervention Lesson B61 **185**

Math Diagnosis and Intervention System
Intervention Lesson B61

Name ____________________

Dividing by 6 and 7 (continued)

Use the multiplication fact to find each quotient.

10. 6 × 5 = 30
30 ÷ 6 = __5__

11. 7 × 2 = 14
14 ÷ 7 = __2__

12. 6 × 1 = 6
6 ÷ 6 = __1__

13. 7 × 5 = 35
35 ÷ 7 = __5__

14. 6 × __6__ = 36
36 ÷ 6 = __6__

15. 7 × __8__ = 56
56 ÷ 7 = __8__

16. 6 × __4__ = 24
24 ÷ 6 = __4__

17. 6 × 9 = 54
54 ÷ 6 = __9__

18. 6 × 7 = 42
42 ÷ 6 = __7__

Find each quotient.

19. 6)54 = 9
20. 7)42 = 6
21. 6)30 = 5
22. 7)7 = 1
23. 6)42 = 7
24. 7)70 = 10
25. 6)12 = 2
26. 7)14 = 2
27. 6)60 = 10

28. Mrs. Carpenter's class is dividing into groups for group work. There are 28 students in the class and 35 desks. How many students will be in each group if there are 7 groups? __4 students__

29. Reasoning If you know that 6 × 12 = 72, then what is 72 ÷ 6? __12__

186 Intervention Lesson B61

Teacher Notes

Ongoing Assessment

Ask: ***What multiplication fact can help you find 54 ÷ 6?*** 6 × 9 = 54

Error Intervention

If students have trouble remembering the multiplication facts for 6 and 7,

then use G30: Multiplying by 6 or 7.

If You Have More Time

Have students write a division story problem. Have a partner solve the division problem, then write a related multiplication story problem using numbers in the same fact family.

Dividing by 8 and 9

Name ____________________

Math Diagnosis and Intervention System
Intervention Lesson B62

Dividing by 8 and 9

Materials Have counters available for students to use.

You can use multiplication facts to help you divide.

At the museum, 32 students are divided into 8 equal groups.
How many students are in each group?

Find 32 ÷ 8.

1. To find 32 ÷ 8, think about the related multiplication problem.
   8 times what number equals 32? 8 × __4__ = 32
2. Since you know 8 × 4 = 32, then you know 32 ÷ 8 = __4__.
3. How many students are in each group at the museum? __4__ students

Find 36 ÷ 9.

4. To find 36 ÷ 9, think about the related multiplication problem.
   9 times what number equals 36? 9 × __4__ = 36
5. Since you know 9 × 4 = 36, then you know 36 ÷ 9 = __4__.

Find 8)80.

6. To find 8)80, think about the related multiplication problem.
   8 times what number equals 80? 8 × __10__ = 80
7. Since you know 8 × 10 = 80, then you know 8)80 = __10__.
8. **Reasoning** Explain how to find 56 ÷ 8.
   Think: 8 times what number equals 56. Since 8 × 7 = 56, 56 ÷ 8 = 7.

Intervention Lesson B62 **187**

Name ____________________

Math Diagnosis and Intervention System
Intervention Lesson B62

Dividing by 8 and 9 (continued)

Use the multiplication fact to find each quotient.

9. 8 × 2 = 16
   16 ÷ 8 = __2__
10. 9 × 5 = 45
    45 ÷ 9 = __5__
11. 8 × 3 = 24
    24 ÷ 8 = __3__
12. 9 × 6 = 54
    54 ÷ 9 = __6__
13. 8 × __4__ = 32
    32 ÷ 8 = __4__
14. 8 × __6__ = 48
    48 ÷ 8 = __6__
15. 9 × __3__ = 27
    27 ÷ 9 = __3__
16. 9 × __10__ = 90
    90 ÷ 9 = __10__
17. 8 × __9__ = 72
    72 ÷ 8 = __9__

Find each quotient.

18. 9)63 = 7
19. 8)32 = 4
20. 9)36 = 4
21. 8)64 = 8
22. 9)81 = 9
23. 8)16 = 2
24. 9)45 = 5
25. 8)56 = 7
26. 8)40 = 5
27. **Reasoning** If you know that 8 × 12 = 96, then what is 96 ÷ 8? __12__
28. Nine friends go to lunch and split the $54 ticket evenly. How much does each friend pay? __$6__

188 Intervention Lesson B62

Teacher Notes

Ongoing Assessment

Ask: ***What two division facts can be written using 8 × 9?*** 72 ÷ 8 = 9 and 72 ÷ 9 = 8

Error Intervention

If students have trouble remembering the multiplication facts for 8 or 9,

then use G26: Multiplying by 9 and G31: Multiplying by 8.

If You Have More Time

Have partners make a game like Memory. The partners write the expression on one card and the quotient on another card for the 8 and 9 division facts. Have partner A write the eight 8s facts beginning with 16 ÷ 8 = 2 and ending with 72 ÷ 8 = 9. Have partner B write the eight 9s facts beginning with 18 ÷ 9 = 2 and ending with 81 ÷ 9 = 9. Shuffle all cards and then place face down in a 4 by 8 array. Partner A turns over two cards, if they go together the player keeps the two cards and goes again. When a match is not made the cards are turned back over, and it is the other partner's turn. The game is finished when all cards are matched. The partner with the most matches wins.

0 and 1 in Division

Math Diagnosis and Intervention System
Intervention Lesson B63

Name ______

0 and 1 in Division

Think about related multiplication facts to help you divide.

Find 5 ÷ 1.

1. Think: 1 times what number equals 5? 1 × 5 = 5

2. Since you know 1 × 5 = 5, then you know 5 ÷ 1 = 5.

3. If Karina had 5 oranges to put equally in 1 basket, how many oranges would go in each basket? 5 oranges

Find 9 ÷ 1.

4. 1 × 9 = 9 So, 9 ÷ 1 = 9.

5. What is the result when any number is divided by 1? The number

Find 0 ÷ 7.

6. Think: 7 times what number equals 0? 7 × 0 = 0

7. Since you know 7 × 0 = 0, then you know 0 ÷ 7 = 0.

8. If Karina had 0 oranges to put equally in 7 baskets, how many oranges would go in each basket? 0 oranges

Find 0 ÷ 2.

9. 2 × 0 = 0 So, 0 ÷ 2 = 0.

10. What is the result when zero is divided by any number (except 0)? 0

Find 5 ÷ 0.

11. Reasoning If Karina had 5 oranges to put equally in 0 baskets, how many oranges would go in each basket? Explain.

Karina can not put 5 oranges into 0 baskets.

You cannot divide a number by 0.

Math Diagnosis and Intervention System
Intervention Lesson B63

Name ______

0 and 1 in Division (continued)

Find 4 ÷ 4.

12. Think: 4 times what number equals 4? 4 × 1 = 4

13. Since you know 4 × 1 = 4, then you know 4 ÷ 4 = 1.

14. If Karina had 4 oranges to put equally in 4 baskets, how many oranges would go in each basket? 1 orange

Find 8 ÷ 8.

15. 8 × 1 = 8 So, 8 ÷ 8 = 1.

16. What is the result when any number (except 0) is divided by itself? 1

Find each quotient.

17. 4 ÷ 1 = 4 **18.** 0 ÷ 5 = 0 **19.** 6 ÷ 6 = 1

20. $3\overline{)0}$ 0 **21.** $9\overline{)9}$ 1 **22.** $5\overline{)5}$ 1

23. $1\overline{)6}$ 6 **24.** $1\overline{)1}$ 1 **25.** $8\overline{)0}$ 0

26. Reasoning Use the rule for division by 1 to find 247 ÷ 1. Explain.

A number divided by 1 equals the same number, so 247 ÷ 1 = 247.

27. Larry has 3 friends who would like some cookies but he has no cookies to give them. How many cookies can Larry give each friend?

Each friend gets zero cookies.

Teacher Notes

Ongoing Assessment

Ask: ***What is 0 ÷ 245?*** 0 ***What is 245 ÷ 1?*** 245

Error Intervention

If students have trouble understanding that division is actually taking place,

then encourage them to use counters or draw pictures to "see" what is being done. For example, 5 ÷ 1 can be 5 counters put into 1 group to find how many are in the group. And 0 ÷ 7 can be 0 counters put into 7 groups to find how many are in each group.

If You Have More Time

Place students in groups of 3. One student acts as a referee. The referee says a number from 2 to 9 and then says, "On your mark, get set, go." On go, the referee holds out a fist for 0 or a hand with 1 finger up for one. The other two students race to say the product of 0 or 1 and the number between 2 and 9. The student who says the product first gets a point. The first student to 5 wins. Let students play again, until each one has a turn as referee.

Name ______________________________

Addition

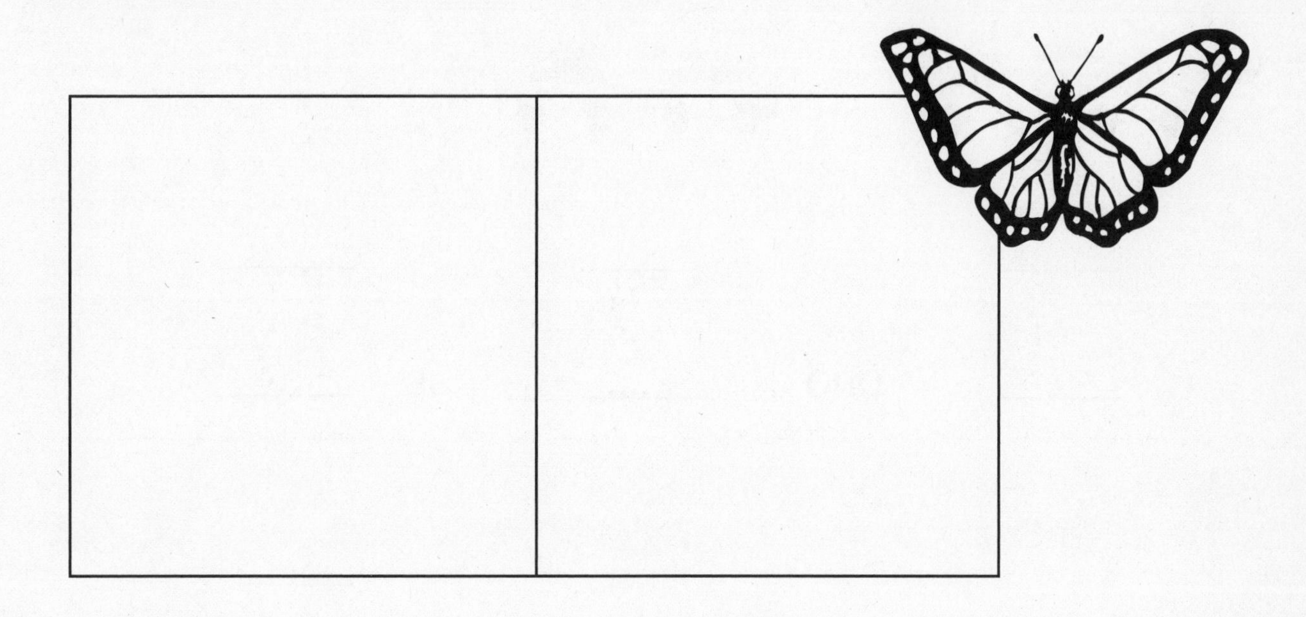

1. 2 and 3 is 5

2. ____ and ____ is ____

3. ____ and ____ is ____

Materials: Counters, 6 per child

1. Say: ***Two butterflies are on a branch.*** Have children put 2 counters in the first box for the 2 butterflies and write 2. Say: ***Three butterflies join them.*** Have children put 3 counters in the second box and write 3. Ask: ***How many butterflies are on the branch in all?*** Have children write 5.
2. Say: ***One butterfly is flying around.*** Have children show one counter in the first box for the 1 butterfly and write 1. Say: ***Two more butterflies join them.*** Have children put 2 counters in the second box and write 2. Ask: ***How many butterflies are flying around in all?*** Have children write 3.
3. Have children do $4 + 2 = 6$ similarly.

Name ______________________________

Addition (continued)

Write the numbers.

4.   

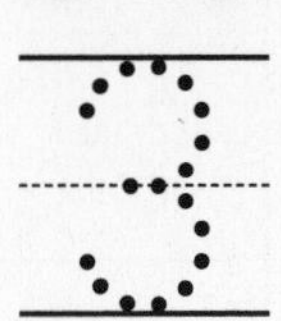 and 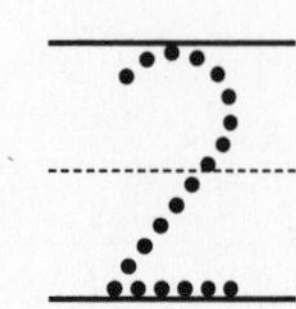 is 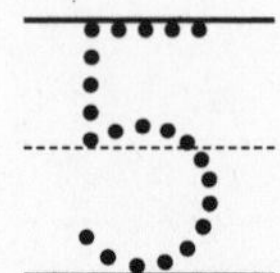

5. 

____ and ____ is ____

6. 

____ and ____ is ____

7. 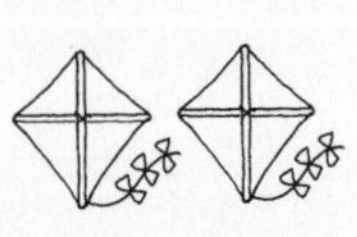

____ and ____ is ____ 

Name ______________________________

Subtraction

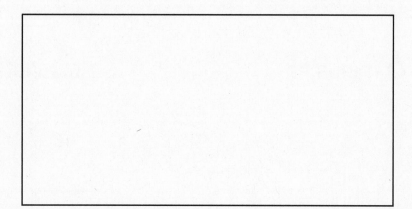

1. ___1___ left
2. ______ left
3. ______ left
4. ______ left
5. ______ left
6. ______ left

Materials: Counters, 6 per child

1. Say: ***Four owls were in a tree.*** Have children put 4 counters in the box for the owls. Say: ***Three owls flew away.*** Have children take 3 counters out of the box for the 3 owls that flew away. Ask: ***How many owls are left in the tree?*** Have children write 1.
2. Say: ***Five owls were on top of the barn.*** Have children put 5 counters in the box for the owls. Say: ***Two owls flew into the barn.*** Have children take 2 counters out of the box for the two owls. Ask: ***How many owls are left on top of the barn?*** Have children write 3.
3. Do similarly, stories with owls on the barn flying away, owls flying out of the barn, owls flying from the barn to the tree, owls flying from the tree to the barn, and owls going to sleep. Do 6 − 4, 3 − 2, 5 − 1, and 4 − 2.

Name ______________________________

Subtraction (continued)

Write how many are left.

7.

6 minus 4

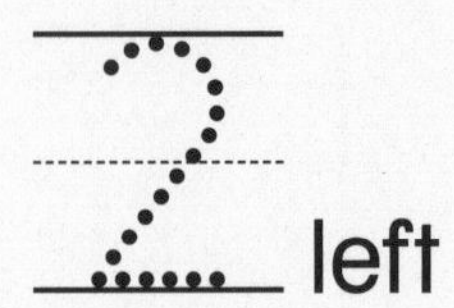

left

8.

5 minus 1 ______ left

9.

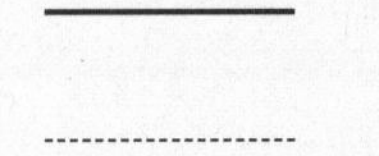

3 minus 2 ______ left

10.

6 minus 3 ______ left

11.

6 minus 1 ______ left

Name ______________________________

Finding Sums

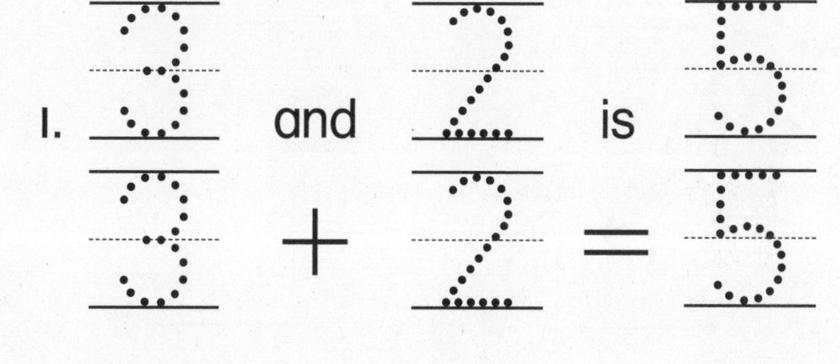

1. 3 and 2 is 5
3 + 2 = 5

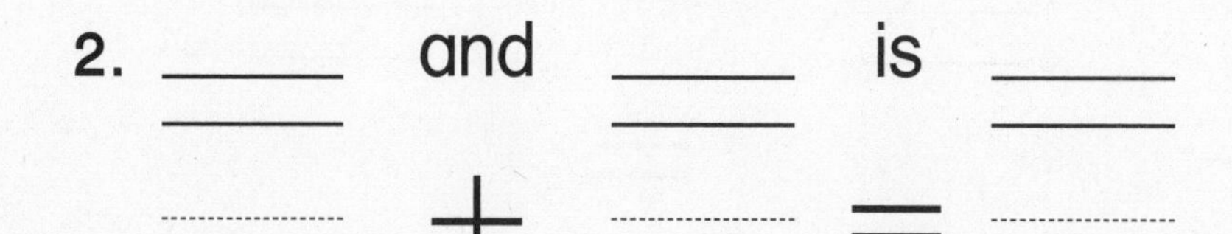

2. ____ and ____ is ____
____ + ____ = ____

Materials: Counters, 6 per child

1. Say: ***Three frogs are on the log.*** Have children put 3 counters next to the picture and write 3. Say: ***Two frogs hop onto the log to join them.*** Have children add 2 more counters and write 2. Ask: ***How many frogs are on the log then?*** Have children write 5.
2. Write the + sign on the board or overhead. Say ***This sign means add or plus. Use it for joining stories.*** Write 3 + 2 = 5 on the board or overhead. Say: ***This number sentence describes the story about the frogs.*** Point to each part as you say: ***Three plus two equals five.*** Have children complete the addition sentence.
3. For Problem 2, say: ***Two ducks are swimming.*** Have children put two counters next to the picture and write 2. Say: ***The two ducks on this side of the log decide to join them.*** Have children show 2 more counters and write 2 again. Ask: ***How many ducks will be swimming then?*** Have children write 4.
4. Have children complete the addition sentence.

Name ____________________

Finding Sums (continued)

Write the numbers.

3. 

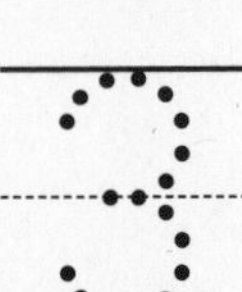 and 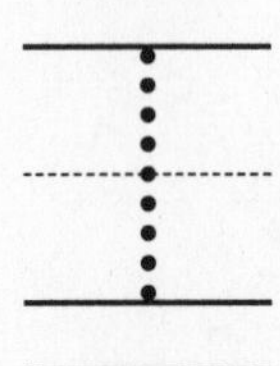 is 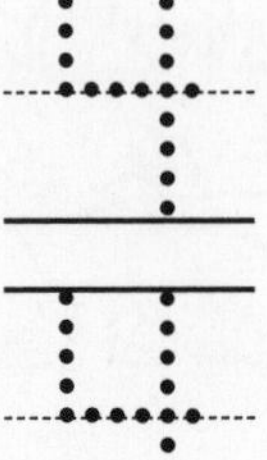

\+ =

4. 

____ and ____ is ____

____ + ____ = ____

5. Draw to show each number

4 + 2 = ____

Name ______________________

Finding Differences

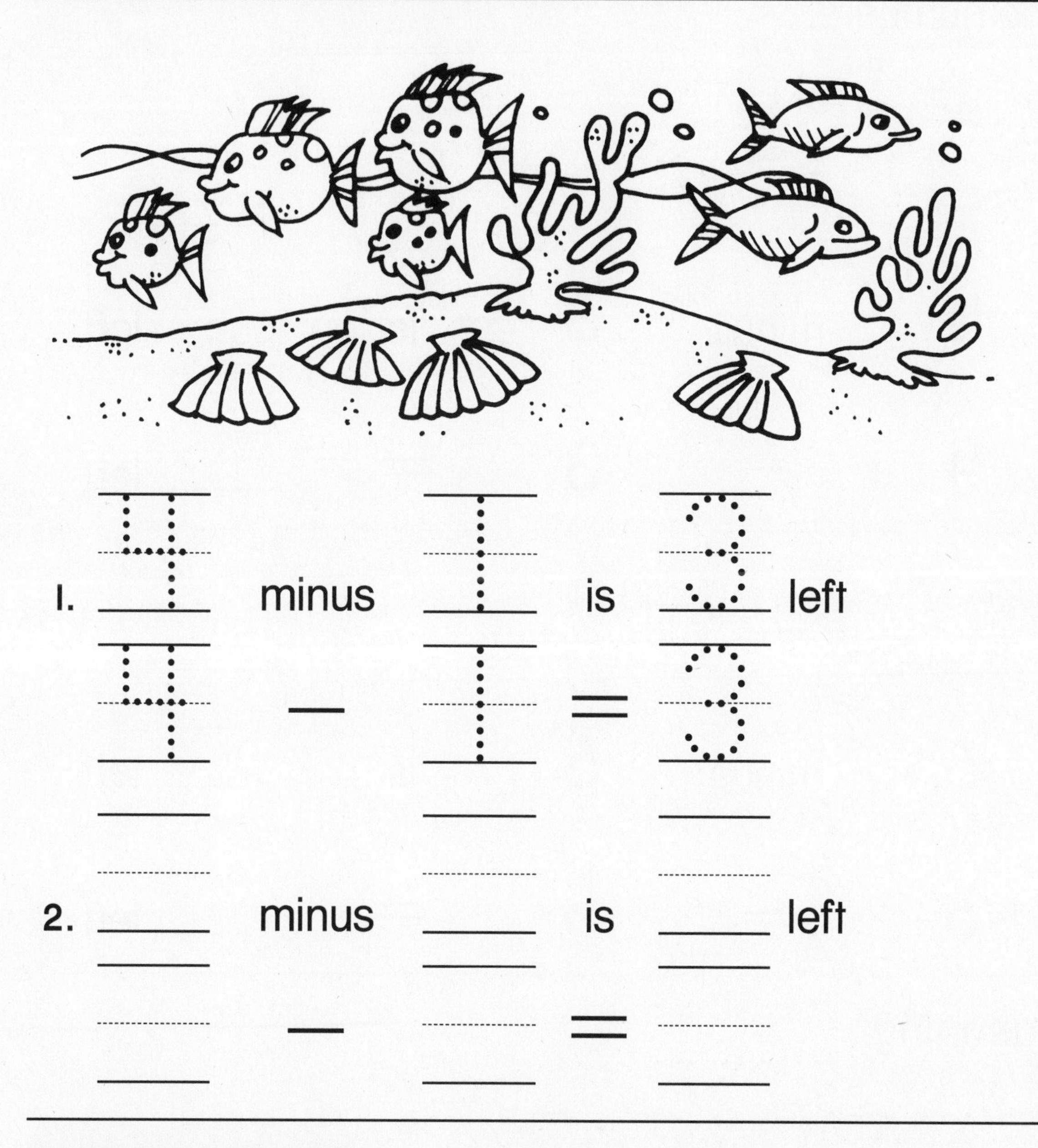

1. 4 minus 1 is 3 left
4 − 1 = 3
2. ____ minus ____ is ____ left
____ − ____ = ____

Materials: Counters, 6 per child

1. Say: ***Four shells are together on the ocean floor.*** Have children show 4 counters and write 4. Say: ***One shell floated away.*** Have children separate one of the counters from the 4 and write 1. Ask: ***How many shells are left?*** Have children write 3.
2. Write the − sign on the board or overhead. Say: ***This sign means minus. Use it for separating stories.*** Write 4 − 1 = 3 on the board or overhead. Say: ***This number sentence describes the story about the shells.*** Point to each part as you say: ***Four minus one equals three.*** Have children complete the subtraction sentence.
3. For Problem 2, say: ***Six fish are together.*** Have children show 6 counters and write 6. Say: ***Two fish swam away.*** Have children show 2 counters and write 2. Ask: ***How many fish are left?*** Have children write 4. Have children complete the subtraction sentence.

Name ______________________

Finding Differences (continued)

Write the numbers.

3. 

4 minus 3 is ____ left

4 − 3 = ____ left

4. 

6 minus 5 is ____ left

6 − 5 = ____ left

5. **Reasoning**

____ − ____ = ____

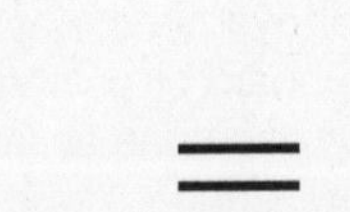

Name ______________________________

Making 6 and 7

1. 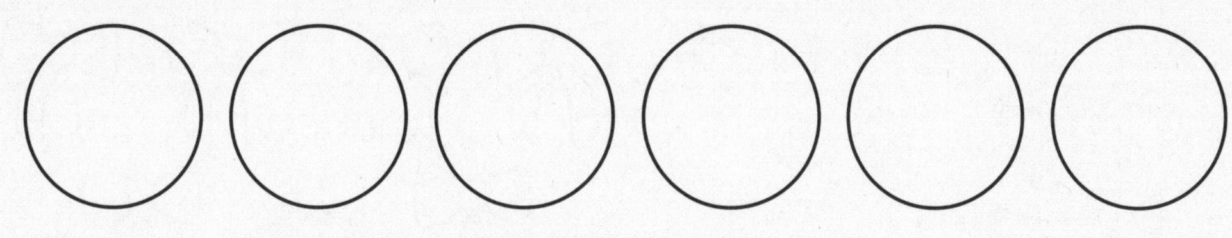

2 and 4 is 6 in all.

2. 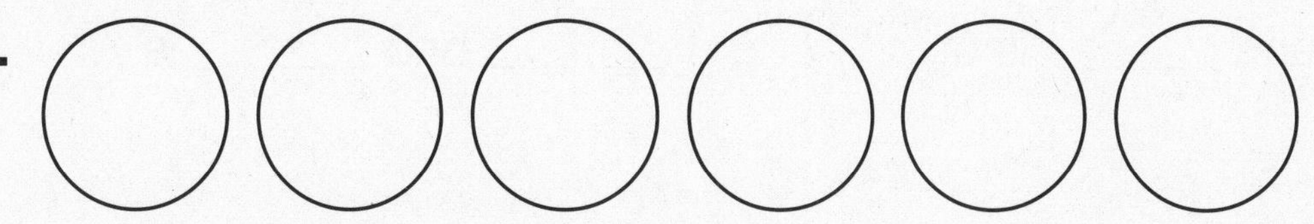

_______ and _______ is 6 in all.

3. 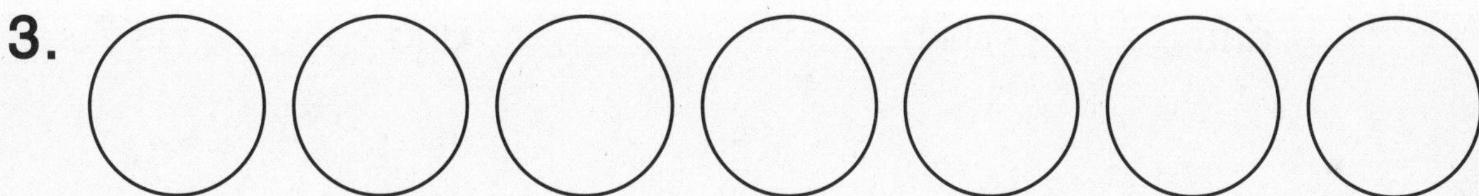

_______ and _______ is 7 in all.

4. 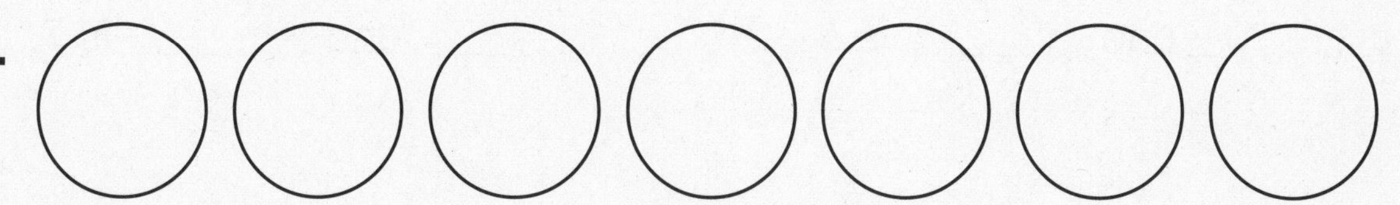

_______ and _______ is 7 in all.

Materials: Crayons or markers

1. Have children color the first two circles one color and write 2. Have them color the rest of the circles another color and write 4. Say: ***One way to make 6 is 2 and 4.***
2. Have children color the circles and write numbers to show another way to make 6.
3. Have children color the first 3 circles one color and write 3. Have children color the next 4 another color and write 4. Say: ***One way to make 7 is 3 and 4.***
4. Have children color the circles and write numbers to show another way to make 7.

Name ________________________

Making 6 and 7 (continued)

Find different ways to make 6 and 7.

5. 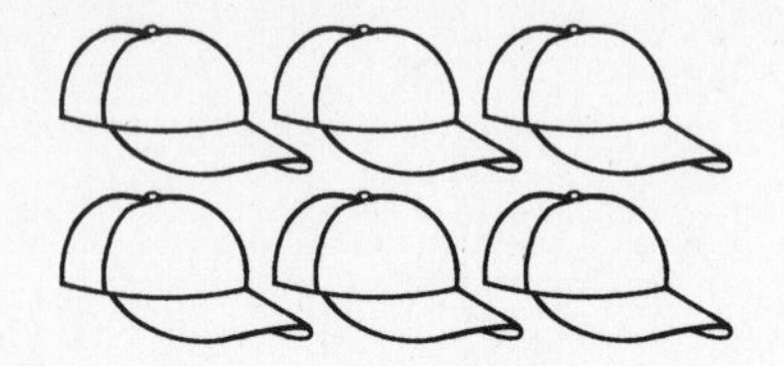

1 and 5 is 6.

_____ and _____ is 6.

_____ and _____ is 6.

_____ and _____ is 6.

_____ and _____ is 6.

6. 

1 and 6 is 7.

_____ and _____ is 7.

_____ and _____ is 7.

_____ and _____ is 7.

_____ and _____ is 7.

_____ and _____ is 7.

7. 

3 and _____ is 5.

Name ______________________________

Making 8 and 9

1. ○ ○ ○ ○ ○ ○ ○ ○

___3___ and ___5___ is 8 in all.

2. ○ ○ ○ ○ ○ ○ ○ ○

______ and ______ is 8 in all.

3. ○ ○ ○ ○ ○ ○ ○ ○ ○

______ and ______ is 9 in all.

4. ○ ○ ○ ○ ○ ○ ○ ○ ○

______ and ______ is 9 in all.

Materials: Crayons or markers

1. Have children color the first three circles one color and write 3. Have them color the rest of the circles another color and write 5. Say: ***One way to make 8 is 3 and 5.***
2. Have children color the circles and write numbers to show another way to make 8.
3. Have children color the first 2 circles one color and write 2. Have children color the next 7 another color and write 7. Say: ***One way to make 9 is 2 and 7.***
4. Have children color the circles and write numbers to show another way to make 9.

Name ______________________________

Making 8 and 9 (continued)

Find different ways to make 8 and 9.

5.

1 and 7 is 8.

_____ and _____ is 8.

_____ and _____ is 8.

_____ and _____ is 8.

_____ and _____ is 8.

_____ and _____ is 8.

_____ and _____ is 8.

6.

1 and 8 is 9.

_____ and _____ is 9.

_____ and _____ is 9.

_____ and _____ is 9.

_____ and _____ is 9.

_____ and _____ is 9.

_____ and _____ is 9.

_____ and _____ is 9.

Name ______________________

Joining Stories

I.

2 + 3 = 5 in all

2.

_____ + _____ = _____ in all

3.

_____ + _____ = _____ in all

Materials: Counters, 9 per child

1. Say: ***Two frogs are by the pond.*** Have children place a counter on each frog in the first group, use the counters to count the frogs, and then write the number. Say: ***Three more frogs join them.*** Have children place a counter on each frog in the second group, use the counters to count the frogs, and then write the number. Ask: ***How many frogs are by the pond now?*** Have students use the counters to find how many in all and write the number.
2. Say: ***Four ducks are swimming on the pond. Three more ducks land on the pond and start swimming. How many ducks are on the pond now?*** Have children use counters to solve as in the previous problem.
3. Say: ***What if there are 5 frogs by the pond and 3 frogs join them? How many frogs are by the pond now?*** Have students solve similarly.

Name ______________________

Joining Stories (continued)

Write a number sentence for each picture.

4.  

2 + 2 = 4

5.  

____ + ____ = ____

6.  

____ + ____ = ____

7.  

____ + ____ = ____

8.  

____ + ____ = ____

9.  

____ + ____ = ____

10.  

____ + ____ = ____

11. 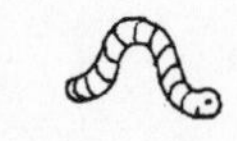 

____ + ____ = ____

Reasoning Complete each number sentence.

12. 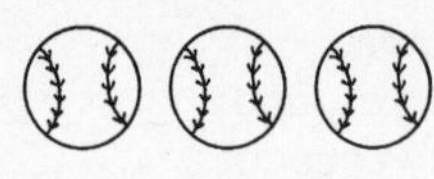

____ + 2 = ____

13.  

3 + ____ = ____

Name ______________________

Adding Across and Down

1. 

2 + 5 = 7

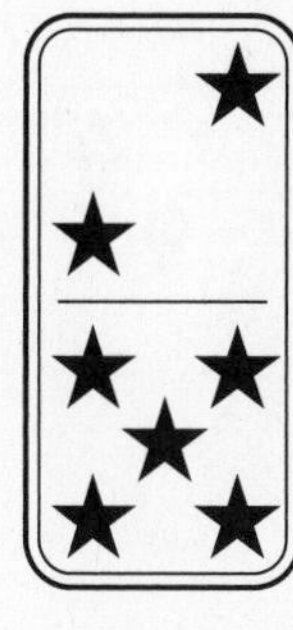

$$\begin{array}{r} 2 \\ +\ 5 \\ \hline 7 \end{array}$$

2. 

_____ + _____ = _____

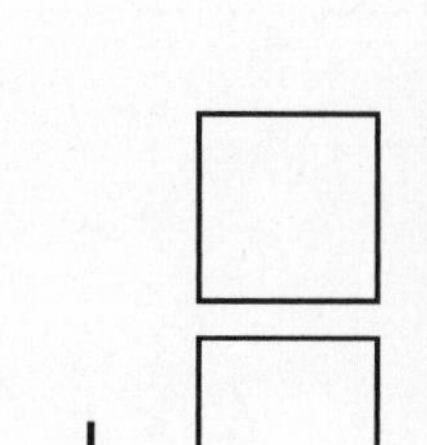

3. 4 + 1 = _____

$$\begin{array}{r} 4 \\ +\ 1 \\ \hline \end{array}$$

4. 3 + 6 = _____

$$\begin{array}{r} 3 \\ +\ 6 \\ \hline \end{array}$$

Materials: Counters, 9 per child

1. Ask: ***How many stars are in the first part of the domino?*** Have children write 2. Ask: ***How many are in the second part?*** Have children write 5. Ask: ***How many in all?*** Have children write 7.
2. Say: ***There is another way to write two plus five equals seven.*** Write the vertical form on the board or overhead and have children write the numbers.
3. For Problem 2, have children write the numbers for the number of hearts in each part and how many in all. Have them complete the other number sentence.
4. For remaining problems, have children use counters to find each sum, written both ways.

Name ______________________________

Math Diagnosis and Intervention System
Intervention Lesson **B8**

Adding Across and Down (continued)

Write the numbers. Add.

5. 

_____ + _____ = 7

$+$ ☐

7

Add. Use counters if you like.

6. 6 + 1 = 7	**7.** 2 + 3 = _____	**8.** 5 + 3 = _____
9. 3 + 3 = _____	**10.** 7 + 1 = _____	**11.** 1 + 3 = _____
12. 6 + 2 = _____	**13.** 4 + 2 = _____	**14.** 4 + 1 = _____
15. 2 + 5	**16.** 5 + 1	**17.** 2 + 2
18. 1 + 2	**19.** 5 + 3	**20.** 3 + 2

Name ______________________

Adding in Any Order

1. 

3 + 2 = 5

  3
+ 2
___

2 + 3 = 5

□
+ □
___

2. 7 + 1 = 8

1 + 7 = ______

  7
+ 1
___

  1
+ 7
___

3. 4 + 5 = 9

______ + ______ = ______

  4
+ 5
___

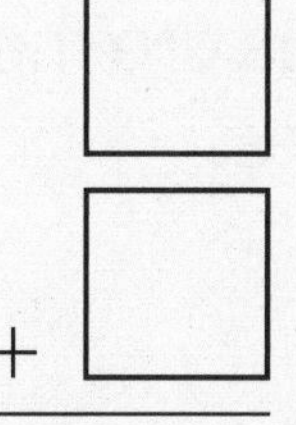

Materials: Counters, 9 per child

1. Have children find each sum. Ask: ***What is the same about these two problems?*** The amount in all is the same. The numbers being added are the same, just in a different order. Say: ***The amount in all is called the sum. You can change the order and the sum will always be the same.***
2. Have children find the sum that is written vertically. Have them change the order, write the numbers, and write the sum.
3. For Problem 2, have children use the first sum to write each sum. Let them use counters if they need them.
4. For Problem 3, have children write each sum a different way and write the sums. Let them use counters if they need them.

Name ______________________

Adding in Any Order (continued)

Add. Then change the order.
Use counters if you like.

4. $3 + 4 =$ 7

4 + 3 = 7

5. $1 + 4 =$ ______

______ + ______ = ______

6. $\begin{array}{r} 7 \\ +\ 1 \\ \hline \end{array}$

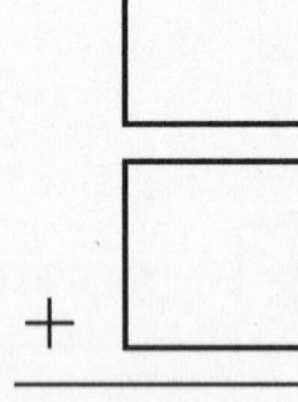

7. $\begin{array}{r} 1 \\ +\ 3 \\ \hline \end{array}$

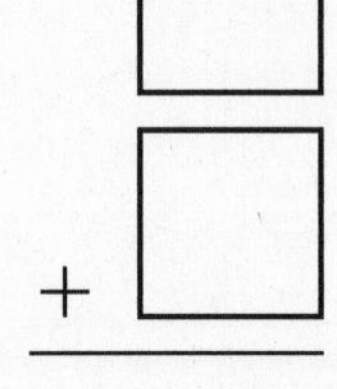

8. **Reasoning** Look at the picture. How many butterflies are there in all? Write two addition sentences.

______ + ______ = ______

______ + ______ = ______

9. **Reasoning** If $5 + 3 = 8$, what is $3 + 5$? ______

Name ________________________________

Parts of Ten

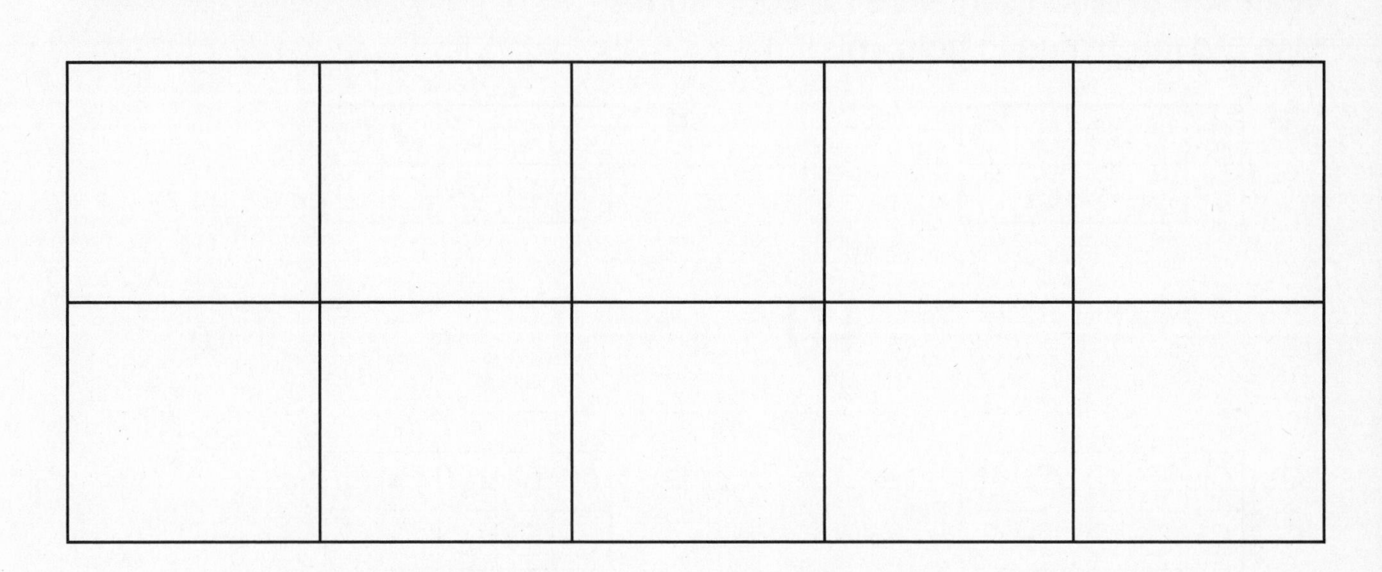

1. 7 + 3 = 10

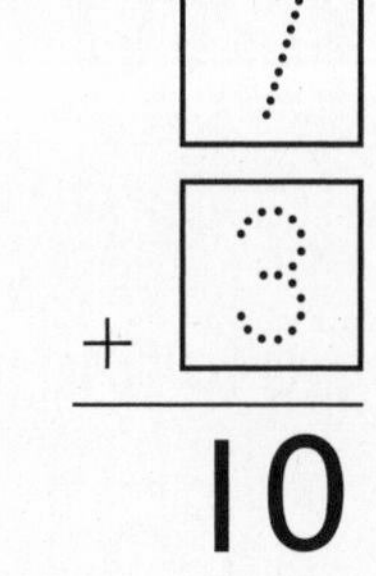

2. ______ + ______ = 10

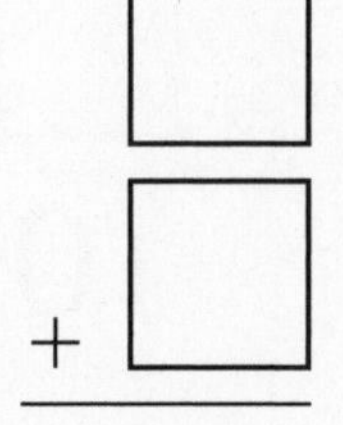

Materials: Two-color counters, 10 per child

1. Have children put 7 red counters in the ten-frame and write 7. Have children finish filling the ten-frame with yellow counters. Ask: ***How many yellow counters did you use?*** Have children write 3. Say: ***So, 7 plus 3 equals 10.***
2. Have children put 1 red counter in the ten-frame and write 1. Have them finish filling the ten-frame with yellow counters. Have children complete the number sentences.

Name ______________________________

Parts of Ten (continued)

Write the addition sentence for each sum.
Use the ten-frame to help you.

3. 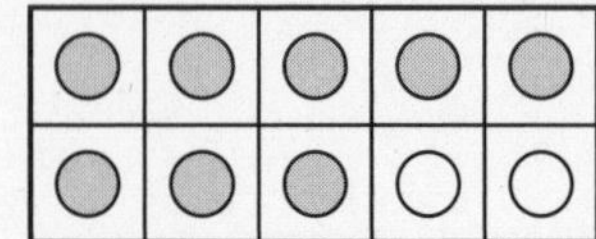

8 + 2 = 10

4. 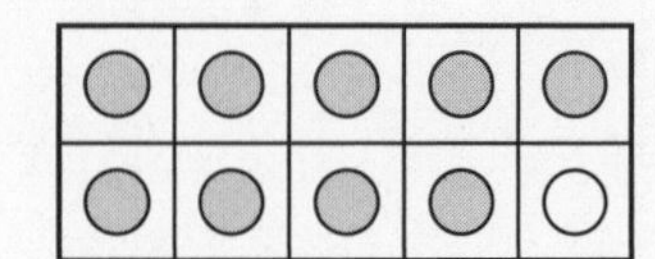

_____ + _____ = 10

5. 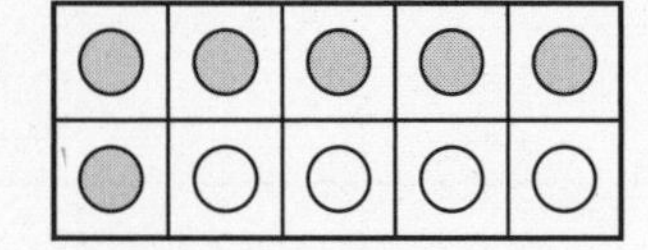

_____ + _____ = 10

6. 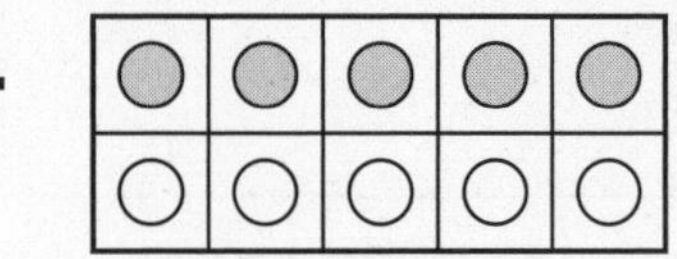

_____ + _____ = 10

Fill in the missing numbers to find each sum of 10.

7. 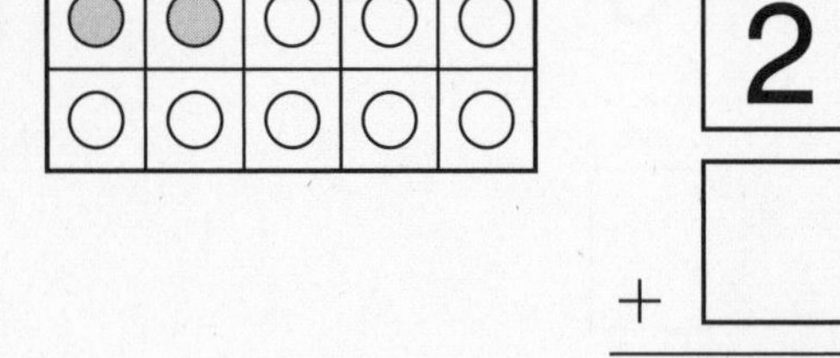

$$\begin{array}{r} 2 \\ + \square \\ \hline 10 \end{array}$$

8. 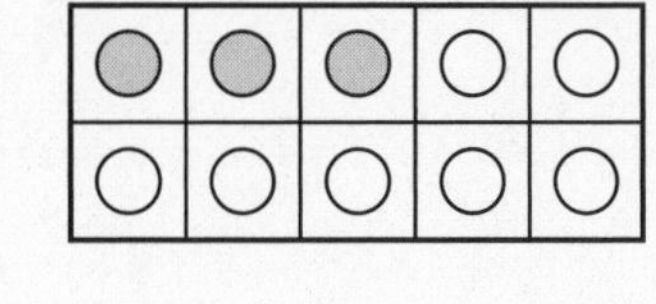

$$\begin{array}{r} 3 \\ + \square \\ \hline 10 \end{array}$$

9. 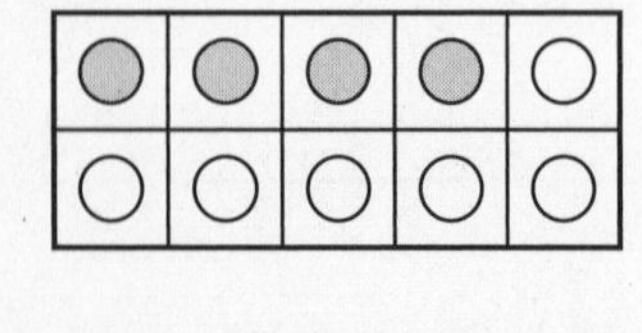

$$\begin{array}{r} 4 \\ + \square \\ \hline 10 \end{array}$$

10. 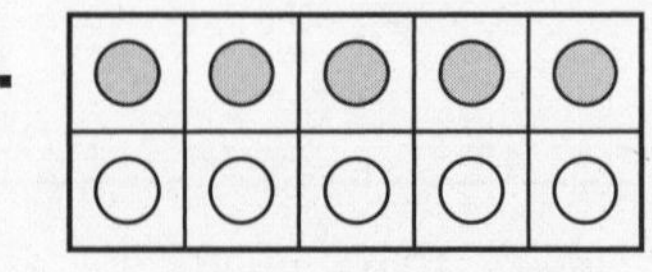

$$\begin{array}{r} 5 \\ + \square \\ \hline 10 \end{array}$$

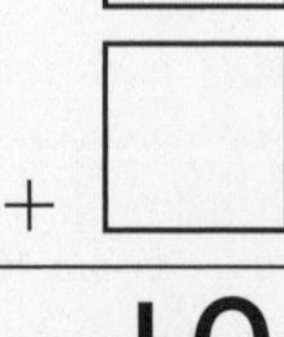

Name ____________________

Adding with 0, 1, 2

1.

5 , 6

4 + 2 = 6

2. 7 + 1 = ____

3. 1 + 6 = ____

4.

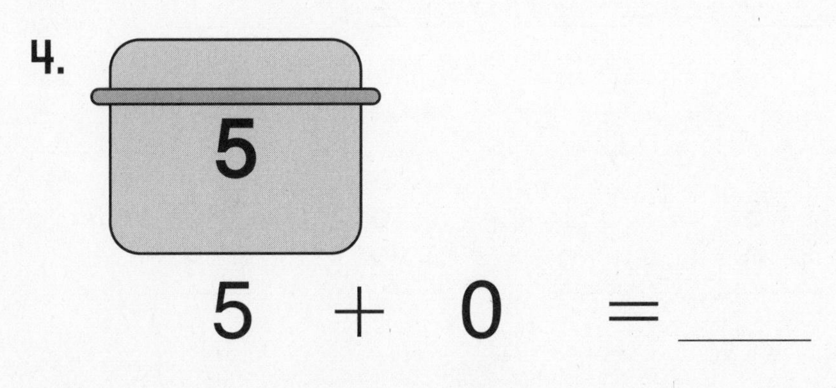

5 + 0 = ____

5. **Reasoning** 3 + 0 = ____

Materials: Have counters available for children who need them, 12 for each child.

1. Say: ***There are 4 cars in the box. Count on to find the sum.*** Have children count on from 4 and write 5 and 6. Say: ***So 4 plus 2 is 6.*** Have children write 6.
2. Have children count on from 7 to find 7 + 1. Have them write the sum.
3. Say: ***You can count on from any number.*** Have children count on from the 6 to find 1 + 6.
4. Say: ***If there are 5 cars in the box, how many cars are there in all?*** 5 Say: ***So, 5 + 0 is 5.*** Have children write the 5. Have children answer the reasoning question.

Name ______________________

Adding with 0, 1, 2 (continued)

Add. Use counters if you like.

6. 

_____, _____

8 + 2 = _____

7.

6	5	4	7	1	8
+ 1	+ 1	+ 2	+ 2	+ 2	+ 1

8.

0	6	0	7	3	4
+ 1	+ 2	+ 3	+ 0	+ 2	+ 1

9.

2	6	8	1	5	0
+ 2	+ 0	+ 0	+ 9	+ 2	+ 3

10. **Reasoning** When you add any number to zero what is your sum?

Name ____________________

Adding Doubles

1. 4 + 4 = 8

2.  

____ + ____ = ____

3. 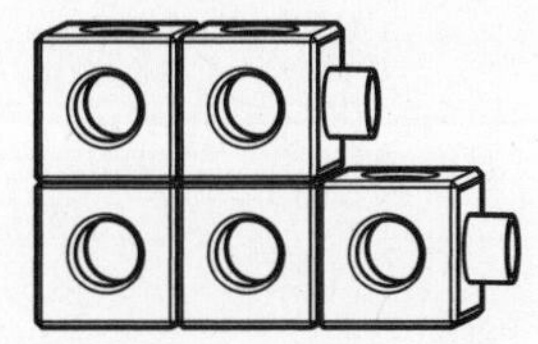 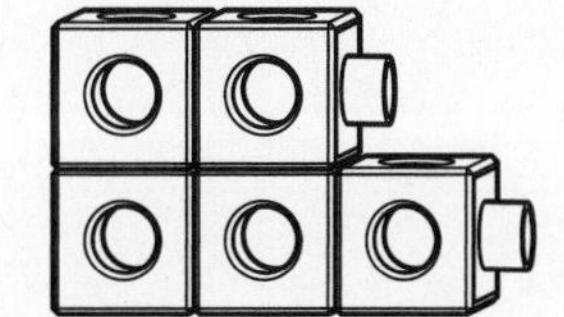

____ + ____ = ____

4. 3 + 3 = ____

5. 6 + 6 = ____

6. 1 + 1 = ____

Materials: Snap cubes, 12 for each child

1. Have children make 2 trains of 4 snap cubes each and write the 4s. Ask: ***How much is 4 plus 4?*** Have children write 8.
2. Ask: ***What is special about the sum 4 plus 4?*** The numbers are the same. Say: ***When the numbers are the same, the addition fact is a double.***
3. Have children use snap cubes to find the other doubles.

Name ______________________________

Adding Doubles (continued)

Add to find the double.

7. 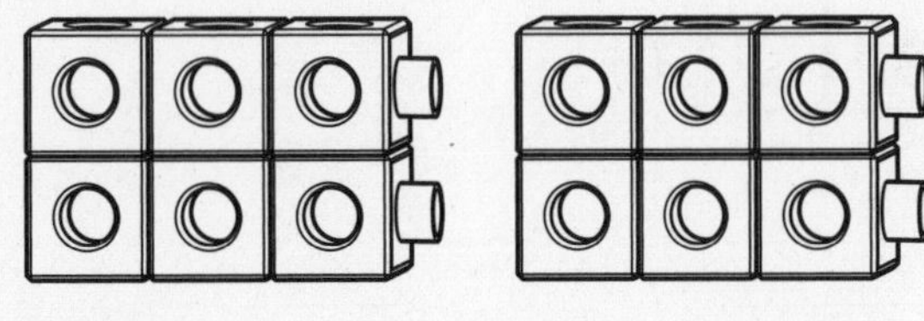

6 + 6 = 12

8. 

_____ + _____ = _____

9. 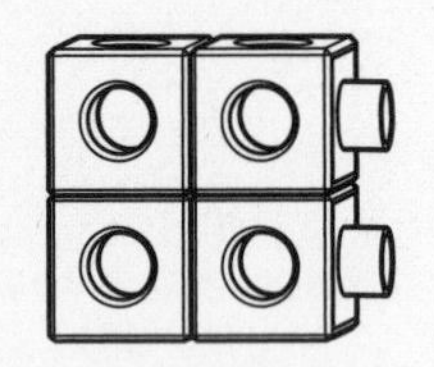 

_____ + _____ = _____

10.  

_____ + _____ = _____

Add. Circle the doubles facts.

11.

5	4	2	2	1	3
+ 2	+ 4	+ 2	+ 6	+ 8	+ 3

Reasoning Write the missing number that makes each sentence true.

12. _____ + 5 = 10

13. 3 + _____ = 6

Name ____________________

Using Doubles to Add

1.

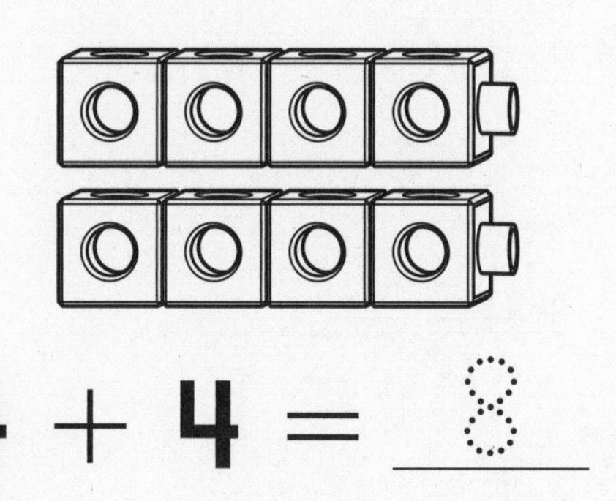

4 + 4 = 8

4 + 5 = 9

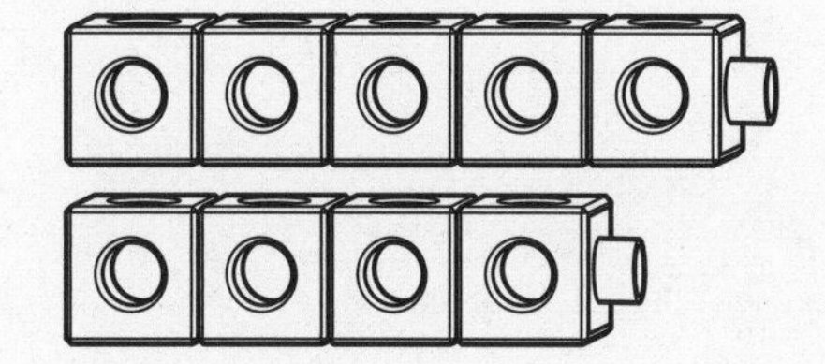

5 + 4 = 9

2. 2 + 3

___ + ___ = ___

2 + 3 = ___

3 + 2 = ___

3. 6 + 5

___ + ___ = ___

6 + 5 = ___

5 + 6 = ___

Materials: Snap cubes, 11 for each child

1. Have children form 2 trains of 4 and write the sum of the double 4 + 4. Then, have children add one more cube to the second train. Say: ***Four plus 5 is 4 plus 4 and one more. What is one more than 8?*** 9 Say: ***So, 4 plus 5 equals 9.*** Have children write 9.
2. Have children show 4 + 4 again. Have them add one cube to the first train of 4. Say: ***Five plus 4 is also one more than 4 plus 4. What is 5 plus 4?*** Have children write 9.
3. Ask: ***What double can you use to find 2 + 3?*** Have children write 2 and 2. Have children form two trains with 2 cubes each and write the sum, 4. Have them add cubes to find 2 + 3 and 3 + 2.
4. Ask: ***What double can you use to find 6 plus 5?*** Have children write 5 + 5 = 10 and use the double to find 6 + 5 and 5 + 6.

Name ______________________

Using Doubles to Add (continued)

Find each sum. Think of a double to help you.

4. $1 + 1 =$ 2

$1 + 2 =$ 3

5. $3 + 3 =$ ______

$3 + 4 =$ ______

6. $5 + 5 =$ ______

$5 + 6 =$ ______

7. $4 + 4 =$ ______

$4 + 5 =$ ______

8. $2 + 2 =$ ______ $2 + 3 =$ ______ $3 + 2 =$ ______

9. $3 + 3 =$ ______ $3 + 4 =$ ______ $4 + 3 =$ ______

10. $5 + 5 =$ ______ $5 + 6 =$ ______ $6 + 5 =$ ______

Solve.

11. Reasoning There are 4 birds in a tree. Double that many and one more are flying away. How many birds are flying away?

______ birds

Name ______________________________

Facts with 5 on a Ten-Frame

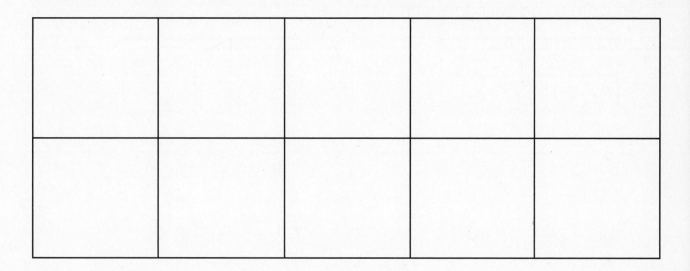

1. 5 + 1 = 6

6 + 4 = 10

2. 5 + 2 = ______

7 + ______ = 10

3. 5 + 3 = ______

8 + ______ = 10

4. 5 + 4 = ______

9 + ______ = 10

5. 5 + 5 = ______

Materials: Two color counters, 10 for each child

1. Have children put 5 red counters in the first row of the ten-frame. Then have them put one yellow counter in the second row. Ask: ***What is 5 plus 1?*** Have children write 6.
2. Ask: ***How many counters would you need to fill the ten-frame?*** 4 Ask: ***So, 6 plus what number equals 10?*** Have children write 4.
3. Have children put 5 red counters in the first row of the ten-frame and two yellow counters in the second row. Ask questions like those above to have children find 5 + 2 and 7 + 3.
4. Do other problems similarly.

Name ______________________

Facts with 5 on a Ten-Frame (continued)

Write an addition fact with 5.
Then write an addition fact with 10.

6. 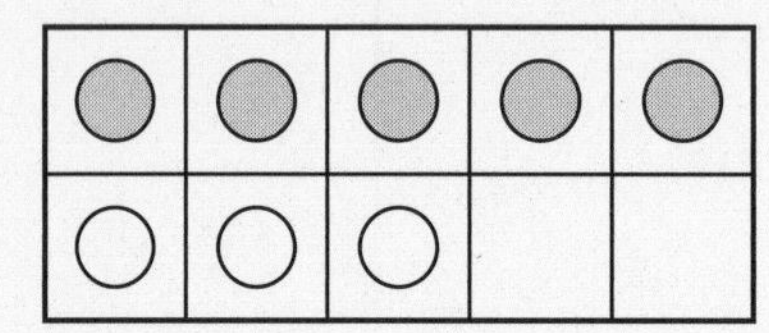

5 + 3 = 8

8 + 2 = 10

7. 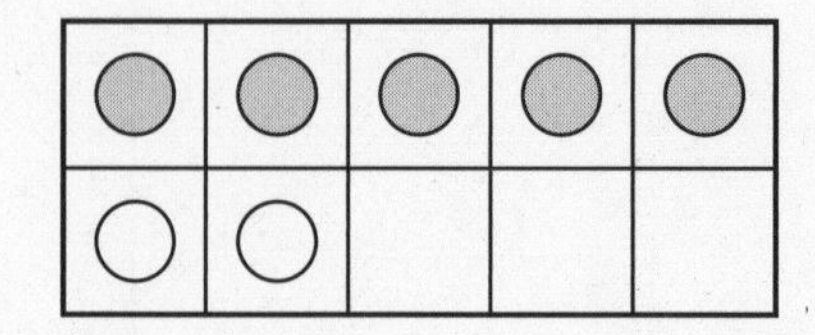

5 + ______ = ______

7 + ______ = 10

8. 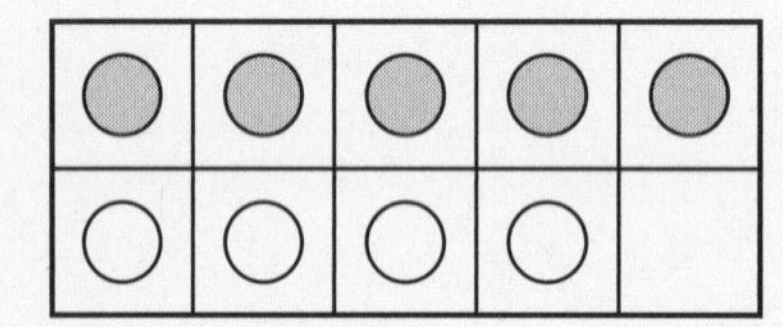

5 + ______ = ______

9 + ______ = 10

9. 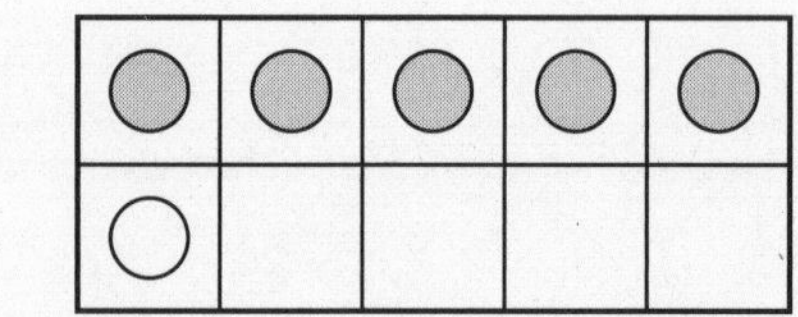

5 + ______ = ______

6 + ______ = 10

Reasoning Write the missing numbers.

10. 5 + ______ = 10

11. 5 + 3 = ______ 3 + 5 = ______

Name ______________________________

Making 10 on a Ten-Frame

1. 10
+ 1
―――
11

2. 10
+ 2
―――

3. 9 + 2 = 10 + ☐

4. 8 + 4 = 10 + ☐

Materials: Two-color counters, 12 for each child

1. Have children fill the ten-frame with yellow counters. Have them put one red counter below the frame. Ask: ***What is 10 plus 1?*** Have children write 11. Do 10 + 2 similarly.
2. Have children put 9 yellow counters in the ten-frame and 2 red counters below. Ask: ***What addition do the counters show?*** 9 plus 2 Then have children move one red counter to fill up the ten-frame. Ask: ***Nine plus 2 is equal to 10 plus what number?*** Have children write 1. Ask: ***If 10 plus 1 equals 11, then what is 9 plus 2?*** Have children write 11 for the sum 9 + 2.
3. Have children put 8 yellow counters in the ten-frame and 4 red counters below. Ask: ***What addition do the counters show?*** 8 plus 4 Then have children move two red counters to fill up the ten-frame. Ask: ***Eight plus 4 is equal to 10 plus what number?*** Have children write 2. Ask: ***If 10 plus 2 equals 12, then what is 8 plus 4?*** Have children write 12 for the sum 8 + 4.

Name ______________________

Making 10 on a Ten-Frame (continued)

Write the missing numbers.
Find the sums.

5. 9 + 3 = 12; 10 + [2]

6. 7 + 4; 10 + [ ]

7. 8 + 3; 10 + [ ]

8. 7 + 5; 10 + [ ]

9. 8 + 4; 10 + [ ]

10. 3 + 9; [ ] + 10

11. **Reasoning** Find 9 + 2.

9 + ______ = 10

1 less than 2 is ______.

So, 9 + 2 = 10 + ______ = ______.

Name ______________________________

Missing Parts

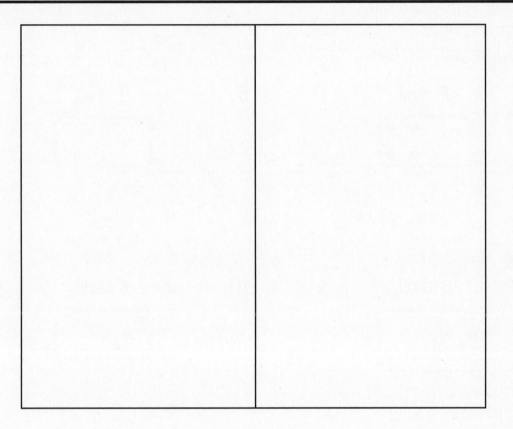

1. 4 + __2__ = 6

2. ______ + 2 = 5

3. 9 = 5 + ______

4. 8 = ______ + 7

5. 7 = ______ + 4

6. 2 + ______ = 4

Materials: Two-color counters, 9 for each child

1. Say: ***There are 6 counters in all.*** Have children count out 6 counters and put 4 in the first box. Ask: ***How many counters go in the second box?*** Have children put 2 counters in the second box and write 2. Say: ***Two is the missing part.***
2. Have children count out 5 counters. Say: ***There are 5 counters in all. Put 2 in the second box. What is the missing part?*** Have children put 3 counters in the first box and write 3.
3. Do the other problems similarly.

Name ________________________________

Missing Parts (continued)

Draw how many are missing.
Write the number.
Use counters if you like.

7. 7 in all

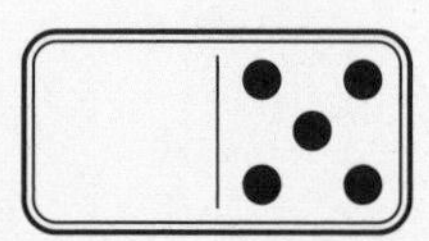

_____ + 5 = 7

8. 4 in all

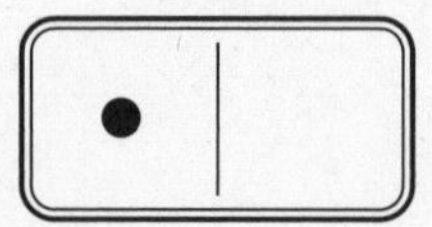

4 = 1 + _____

9. 8 in all

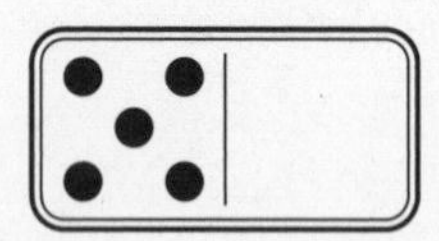

8 = 5 + _____

10. 6 in all

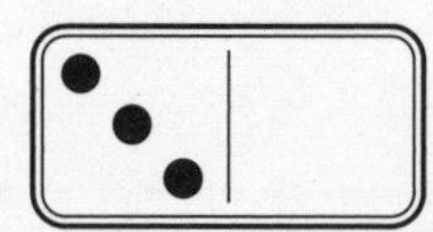

3 + _____ = 6

Write the missing numbers.
Use counters if you like.

11. 4 + _____ = 8

12. 1 + _____ = 7

Reasoning Write the number sentence.
Solve.

13. Fred bought 5 cookies.
His mother gave him some more.
Now Fred has 8 cookies.
How many more did she give him?

8 in all

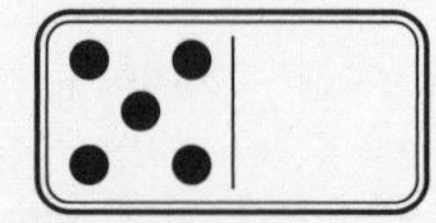

_____ + _____ = _____

Name ______________________

Separating Stories

1. 6 – 2 = 4 bees left

2. ____ – ____ = ____ apples

3. ____ – ____ = ____ balloons

4. ____ – ____ = ____ lions

Materials: Have counters available for children who need them

1. Say: ***Manuella saw 6 bees.*** Have children write 6. Say: ***Two bees flew away.*** Have children write 2 and cross out 2 bees. Ask: ***How many bees are left?*** Have children write 4. Say: ***So 6 minus 2 equals 4.***
2. Say: ***Thomas had 8 apples.*** Have children write 8. Say: ***He ate 1.*** Have children write 1 and cross out 1 apple. Ask: ***How many apples does Thomas have left?*** Have children write 7. Say: ***So, 8 minus 1 equals 7.***
3. Say: ***Rachel had 10 balloons for her party. Three balloons floated away. How many balloons did Rachel have left?*** Have children cross out balloons, solve, and write the number sentence.
4. Say: ***Jamal saw 9 lions outside, at the zoo. Five lions went inside. How many lions were still outside?*** Have children cross out lions, solve, and write the number sentence.

Name ______________________________

Separating Stories (continued)

Write the subtraction sentence.

5. 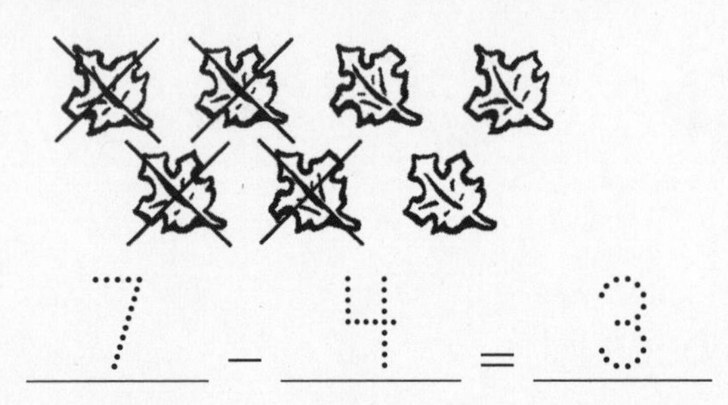

7 – 4 = 3

6. 

_____ – _____ = _____

7. 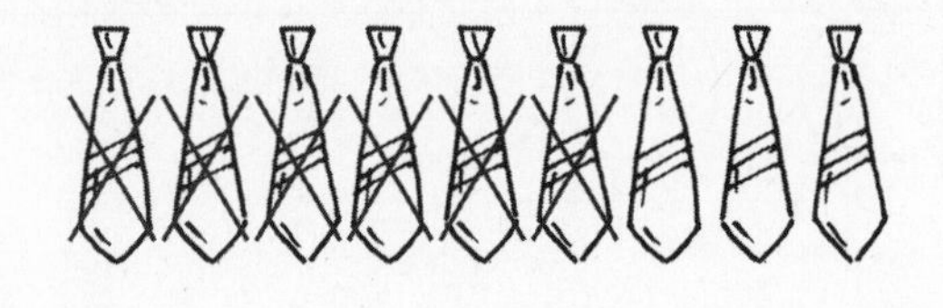

_____ – _____ = _____

8. 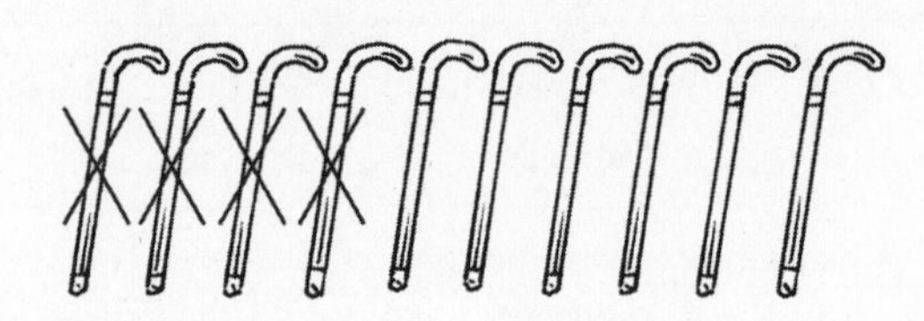

_____ – _____ = _____

9. Kristen had 7 books.
She gave 3 way.
How many books were left?

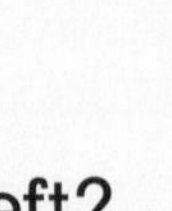    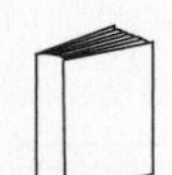 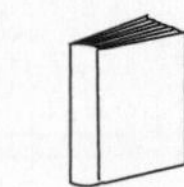

_____ – _____ = _____ books

10. 9 birds were sitting on a fence.
6 birds flew away.
How many birds were left?

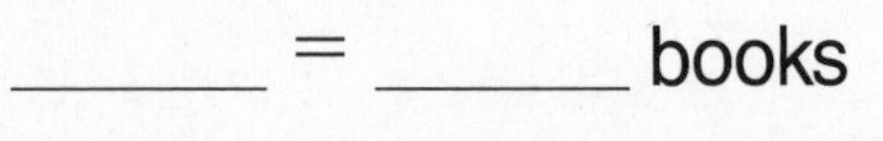

_____ – _____ = _____

11. Ayla has 6 new heart stickers.
She gave 3 of them away.
How many hearts are left?

_____ – _____ = _____ hearts

Name ______________________________

Comparing Stories

1.

7 — 4 = 3

2.

_____ — _____ = _____

3. 

_____ — _____ = _____

1. Say: ***Victor saw 7 elephants and 4 giraffes.*** Have children write 7 and 4. Then have them cross out one elephant and one giraffe, then another elephant and another giraffe. Have them continue until all the giraffes are crossed out. Ask: ***How many more elephants than giraffes did Victor see?*** Have children write 3.
2. Say: ***Miranda saw 6 monkeys and 5 bears.*** Have children write 6 and 5. Then have them cross out one monkey and one bear, then another monkey and another bear. Have them continue until all the bears are crossed out. Ask: ***How many more bears than monkeys did she see?*** Have children write 1.
3. Say: ***Ahmed saw 4 tigers and 2 lions.*** How many more tigers than lions did he see? Have children cross out, solve, and write the number sentence.

Name ____________________

Comparing Stories (continued)

Write the subtraction sentence.

4. Pedro caught 8 butterflies.
David caught 3 butterflies.
How many more butterflies
did Pedro catch?

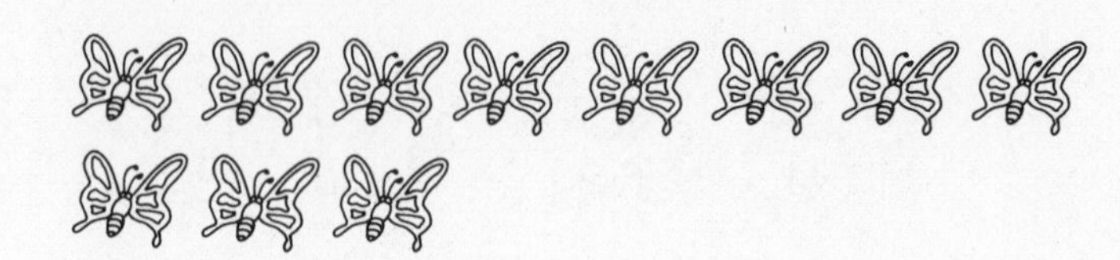

_____ − _____ = _____ butterflies

5. There are 2 ducks in the pond.
There are 8 ducks out of the pond.
How many more ducks are out of
the pond?

_____ − _____ = _____ ducks

6. There are 6 bees and 2 ants.
How many more bees than
ants are there?

_____ − _____ = _____ more

7. **Reasoning** Draw 5 frogs on a log.
Draw 3 frogs on the other log.
How many more frogs are on one
log than the other?
Write a number sentence.

_____ − _____ = _____ more

Name ________________________________

Relating Addition and Subtraction

1. 6 + 3 = 9

2. ____ − ____ = ____

3. ____ − ____ = ____

4.

____ + ____ = ____; ____ − ____ = ____

____ − ____ = ____

5.

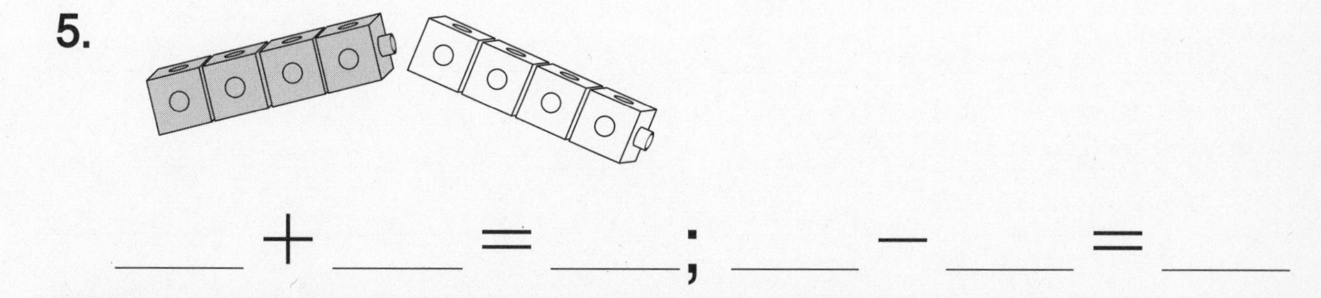

____ + ____ = ____; ____ − ____ = ____

Materials: Snap cubes 6 of one color and 4 of another color for each child

1. Have children make a train of 6 snap cubes, all the same color, and write the number 6. Have them make a train of 3 snap cubes of a different color and write 3. Have them put the two trains together. Ask: ***How long is the train?*** Have children write 9. Say: ***So, 6 plus 3 equals 9.***
2. Have children write 9 in the first blank of the first subtraction sentence. Have them break off the 3 cubes of a different color and write 3. Ask: ***How many cubes are left?*** Have them write 6.
3. Ask: ***If we start with 9 and break off 6, how many cubes will be left?*** Have children write the number sentence 9 − 6 = 3.
4. Ask: ***How are these number sentences alike?*** They all use the same numbers. Say: ***If you know 6 plus 3 equals 9, then you know 9 minus 3 equals 6 and 9 minus 6 equals 3.***
5. Have children form the other trains shown and write corresponding number sentences.

Name ______________________

Relating Addition and Subtraction (continued)

Write two subtraction sentences for each addition sentence. Use cubes if you like.

6. 3 + 4 = 7
7 − 4 = 3
7 − 3 = 4

7. 1 + 7 = 8
___ − ___ = ___
___ − ___ = ___

8. 4 + 2 = 6
___ − ___ = ___
___ − ___ = ___

9. 4 + 5 = 9
___ − ___ = ___
___ − ___ = ___

10. 2 + 7 = 9
___ − ___ = ___
___ − ___ = ___

11. 6 + 1 = 7
___ − ___ = ___
___ − ___ = ___

Write a number sentence.

12. Tonya saw 8 butterflies. 3 flew away. How many butterflies are left?

___ − ___ = ___

13. Jerome found 5 fossils. Kobe found 3 fossils. How many fossils did they find in all?

___ + ___ = ___

Name ______________________

Missing Parts of 10

10

1. 6 ______ part I know   4 ______ missing part
2. ______ part I know   ______ missing part
3. ______ part I know   ______ missing part
4. ______ part I know   ______ missing part

Materials: Counters, 10 for each child

1. Say: ***There are 10 counters in all.*** Have children put 6 of their 10 counters in the first box. Ask: ***How many counters go in the second box?*** Have children write 4. Say: ***Four is the missing part and six is the part you know.***
2. Say: ***There are 10 counters in all and you know 2.*** Have children put 2 counters in the first box and write 2. Ask: ***What is the missing part?*** Have children write 8.
3. Have children do other problems similarly, with 7 counters in the first box and then again with 5 counters.

Name ______________________________

Missing Parts of 10 (continued)

Draw the missing part to make 10 in all.
Write the numbers.

5.

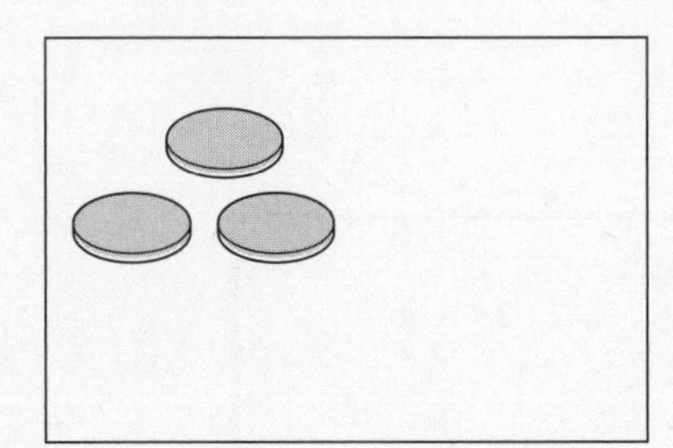

_____ part I know _____ missing part

6.

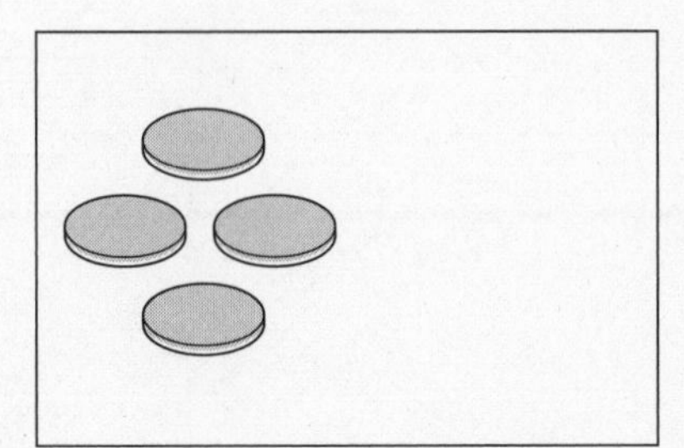

_____ part I know _____ missing part

7.

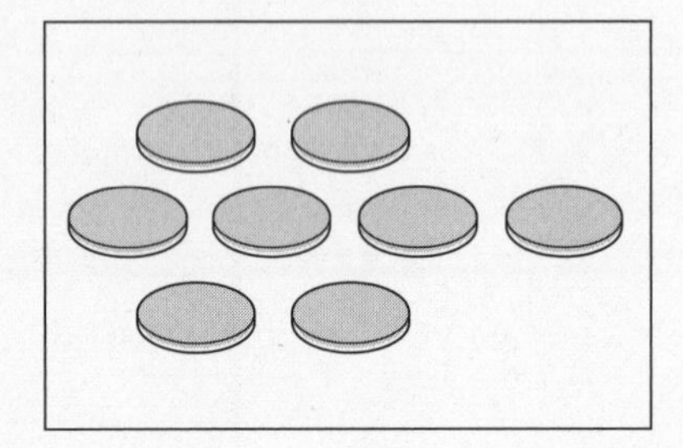

_____ part I know _____ missing part

8.

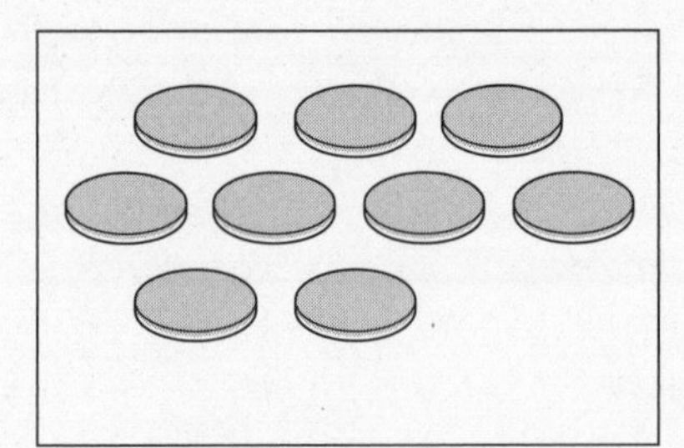

_____ part I know _____ missing part

Reasoning Write the missing number.
Use counters if you like.

9. 5 + _____ = 10

10. 7 + _____ = 10

11. 1 + _____ = 10

12. 6 + _____ = 10

Name ______________________________

Subtracting Across and Down

1.

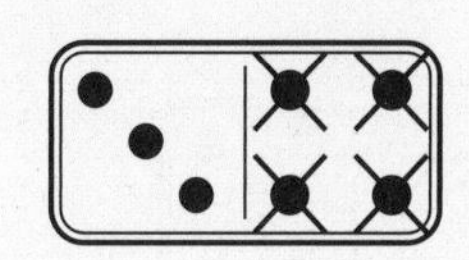

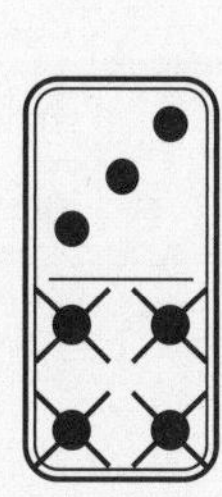

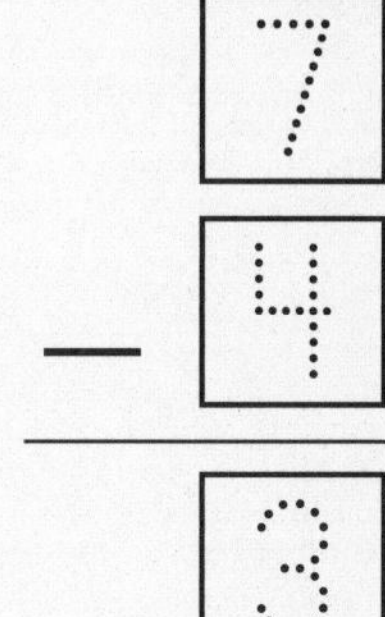

7 − 4 = 3

2.

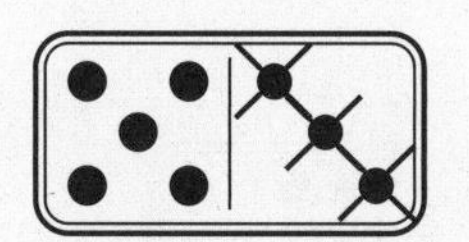

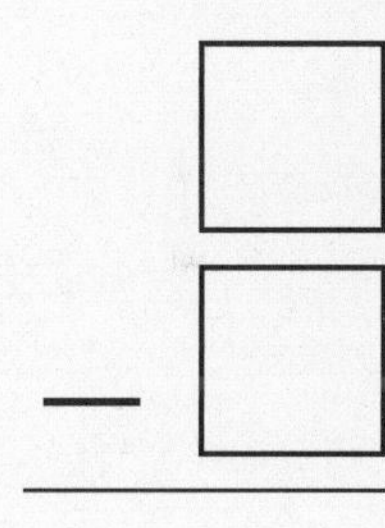

_____ − _____ = _____

3. 6
− 3

_____ − _____ = _____

4. 9
− 4

9 − 4 = _____

Materials: Counters, 9 per child

1. Ask: ***How many dots are in the domino?*** Have children write 7. Ask: ***How many dots are crossed out?*** Have children write 4. Ask: ***How many dots are left?*** Have children write 3.
2. Say: ***There is another way to write seven minus four is three.*** Write the vertical form on the board or overhead and have children write the numbers.
3. For problem 2, have children write the numbers for how many dots in all, how many are crossed out, and how many are left. Have them complete the other number sentence. 8 − 5 = 3
4. For the remaining problems, have children use counters to find each difference, written both ways.

Name ______________________________

Subtracting Across and Down (continued)

Write the numbers. Subtract.

5.

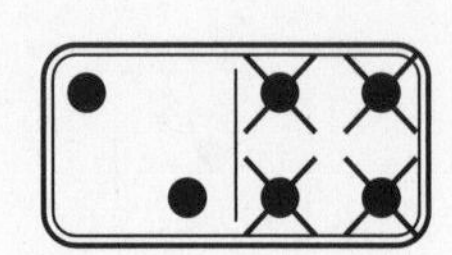

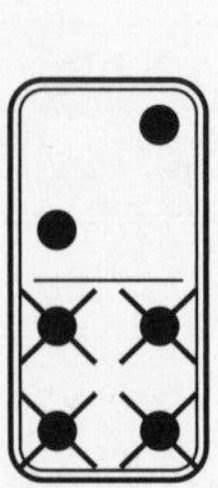

_____ – _____ = _____

6.

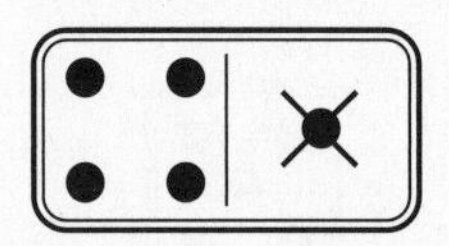

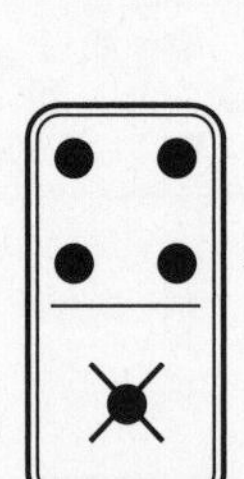

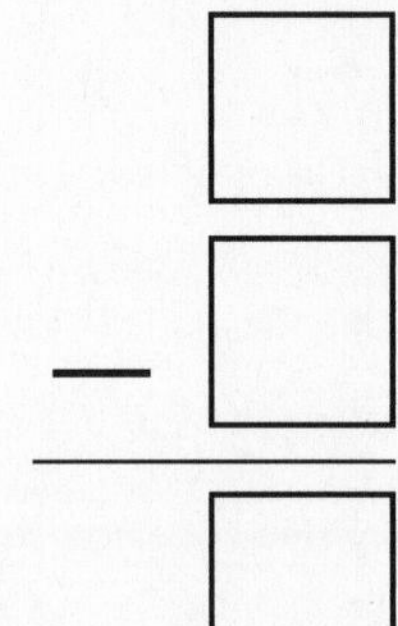

_____ – _____ = _____

Find each difference.
Write the matching subtraction sentence.

7.
$$\begin{array}{r} 8 \\ -\ 3 \\ \hline 8 \end{array}$$

8 – 3 = 5

8.
$$\begin{array}{r} 4 \\ -\ 3 \\ \hline \end{array}$$

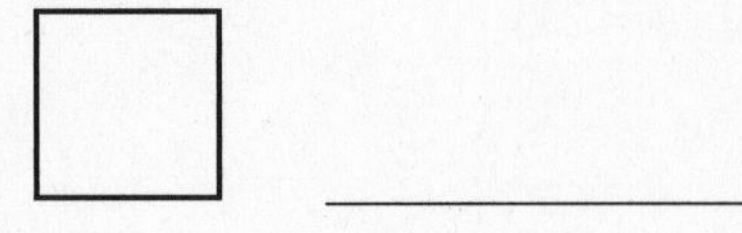

9. **Reasoning** Write the missing number.

$$\begin{array}{r} 9 \\ -\ 3 \\ \hline \end{array}$$

9 – _____ = 6

Name ______________________________

Subtracting with 0, 1, and 2

1.

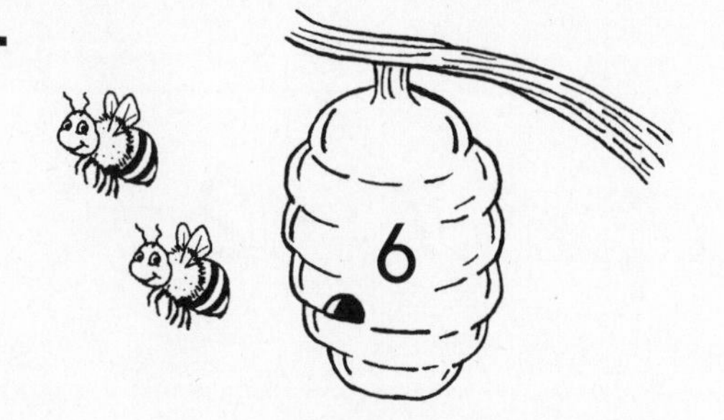

5, 4 $6 - 2 =$ 4

2.

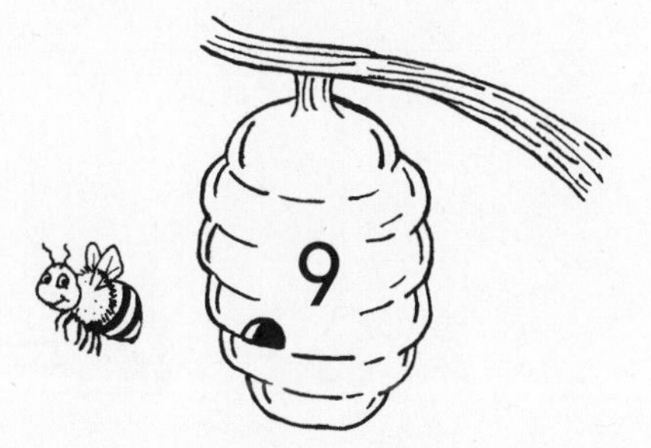

____ $\begin{array}{r} 9 \\ -1 \\ \hline \end{array}$

3.

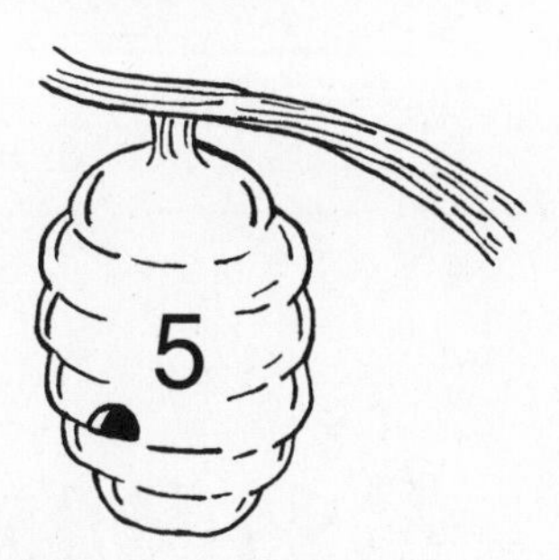

$5 - 0 =$ ____

4. Reasoning

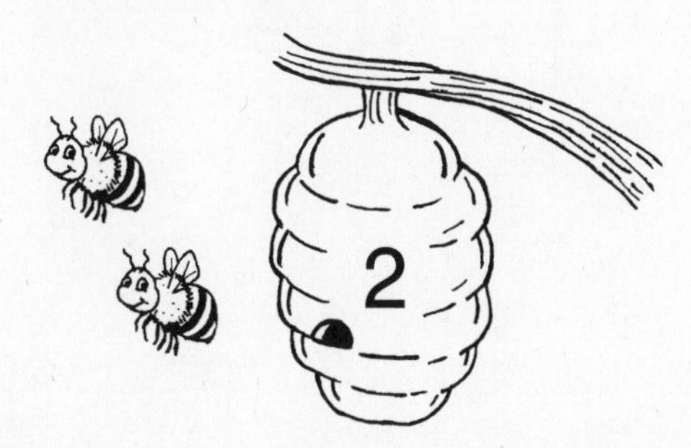

$2 - 2 =$ ____

Materials: Have counters available for children who need them, 9 for each child.

1. Say: ***There were 6 bees in the hive. Two bees flew away. Count back to find how many are still in the hive.*** Have children count back from 6 and write 5 and 4. Say: ***So 6 minus 2 is 4.*** Have children write 4.
2. Have children count back from 9 to find 9 – 1. Have them write the difference.
3. Say: ***If there are 5 bees in the hive and zero fly away, how many bees are left in the hive?*** Have children write 5.
4. Say: ***If there are 2 bees in the hive and 2 fly away, how many bees are left in the hive?*** Have children write zero.

Name ______________________________

Subtracting with 0, 1, and 2 (continued)

Count back to subtract.

5.

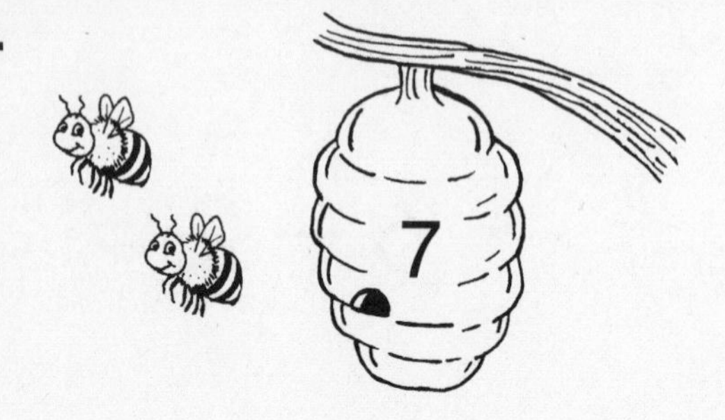

___, ___ $7 - 2 =$ ___

6.

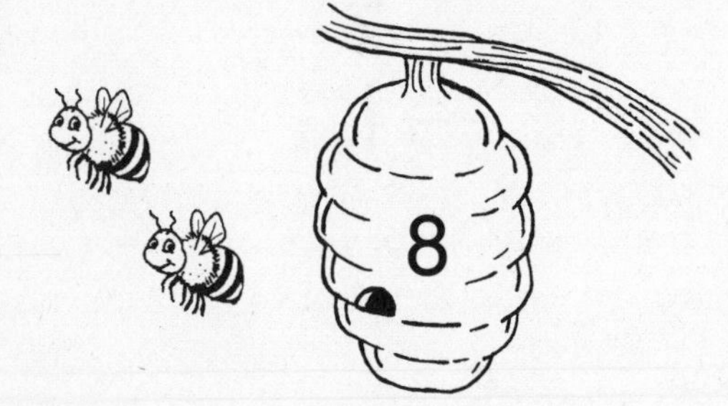

___, ___ $8 - 2 =$ ___

Subtract.

7. 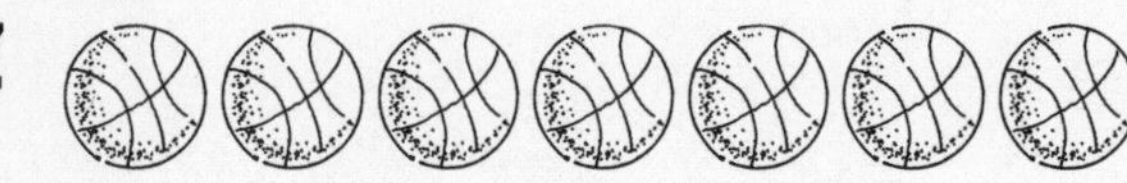

$7 - 0 =$ ___

8. 

$4 - 4 =$ ___

9. $\begin{array}{r} 8 \\ -\ 0 \\ \hline \end{array}$ $\begin{array}{r} 1 \\ -\ 1 \\ \hline \end{array}$ $\begin{array}{r} 4 \\ -\ 2 \\ \hline \end{array}$ $\begin{array}{r} 3 \\ -\ 3 \\ \hline \end{array}$ $\begin{array}{r} 7 \\ -\ 1 \\ \hline \end{array}$ $\begin{array}{r} 6 \\ -\ 6 \\ \hline \end{array}$

10. $\begin{array}{r} 4 \\ -\ 1 \\ \hline \end{array}$ $\begin{array}{r} 8 \\ -\ 1 \\ \hline \end{array}$ $\begin{array}{r} 5 \\ -\ 2 \\ \hline \end{array}$ $\begin{array}{r} 2 \\ -\ 1 \\ \hline \end{array}$ $\begin{array}{r} 4 \\ -\ 2 \\ \hline \end{array}$ $\begin{array}{r} 9 \\ -\ 2 \\ \hline \end{array}$

Name ______________________

Using Doubles to Subtract

1. $3 + 3 =$ 6 So $6 - 3 =$ 3.

2. $4 + 4 =$ ____ So $8 - 4 =$ ____.

3. $6 + 6 =$ ____ So $12 - 6 =$ ____.

4. ____ + ____ = ____

$4 - 2 =$ ____

Materials: Snap cubes, 12 for each child

1. Have children make 2 trains of 3 snap cubes each. Ask: ***How much is 3 plus 3?*** Have children write 6. Have children break the train apart into two trains with 3 each. Ask: ***Since 3 plus 3 is 6, what is 6 minus 3?*** Have children write 3.
2. Say: ***If you know the doubles addition facts, you can use them to subtract.*** Have children use cubes to find 8 – 4 and 12 – 6.
3. Ask: ***What doubles addition fact can you use to find 4 minus 2?*** Have children complete 2 + 2 = 4. Ask: ***What is 4 minus 2?*** Have children write 2.

Name ____________________

Using Doubles to Subtract (continued)

Find the double. Then subtract.
Use cubes if you like.

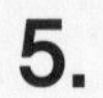 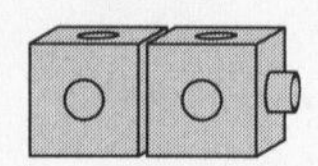 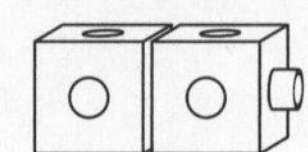

2 + 2 = ______

So 4 − 2 = ______.

6.  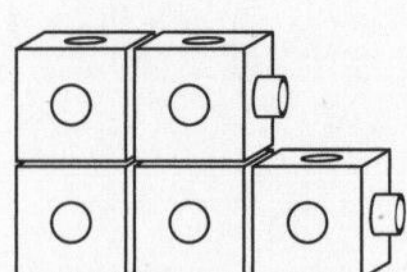

5 + 5 = ______

So 10 − 5 = ______.

Write an addition fact. Then subtract.

7. 1 + 1 = ______ So 2 − 1 = ______.

8. 3 + 3 = ______ So 6 − 3 = ______.

9. 4 + 4 = ______ So 8 − 4 = ______.

10. ______ + ______ = 12 So 12 − 6 = ______.

 Carolyn has 6 apples and 3 oranges.
How many pieces of fruit does she have in all?

______ pieces of fruit

Name ______________________________

Thinking Addition to 12 to Subtract

7

I. 3 + ______ = 7 So 7 − 3 = ______.

2. 5 + ______ = 7 So 7 − 5 = ______.

3. 6 + ______ = 7 So 7 − 6 = ______.

Materials: Counters, 12 for each child

1. Say: ***There are 7 counters in all.*** Have children put 3 of their 7 counters in the first box. Ask: ***How many counters go in the second box?*** Have children write 4. Say: ***Since 3 plus 4 equals 7, what is 7 minus 3?*** Have children write 4.
2. Do the other problems similarly.

Name ______________________________

Thinking Addition to 12 to Subtract (continued)

Draw the missing part. Write the numbers.

4.

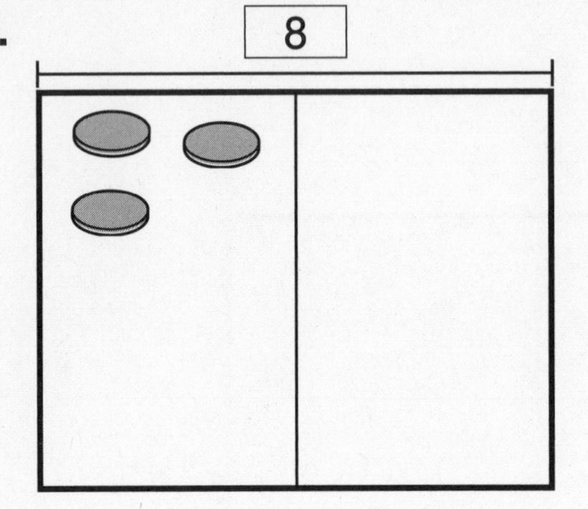

3 + ______ = 8

So 8 − 3 = ______.

5.

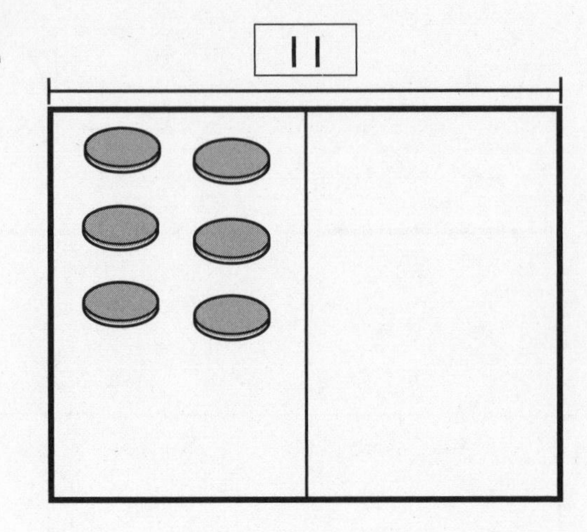

6 + ______ = 11

So 11 − 6 = ______.

6.

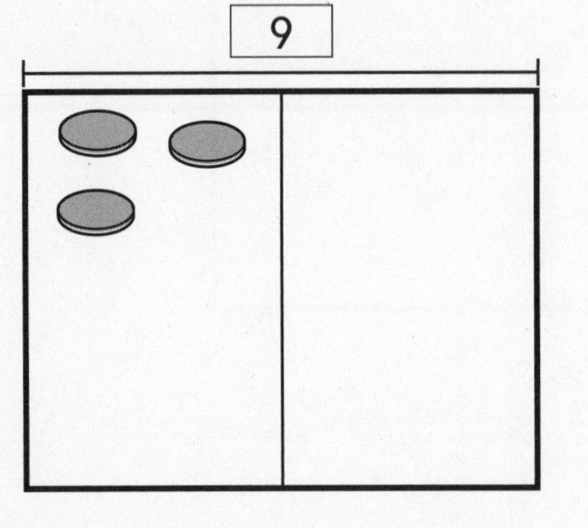

3 + ______ = 9

So 9 − 3 = ______.

7.

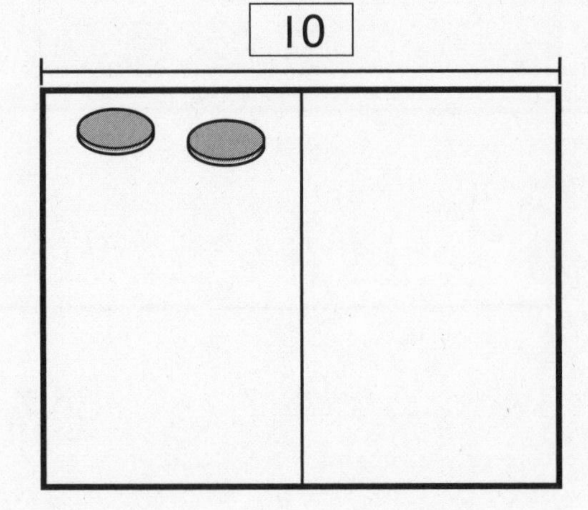

2 + ______ = 10

So 10 − 2 = ______.

Reasoning Write the missing number. Use counters if you like.

8. 4 + ______ = 10 So 10 − 4 = ______.

9. 7 + ______ = 11 So 11 − 7 = ______.

Name ______________________

Stories about Joining

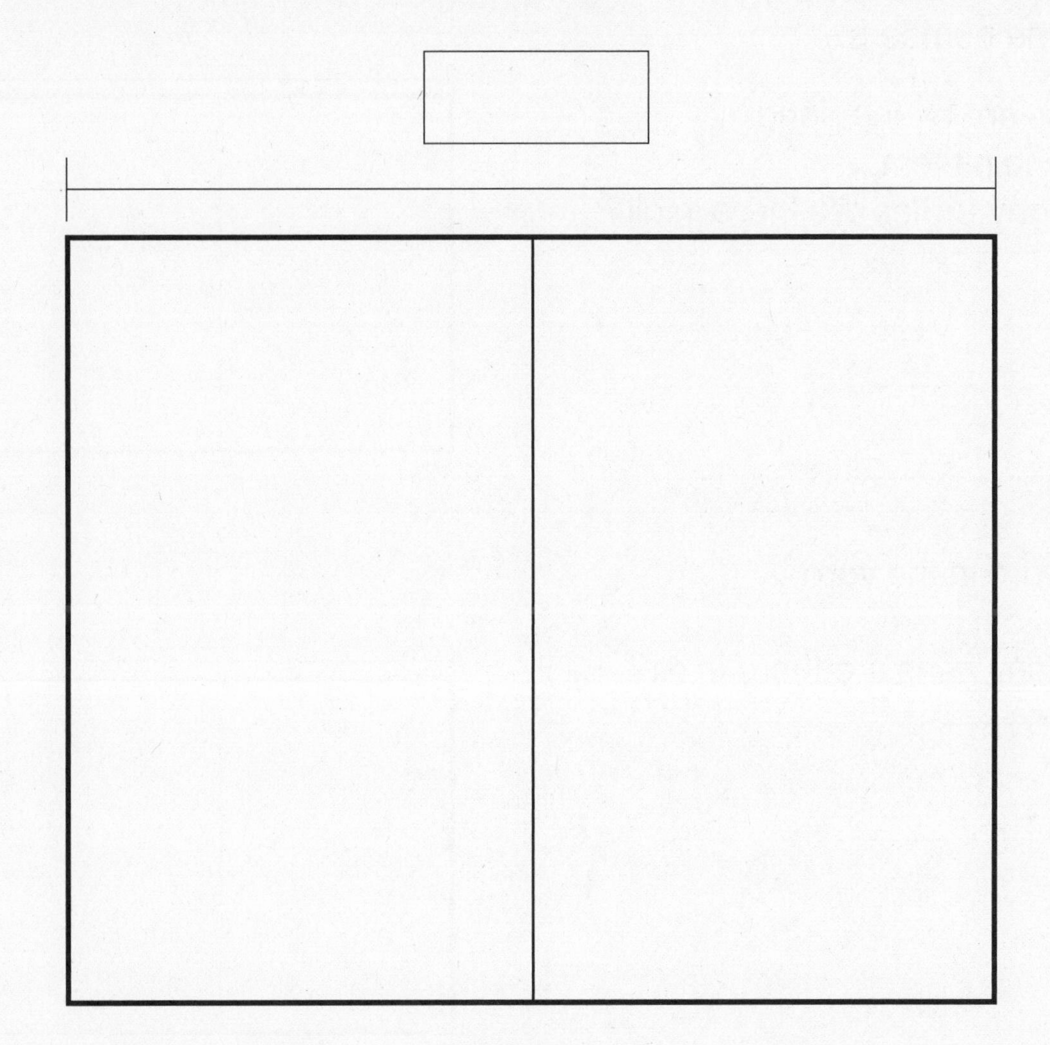

1. 8 + 7 = 15 2. ____ + ____ = ____

3. ____ + ____ = ____ 4. ____ + ____ = ____

Materials: Counters, 18 for each child

1. Say: ***Anna has 8 leaves.*** Have children put 8 counters in the first box and write 8. Say: ***Anna found 7 more leaves.*** Have children put 7 counters in the second box and write 7. Ask: ***How many leaves does Anna have now?*** Have children use the counters to find 8 + 7 and write 15.
2. Say: ***Ahmed had 5 sports cards.*** Have children put 5 counters in the first box and write 5. Say: ***Ahmed got 9 more sports cards as a gift.*** Have children put 9 counters in the second box and write 9. Ask: ***How many sports cards does Ahmed have now?*** Have children use the counters to find 5 + 9 and write 14.
3. Create joining stories as a class for 6 + 7 = 13 and 9 + 8 = 17.

Name ___________________________

Stories about Joining (continued)

Draw a picture to find the sum.
Then write the numbers.

5. 9 turtles are by the pond.
7 more join them.
How many turtles are there in all?

9 + 7 = ______

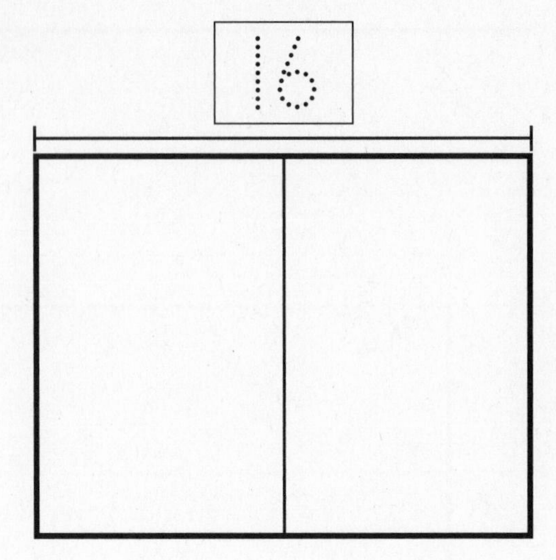

6. 8 hens are in the yard.
6 more join them.
How many hens are there in all?

______ + ______ = ______

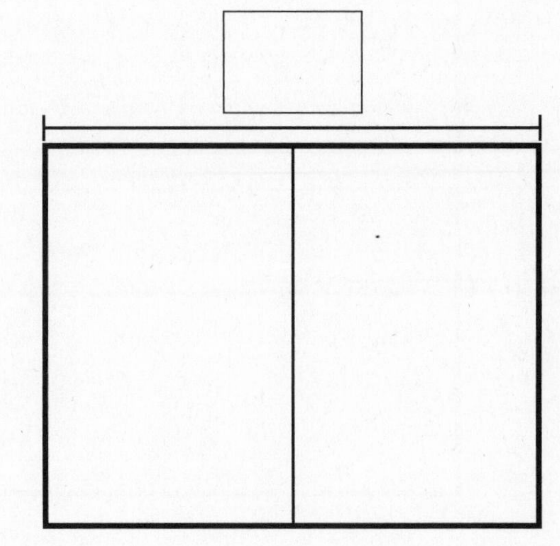

7. 9 cows are in the barn.
9 more join them.
How many cows are there in all?

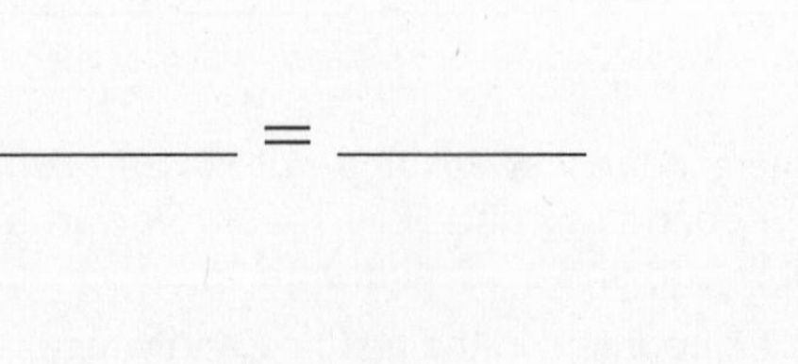

______ + ______ = ______

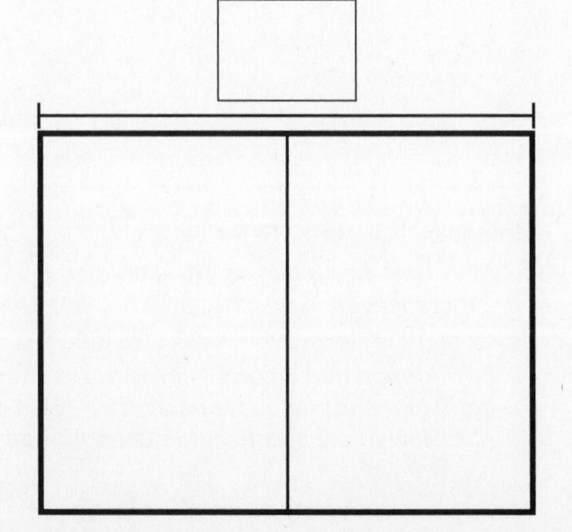

Name ______________________________

Doubles to 18

1. 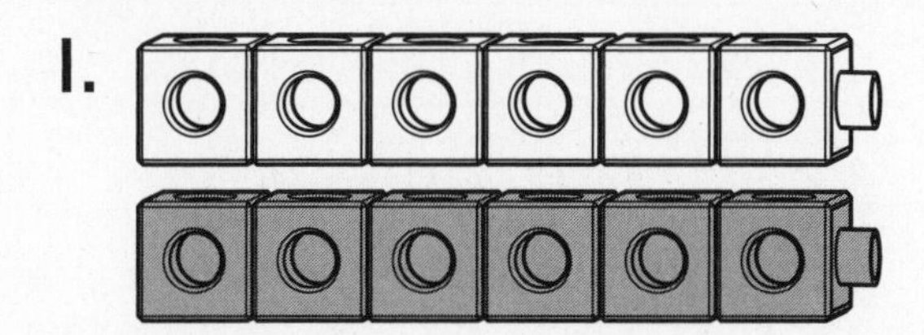

$6 + \underline{6} = \underline{12}$

2.

$5 + \underline{5} = \underline{10}$

3. 7 + ______ = ______

4. 4 + ______ = ______

5. 9 + ______ = ______

6. 8 + ______ = ______

7. **Reasoning** Is 6 a double? yes or no

8. ______ + ______ = 6

9. **Reasoning** Is 9 a double? yes or no

Materials: Snap cubes, 18 for each child

1. Have children make a train of 6 snap cubes. Ask: ***How many snap cubes do you need to add to make this addition fact a double?*** Have children make another train of 6 snap cubes and write the 6. Ask: ***How much is 6 plus 6?*** Have children write 12.
2. Do 5 + 5 similarly.
3. Have children use the snap cubes to find the other doubles.
4. Have children make a train of 6 snap cubes. Ask: ***Can 6 be the sum of a double?*** Give children time to break apart the 6-trains. Have children circle yes.
5. Ask: ***What number can be doubled to give the sum of 6?*** Have children write the 3s.
6. Have children make a train of 9 snap cubes. Ask: ***Can 9 be the sum of a double?*** Give children time to break apart the 9-trains. Have children circle no.

Name ______________________________

Doubles to 18 (continued)

Add.
Circle the doubles. Use cubes if you like.

10. $3 + 3 =$ ______ $8 + 2 =$ ______ $9 + 9 =$ ______

11. $2 + 9 =$ ______ $8 + 8 =$ ______ $7 + 3 =$ ______

12.

$$\begin{array}{r} 6 \\ +\ 3 \\ \hline \end{array} \quad \begin{array}{r} 1 \\ +\ 1 \\ \hline \end{array} \quad \begin{array}{r} 4 \\ +\ 4 \\ \hline \end{array} \quad \begin{array}{r} 3 \\ +\ 5 \\ \hline \end{array} \quad \begin{array}{r} 4 \\ +\ 9 \\ \hline \end{array} \quad \begin{array}{r} 5 \\ +\ 5 \\ \hline \end{array}$$

Reasoning Solve.

13. Thomas picked 12 flowers. He picked the same number of yellow flowers as red flowers. How many flowers of each color does he have?

______ yellow ______ red

14. Rhonda has 16 flowers altogether. She has 2 more yellow flowers than blue flowers. How many flowers of each color does she have?

______ yellow ______ blue

15. Is 7 a double? yes or no

16. Is 14 a double? yes or no

Name ______________________

Using Doubles to Add

1.

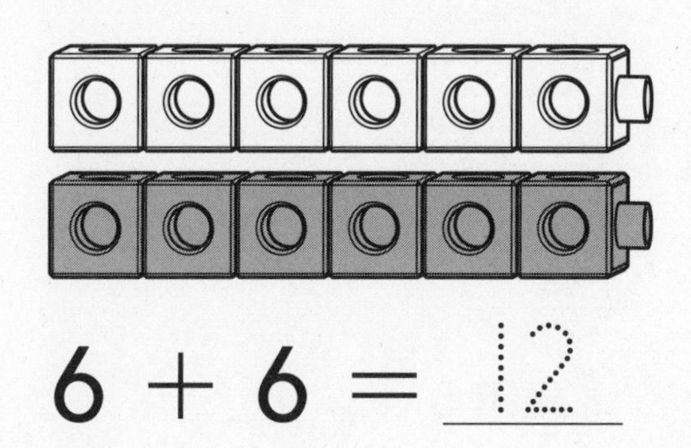

6 + 6 = 12

6 + 7 = 13

7 + 6 = ____

2. 5 + 6

____ + ____ = ____

5 + 6 = ____

6 + 5 = ____

3. 8 + 7

____ + ____ = ____

8 + 7 = ____

7 + 8 = ____

Materials: Snap cubes, 15 for each child

1. Have children use snap cubes to form 2 trains of 6 and write the sum of the double 6 + 6. Then, have children add one more cube to the second train. Say: ***Six plus 7 is 6 plus 6 and one more. What is one more than 12?*** 13; Say: ***So, 6 plus 7 equals 13.*** Have children write 13.
2. Have children show 6 + 6 again. Have them add one cube to the first train of 6. Say: ***Seven plus 6 is also one more than 6 plus 6. What is 7 plus 6?*** Have children write 13.
3. Ask: ***What double can you use to find 5 + 6?*** Have children write 5 and 5. Have children form two trains with 5 cubes each and write the sum, 10. Have them add cubes to find 5 + 6 and 6 + 5.
4. Ask: ***What double can you use to find 8 plus 7?*** Have children write 7 + 7 = 14 and use the double to find 8 + 7 and 7 + 8.

Name ______

Using Doubles to Add (continued)

Find each sum. Think of a double to help you.

4. 2 + 2 = 4

   2 + 3 = 5

5. 5 + 5 = ______

   5 + 6 = ______

6. 8 + 8 = ______

   8 + 9 = ______

7. 4 + 4 = ______

   4 + 5 = ______

8. 7 + 7 = ______ 7 + 8 = ______ 8 + 7 = ______

9. 3 + 3 = ______ 3 + 4 = ______ 4 + 3 = ______

10. 1 + 1 = ______ 1 + 2 = ______ 2 + 1 = ______

11. 6 + 6 = ______ 6 + 7 = ______ 7 + 6 = ______

12. **Reasoning** There are 8 bees near a hive. There are double that many and one more in the hive. How many bees are in the hive?

______ bees

Name ______________________________

Adding 10

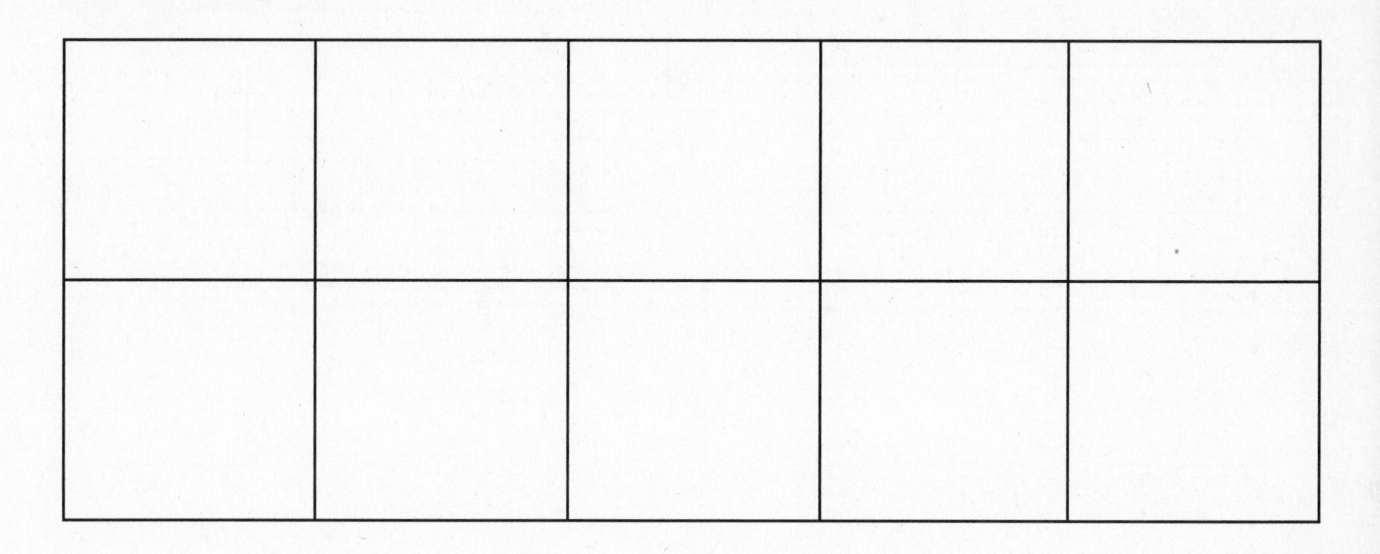

1. 10 + 4 = ______
2. 10 + 5 = ______
3. 10 + 1 = ______
4. 10 + 2 = ______
5. 10 + 7 = ______
6. 10 + 10 = ______

Materials: Two-color counters, 20 for each child

1. Have children fill the ten-frame with yellow counters. Have them put four red counters below the frame. Have them count on from ten, 11, 12, 13, 14. Ask: ***What is 10 plus 4?*** Have children write 14.
2. Do 10 + 5 similarly.
3. Ask: ***How could you use tens and ones to find 10 + 5?*** Sample answer: The sum of 10 + 5 is 15, which is one ten and 5 ones.
4. Have children use the ten-frame or the pattern in tens and ones to find the other sums.

Name ____________________

Adding 10 (continued)

Write the addition sentence for each ten-frame.

7.

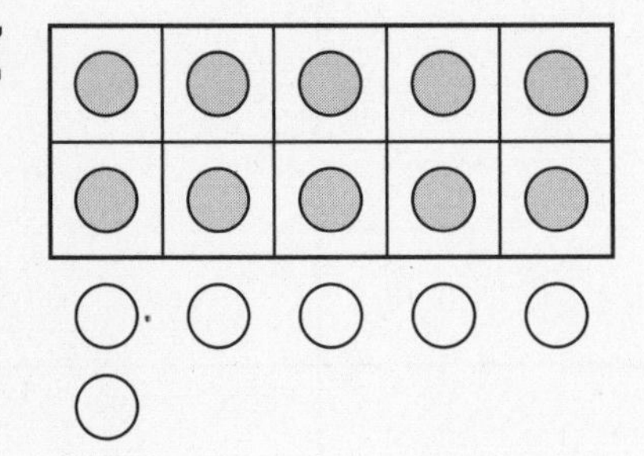

10 + 6 = ______

8.

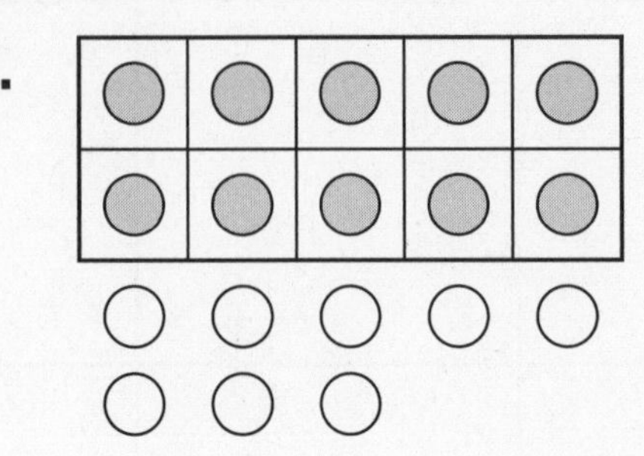

______ + ______ = ______

9.

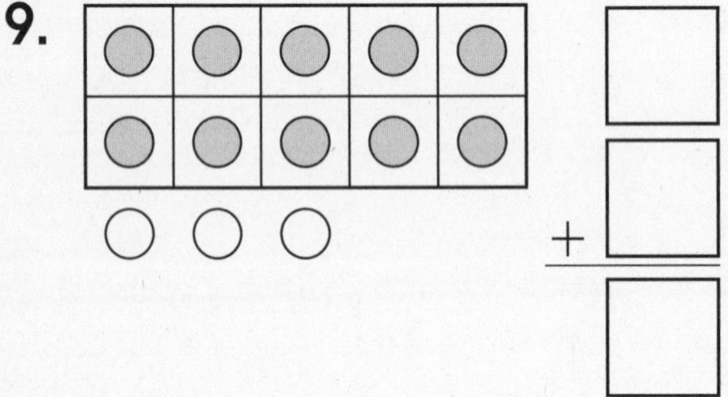

10.

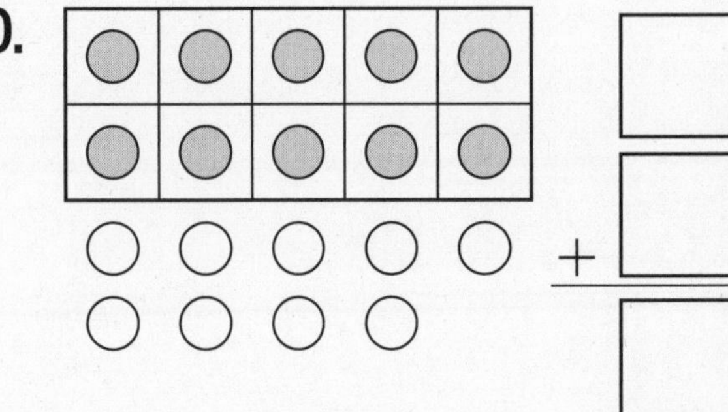

11. **Reasoning** Look at the addition sentences.

10 + 1 = 11　　10 + 2 = 12　　10 + 3 = 13

10 + 4 = 14　　10 + 5 = 15　　10 + 6 = 16

Tell what happens when you add 10 + 8.

Name ______________________________

Making 10 to Add 9

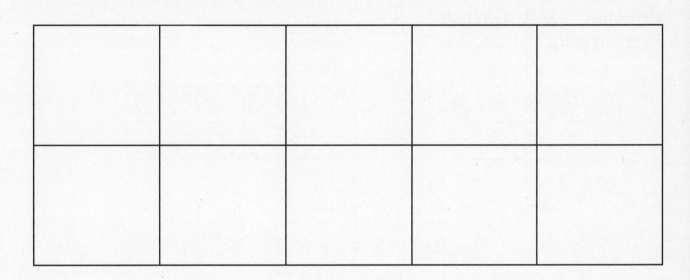

1. $\begin{array}{r} 9 \\ +\ 6 \\ \hline \end{array}$ $\begin{array}{r} 10 \\ +\ \square \\ \hline \end{array}$

2. $\begin{array}{r} 9 \\ +\ 8 \\ \hline \end{array}$ $\begin{array}{r} 10 \\ +\ \square \\ \hline \end{array}$

Materials: Two-color counters, 17 for each child

1. Have children put 9 yellow counters in the ten-frame and 6 red counters below. Ask: ***What addition do the counters show?*** 9 plus 6; Then have children move one red counter to fill up the ten-frame. Ask: ***Nine plus 6 is equal to 10 plus what number?*** Have children write 5. Ask: ***What is 10 + 5?*** Have children write 15 for the sum of 10 + 5. Ask: ***If 10 plus 5 equals 15, then what is 9 plus 6?*** Have children write 15 for the sum of 9 + 6.
2. Do 9 + 8 similarly.

Name ___________________________

Making 10 to Add 9 (continued)

Draw more counters to add.
Write the missing numbers.
Find the sums.

3. 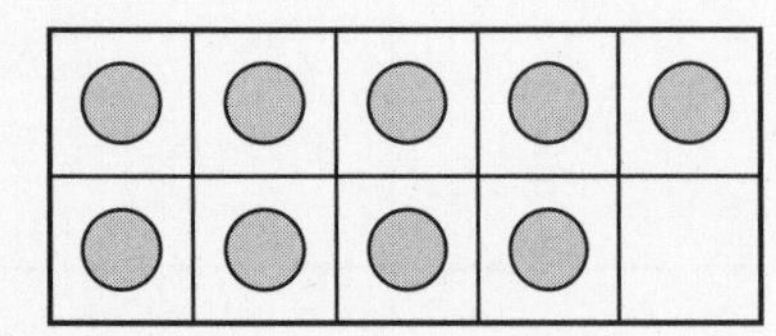

$$\begin{array}{r} 9 \\ +\ 3 \\ \hline \end{array} \qquad \begin{array}{r} 10 \\ +\ \square \\ \hline \end{array}$$

4. 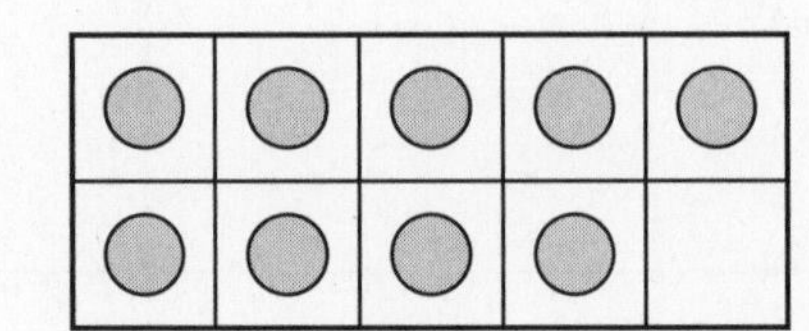

$$\begin{array}{r} 9 \\ +\ 7 \\ \hline \end{array} \qquad \begin{array}{r} 10 \\ +\ \square \\ \hline \end{array}$$

5. 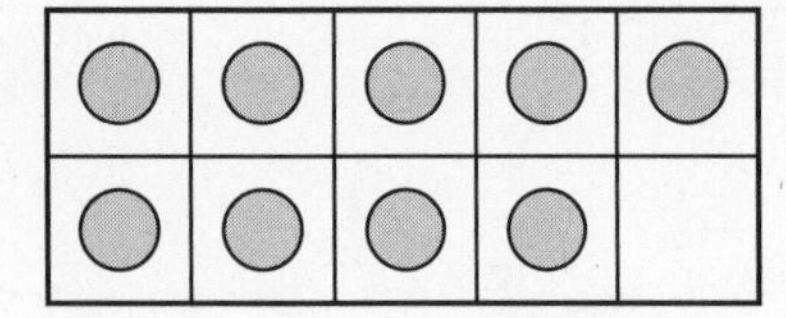

$$\begin{array}{r} 9 \\ +\ 9 \\ \hline \end{array} \qquad \begin{array}{r} 10 \\ +\ \square \\ \hline \end{array}$$

6. 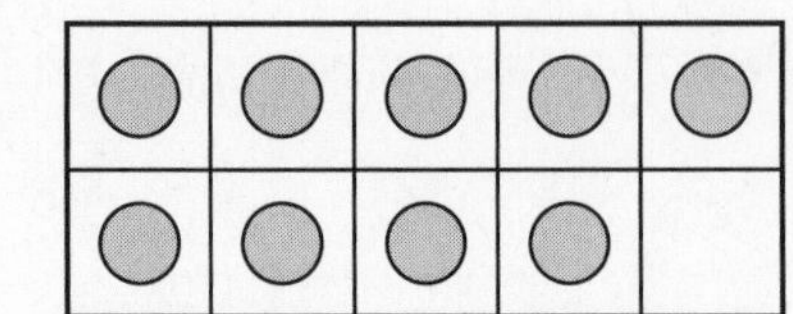

$$\begin{array}{r} 9 \\ +\ 5 \\ \hline \end{array} \qquad \begin{array}{r} 10 \\ +\ \square \\ \hline \end{array}$$

Name ______________________________

Making 10 to Add 8

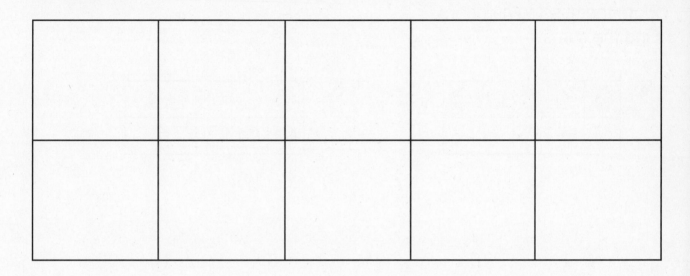

I. $\begin{array}{r} 8 \\ + 6 \\ \hline \end{array}$ $\begin{array}{r} 10 \\ + \square \\ \hline \end{array}$

2. $\begin{array}{r} 8 \\ + 9 \\ \hline \end{array}$ $\begin{array}{r} 10 \\ + \square \\ \hline \end{array}$

3. Reasoning 8 + 5 = 10 + ______ = ______

Materials: Two-color counters, 17 for each child

1. Have children put 8 yellow counters in the ten-frame and 6 red counters below. Ask: ***What addition do the counters show?*** 8 plus 6; Then have children move two red counters to fill up the ten-frame. Ask: ***Eight plus 6, is equal to 10 plus what number?*** Have children write 4. Ask: ***What is 10 + 4?*** Have children write 14 for the sum 10 + 4. Ask: ***If 10 plus 4 equals 14, then what is 8 plus 6?*** Have children write 14 for the sum 8 + 6.
2. Do 8 + 9 similarly.
3. Ask: ***Is 4, two less than 6?*** yes ***Is 7, two less than 9?*** yes; ***Is 8 + 5 equal to 10 plus 2 less than 5?*** yes; ***What is 2 less than 5?*** Have children write 3 and find the sum.

Name ______________________________

Making 10 to Add 8 (continued)

Draw more counters to add.
Write the missing numbers.
Find the sums.

4. 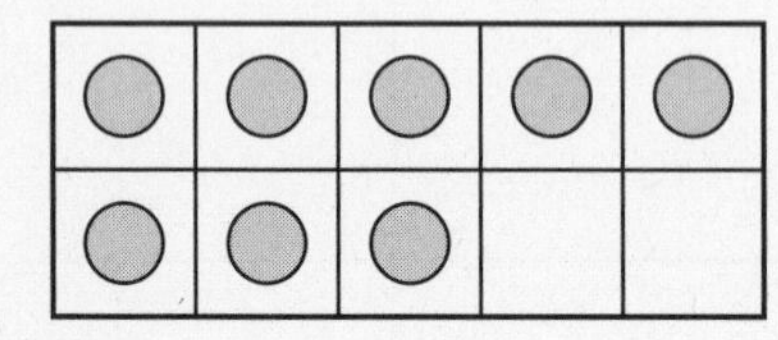

$$\begin{array}{r} 8 \\ +\ 7 \\ \hline 15 \end{array} \qquad \begin{array}{r} 10 \\ +\ \boxed{5} \\ \hline \end{array}$$

5. 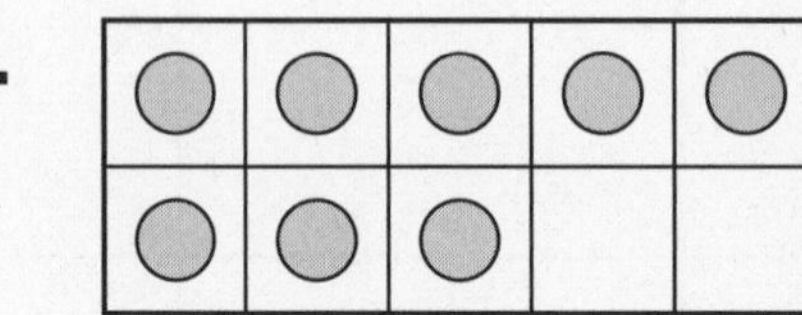

$$\begin{array}{r} 8 \\ +\ 5 \\ \hline \end{array} \qquad \begin{array}{r} 10 \\ +\ \boxed{} \\ \hline \end{array}$$

6. 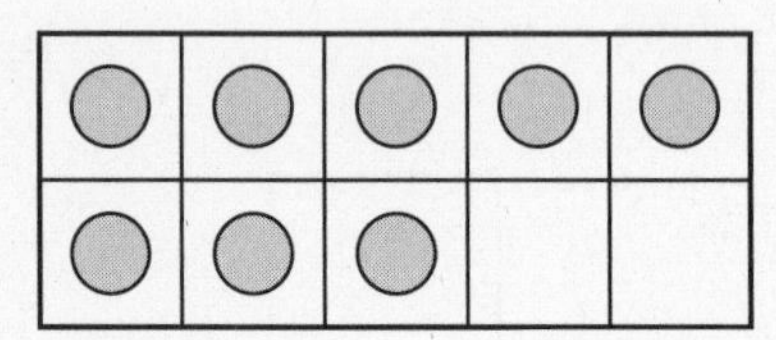

$$\begin{array}{r} 8 \\ +\ 8 \\ \hline \end{array} \qquad \begin{array}{r} 10 \\ +\ \boxed{} \\ \hline \end{array}$$

7. 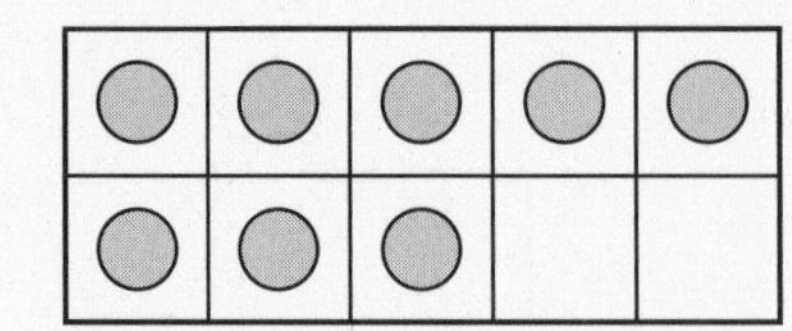

$$\begin{array}{r} 8 \\ +\ 4 \\ \hline \end{array} \qquad \begin{array}{r} 10 \\ +\ \boxed{} \\ \hline \end{array}$$

8. **Reasoning** $8 + 9 = 10 +$ ______ $=$ ______

Name ______________________________

Adding Three Numbers

1. 5, 3, + 2 → 8 + 2 = 10 | 5, 3, + 2 → □ + □ = □ | 5, 3, + 2 → □ + □ = □

2. 7, 4, + 3 → □ + □ = □ | 7, 4, + 3 → □ + □ = □

Materials: Counters, 18 for each child

1. Have children put 5 counters in the first box, 3 counters in the next box, and 2 counters in the last box.
2. Ask: ***What are the first two numbers?*** Have children circle the 5 and 3. Say: ***Move the 3 counters to the box with the 5 counters. What is 5 plus 3?*** Have the children write 8. Ask: ***What number do you still need to add?*** Have children write 2. Ask: ***What is 8 plus 2?*** Have children write 10.
3. Add 5 + 3 + 2, two more times similarly, adding 3 and 2 first and then adding 5 and 2 first. Ask: ***Is the sum the same every time?*** yes ***When adding 3 numbers, you can add any two numbers first. You will always get the same sum.*** Have children tell which way was easiest and explain why. Say: ***Try to choose ways that make the addition easier for you.***
4. Have children show 7 + 4 + 3 with counters in the boxes. Say: ***One way to make the addition easy is to make a 10. In 7 + 4 + 3, what two numbers make a 10?*** Have children circle the 7 and 3 and write 10. Ask: ***What number do you still need to add?*** Have children write 4. Ask: ***What is 10 plus 4?*** Have children write 14.
5. Say: ***Another way to make the addition easy is to make a double. In 7 + 4 + 3, what two numbers can you add to make a double of the third number?*** Have children circle 4 and 3 and write the 7s. Ask: ***What is 7 + 7?*** Have children write 14.

Name ______________________________

Adding Three Numbers (continued)

Find each sum.
Circle the numbers you added first.

3. 9 + 6 + 4 (vertical) → □ + □ = □

4. 2 + 6 + 4 (vertical) → □ + □ = □

5. 2 + 9 + 1 = ______

□ + □ = □

6. 3 + 3 + 7 = ______

□ + □ = □

Find each sum.

7.

7	2	5	5	4	8
5	8	6	2	2	3
+ 5	+ 6	+ 1	+ 5	+ 2	+ 5

8. 9 + 1 + 9 = ______

9. 2 + 5 + 7 = ______

10. Reasoning Find the missing number.

2 + □ + 8 = 18

Name ______________________________

Stories about Separating

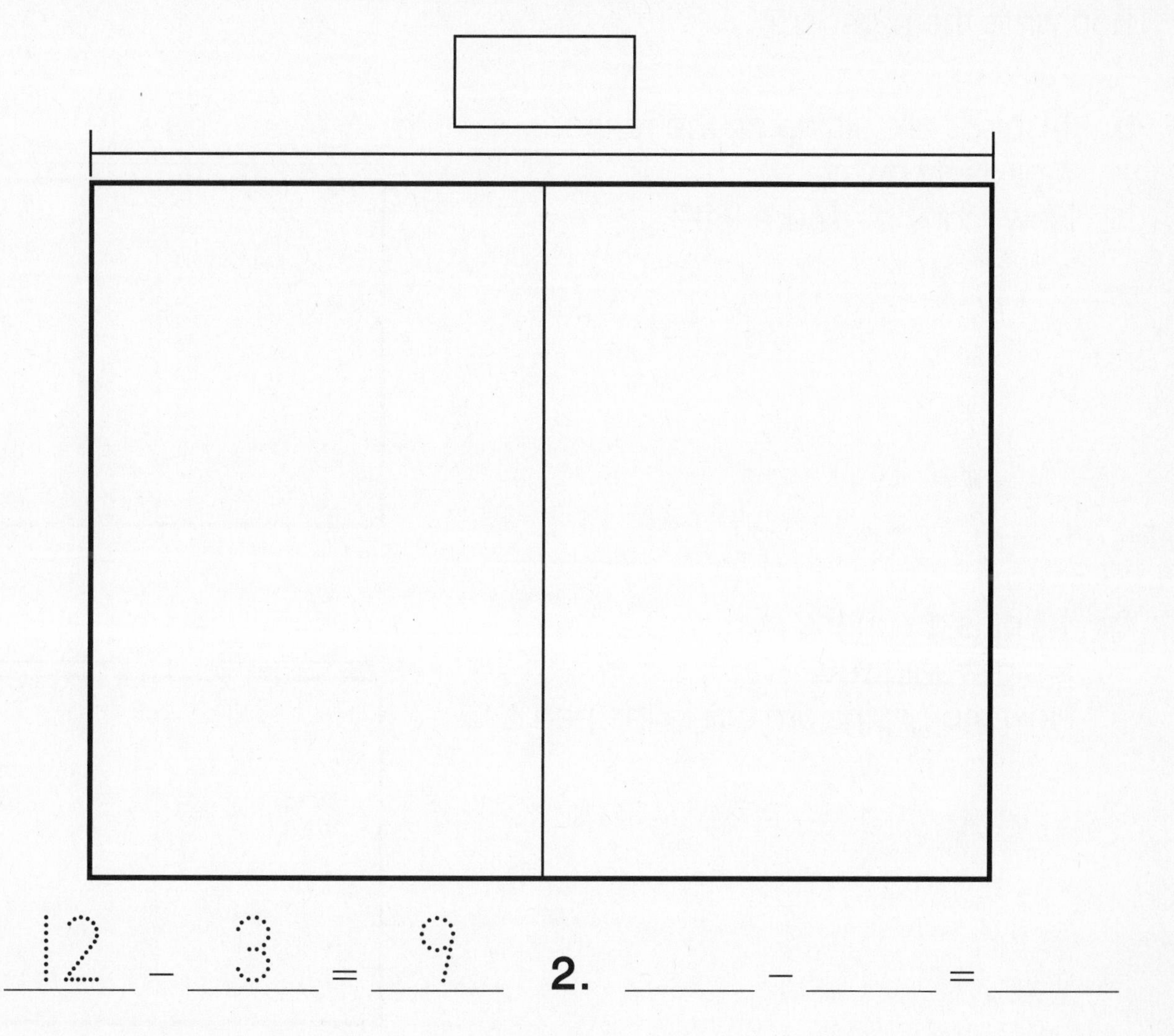

1. 12 − 3 = 9 2. ____ − ____ = ____

3. ____ − ____ = ____ 4. ____ − ____ = ____

Materials: Counters, 18 for each child

1. Say: ***Rosa had 12 balloons.*** Have children put 12 counters in the first box and write 12 in the first line of the number sentence. Say: ***Rosa gave her sister 3 balloons.*** Have children move 3 counters to the second box and write 3. Ask: ***How many balloons did Rosa have then?*** Have children count how many counters are left in the first box and write 9.
2. Say: ***Quaid had 15 marbles.*** Have children put 15 counters in the first box and write 15. Say: ***Quaid gave his brother 7 marbles.*** Have children move 7 counters to the second box and write 7. Ask: ***How many marbles did Quaid have then?*** Have children count how many counters are left in the first box and write 8.
3. Say: ***What if Rosa had 18 balloons and gave away 9? How many balloons would Rosa have then?*** Have children write a number sentence and use counters to solve.
4. Say: ***What if Quaid had 13 marbles and gave 6 away? How many marbles would Quaid have then?*** Have children write a number sentence and use counters to solve.

Name ______________________________

Stories about Separating (continued)

Draw a picture to find the difference.
Then write the numbers.

5. 11 birds are sitting on the fence.
7 birds fly away.
How many birds are left?

11 – ______ = ______

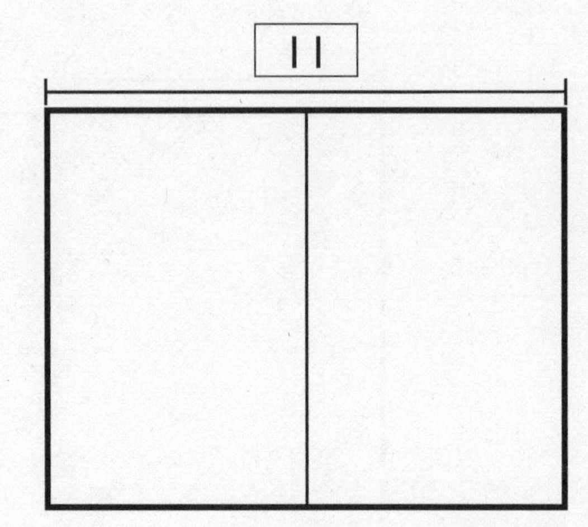

6. 13 pigs are in the pen.
5 pigs run away.
How many pigs are still in the pen?

______ – ______ = ______

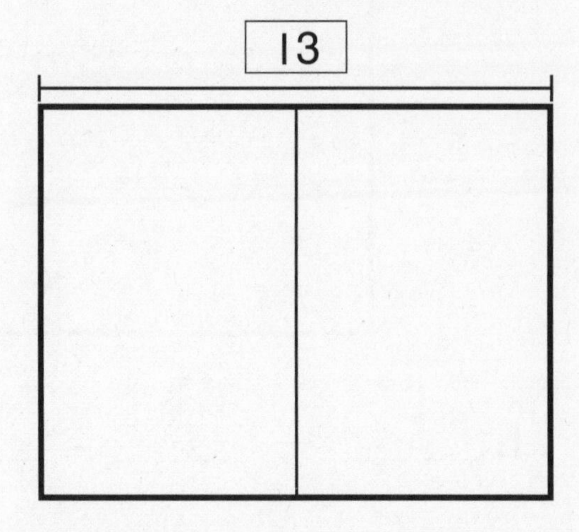

7. 16 ducks are in the pond.
9 ducks swim away.
How many ducks are left?

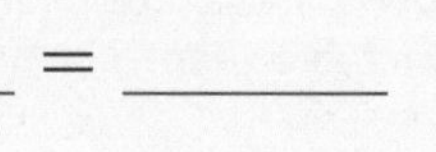

______ – ______ = ______

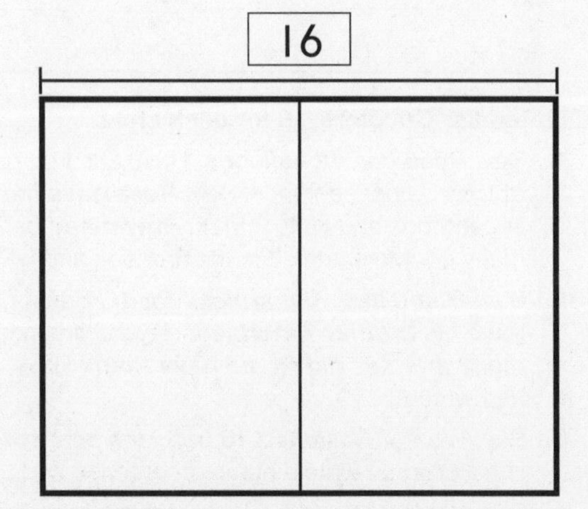

Name ______________________

Stories about Comparing

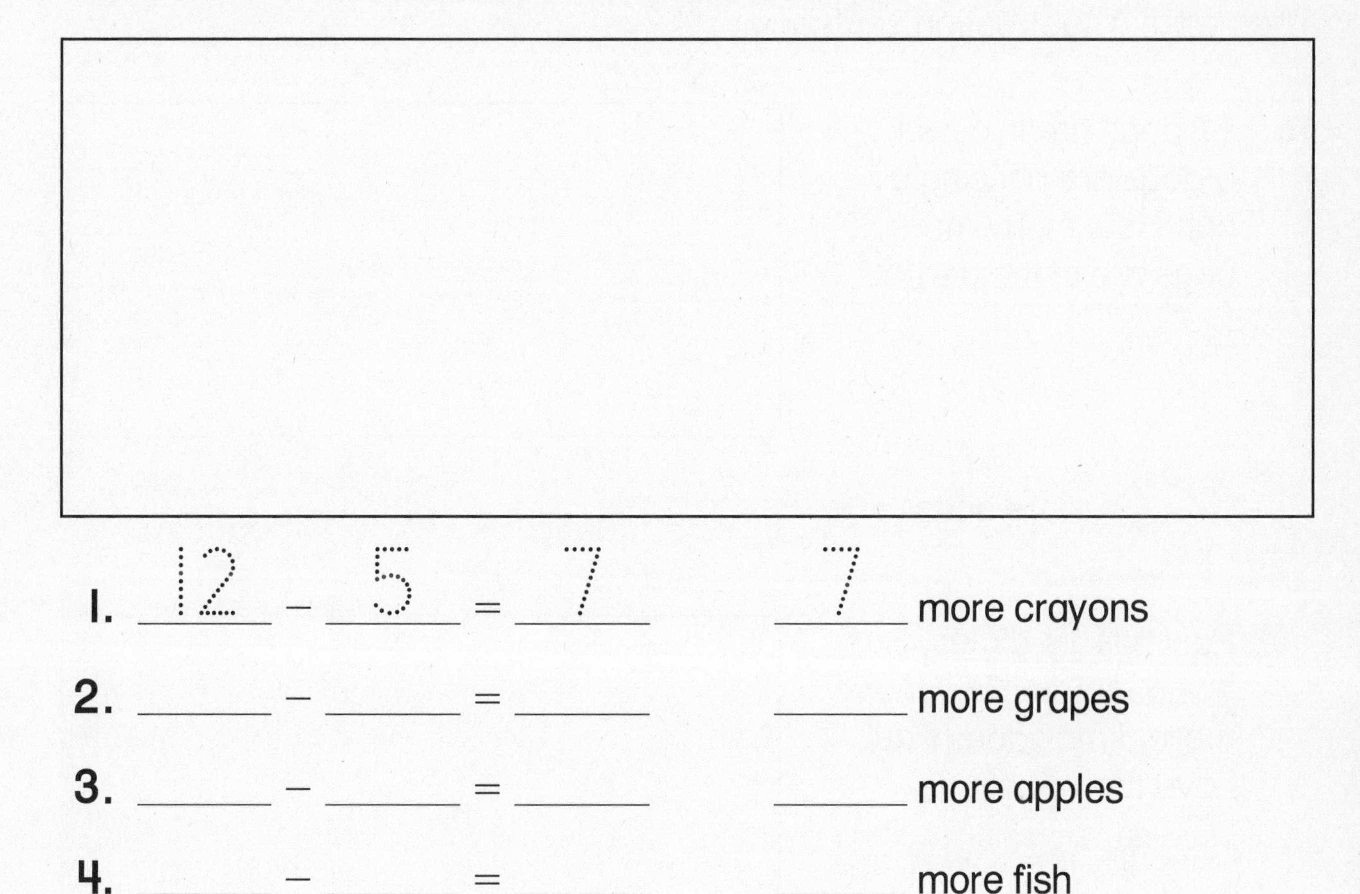

I. 12 – 5 = 7 7 more crayons

2. ____ – ____ = ____ ____ more grapes

3. ____ – ____ = ____ ____ more apples

4. ____ – ____ = ____ ____ more fish

5. ____ – ____ = ____ ____ more hair bows

Materials: Counters, 18 for each child

1. Say: ***Alicia had 12 crayons.*** Have children show 12 counters in a row and write 12. Say: ***Max had 5 crayons.*** Have children show 5 counters in a row below Alicia's and write 5. Say: ***How many more crayons did Alicia have than Max?*** Have children remove 1 counter from each row at the same time. Have them continue removing pairs until all the counters in the bottom row are gone. Have children complete the number sentence by writing 7.
2. Say: ***Jaden had 16 grapes.*** Have children show 16 counters in a row and write 16. Say: ***Rafel had 8 grapes.*** Have children show 8 counters in a row below Jaden's and write 8. Say: ***How many more grapes did Jaden have than Max?*** Have children remove 1 counter from each row at the same time. Have them continue removing pairs until all the counters in the bottom row are gone. Have children complete the number sentence by writing 8.
3. Say: ***Vero had 14 apples and 5 oranges. How many more apples than oranges did she have?*** Have children use counters to write and solve the number sentence.
4. Say: ***Miles had 15 fish. Olivia had 6 fish. How many more fish did Miles have than Olivia?*** Have children use counters to write and solve the number sentence.
5. Say: ***Poppy had 11 hair bows. Lora had 3 hair bows. How many more hair bows did Poppy have than Lora?*** Have children use counters to write and solve the number sentence.

Name ______________________________

Stories about Comparing (continued)

Draw a picture to find the differences.
Then write a subtraction sentence.

6. 11 dogs are in a pen. 5 dogs are chasing a cat. How many more dogs are in the pen?

_____ more dogs   11 − 5 = _____

7. Paul has 14 dimes. Sue has 6 dimes. How many more dimes does Paul have than Sue?

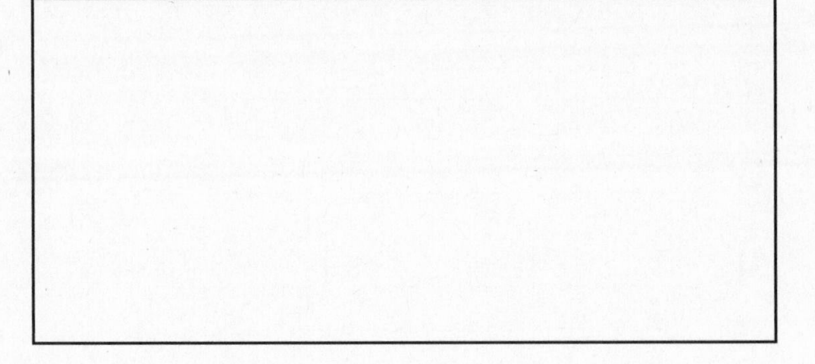

_____ more dimes   _____ − _____ = _____

8. 17 apples are in a basket. 8 apples are on the ground. How many more apples are in the basket?

_____ more apples   _____ − _____ = _____

Name ____________________

Relating Addition and Subtraction to 18

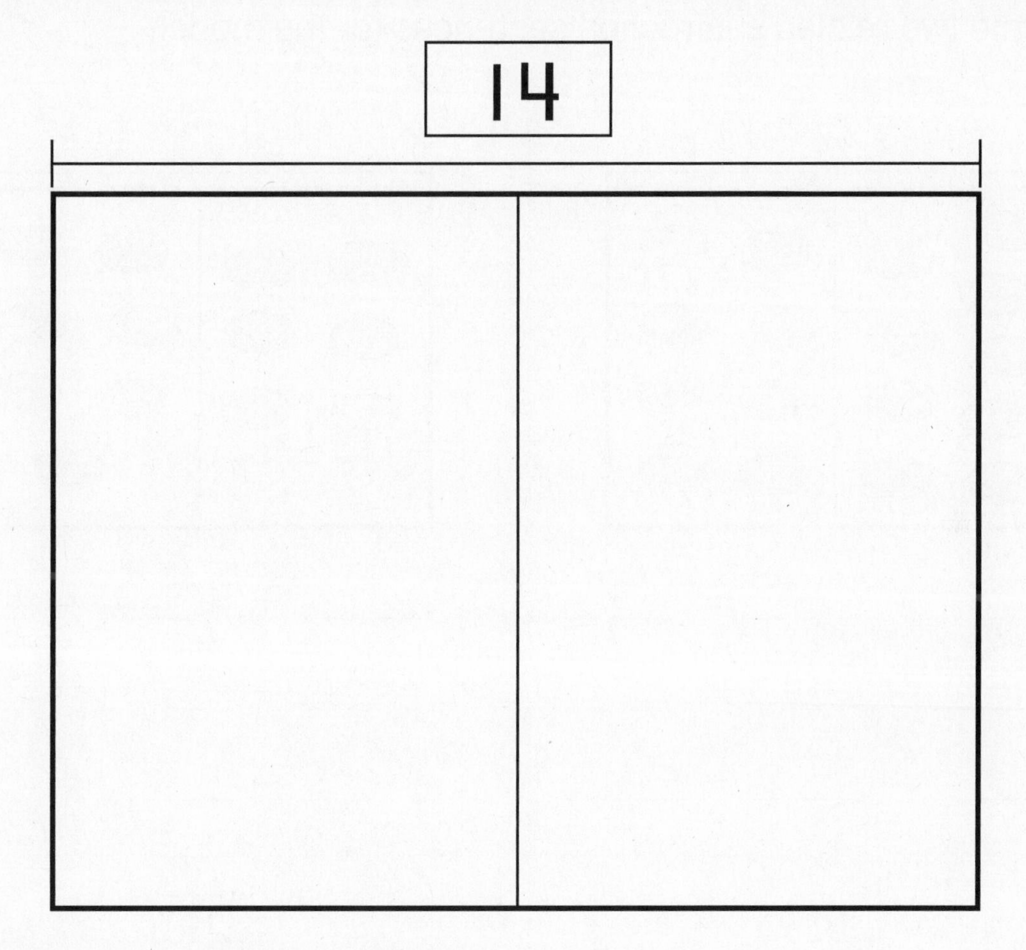

1. 6 + 8 = 14

____ − ____ = ____   ____ − ____ = ____

2. ____ + ____ = ____

____ − ____ = ____   ____ − ____ = ____

Materials: Counters, 14 for each child

1. Say: ***There are 14 counters in all.*** Have children put 6 counters in the first box and 8 counters in the second. Say: ***Write an addition sentence for the counters.*** Have children write 6 + 8 = 14 Say: ***Write two subtraction sentences for the counters.*** Have children write 14 − 8 = 6 and 14 − 6 = 8
2. Do 5 + 9 similarly with 5 counters in the first box and 9 in the second box.

Name ______________________________

Relating Addition and Subtraction to 18 (continued)

Write an addition sentence for the model.
Then write two related subtraction sentences for the model.

3.

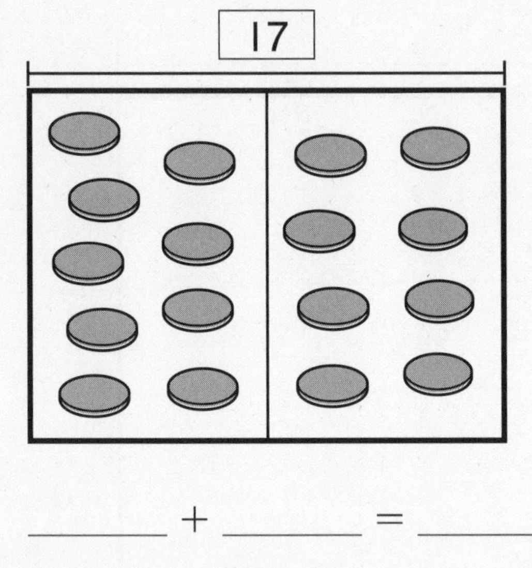

_____ + _____ = _____

_____ − _____ = _____

_____ − _____ = _____

4.

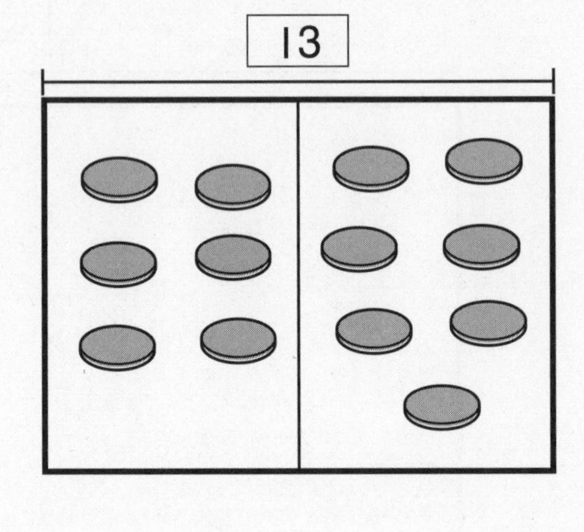

_____ + _____ = _____

_____ − _____ = _____

_____ − _____ = _____

5.

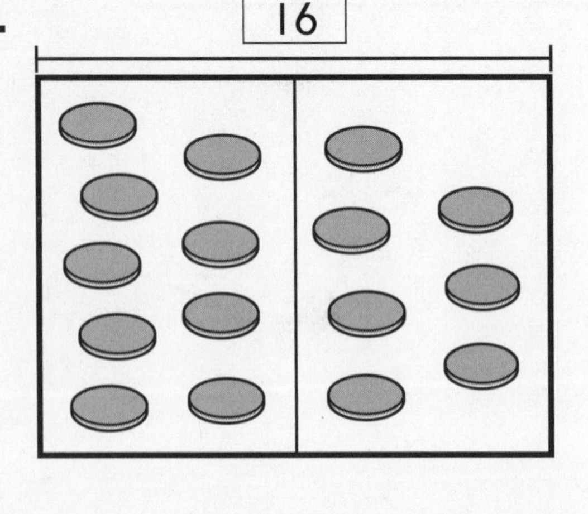

_____ + _____ = _____

_____ − _____ = _____

_____ − _____ = _____

6.

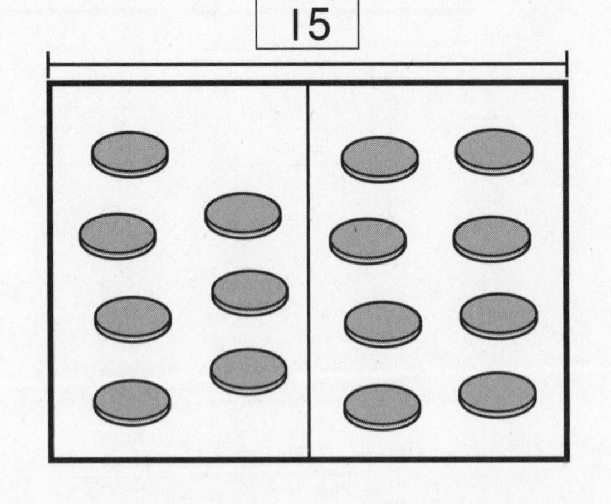

_____ + _____ = _____

_____ − _____ = _____

_____ − _____ = _____

Name ______________________

Fact Families

12

1. 4 + 8 = 12 ______ − ______ = ______

______ + ______ = ______ ______ − ______ = ______

2. ______ + ______ = ______ ______ − ______ = ______

Materials: Counters, 12 for each child

1. Say: ***There are 12 counters in all.*** Have children put 4 counters in the first box and 8 counters in the second box. Say: ***Write two addition sentences for the counters.*** Say: ***Write two subtraction sentences.***
2. Ask: ***How are these number sentences alike?*** They all use the same numbers. Say: ***When addition and subtraction sentences use the same numbers, it is a fact family.***
3. Say: ***Write a fact family using 6 counters in one box and 6 in the other.*** Do similarly as above.

Name ______________________

Fact Families (continued)

Write the fact family for the model.

3. 

____ + ____ = ____ ____ − ____ = ____

____ + ____ = ____ ____ − ____ = ____

4. 

____ + ____ = ____ ____ − ____ = ____

____ + ____ = ____ ____ − ____ = ____

5. 

____ + ____ = ____ ____ − ____ = ____

____ + ____ = ____ ____ − ____ = ____

6. 

____ + ____ = ____ ____ − ____ = ____

7. 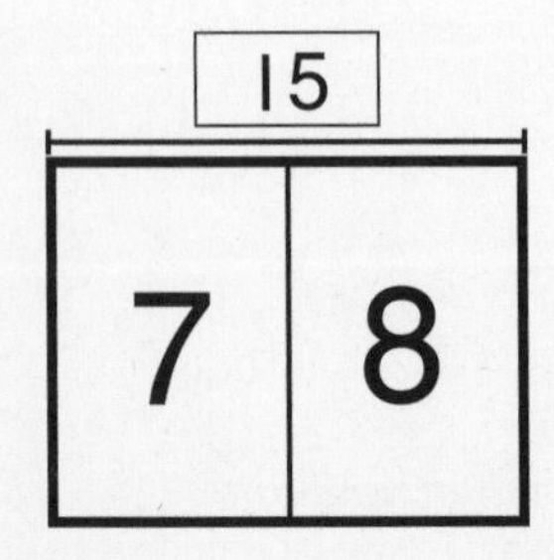

____ + ____ = ____ ____ − ____ = ____

____ + ____ = ____ ____ − ____ = ____

Name ______________________________

Thinking Addition to Subtract Doubles

1.

7 + 7 = 14 So 14 − 7 = 7.

2.

9 + 9 = ______ So 18 − 9 = ______.

3.

8 + 8 = ______ So 16 − 8 = ______.

4. ______ + ______ = ______

12 − 6 = ______

Materials: Snap cubes, 18 for each child

1. Have children make 2 trains of 7 snap cubes each and write the 7s. Ask: ***How much is 7 plus 7?*** Have children write 14. Ask: ***Since 7 plus 7 is 14, what is 14 minus 7?*** Have children write 7.
2. Say: ***If you know the doubles addition facts, you can use them to subtract.*** Have children use cubes to find 18 − 9 and 16 − 8.
3. Ask: ***What doubles addition fact can you use to find 12 minus 6?*** Have children complete 6 + 6 = 12. Ask: ***What is 12 minus 6?*** Have children write 6.

Name ______________________________

Math Diagnosis and Intervention System
Intervention Lesson **B36**

Thinking Addition to Subtract Doubles (continued)

Subtract. Write the doubles fact that helped you.
Use cubes if needed.

5. $18 - 9 =$ ______

______ + ______ = ______

6. $8 - 4 =$ ______

______ + ______ = ______

7. $10 - 5 =$ ______

______ + ______ = ______

8. $6 - 3 =$ ______

______ + ______ = ______

9.

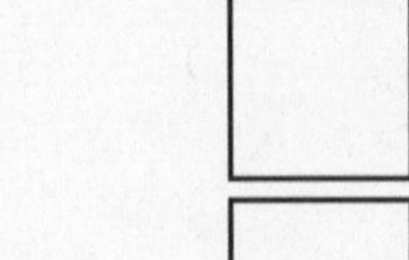

$$\begin{array}{r} 14 \\ -\ 7 \\ \hline \square \end{array} \qquad \begin{array}{r} \square \\ +\ \square \\ \hline \square \end{array}$$

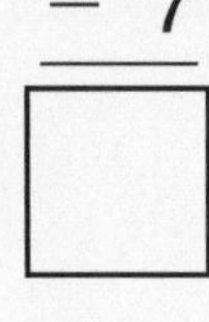

10.

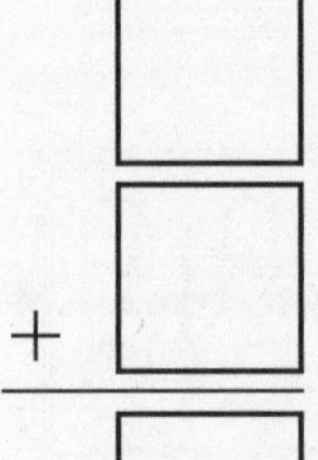

$$\begin{array}{r} 12 \\ -\ 6 \\ \hline \square \end{array} \qquad \begin{array}{r} \square \\ +\ \square \\ \hline \square \end{array}$$

Reasoning

11. Trent has 16 cars. He has the same number of red cars as blue cars. How many of each color does he have?

______ red ______ blue

Name ______________________

Using Addition to 18 to Subtract

1. 9 + ______ = 13 So 13 − 9 = ______.

2. 5 + ______ = 13 So 13 − 5 = ______.

3. 6 + ______ = 13 So 13 − 6 = ______.

Materials: Counters, 13 for each child

1. Say: ***There are 13 counters in all.*** Have children put 9 of their 13 counters in the first box. Ask: ***How many counters go in the second box?*** Have children put the remaining 4 counters in the second box and write 4. Say: ***Since 9 plus 4 equals 13, what is 13 minus 9?*** Have children write 4.
2. Do the other problems similarly.

Name ______________________________

Using Addition to 18 to Subtract (continued)

Complete the model.
Then complete the number sentences.

4.

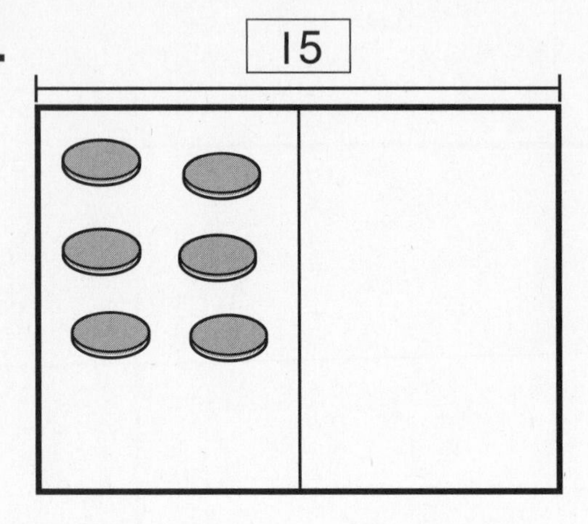

6 + ______ = 15

So 15 − 6 = ______.

5.

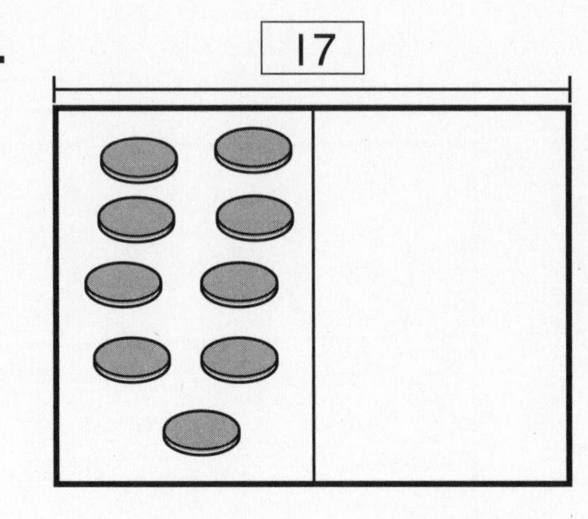

9 + ______ = 17

So 17 − 9 = ______.

6.

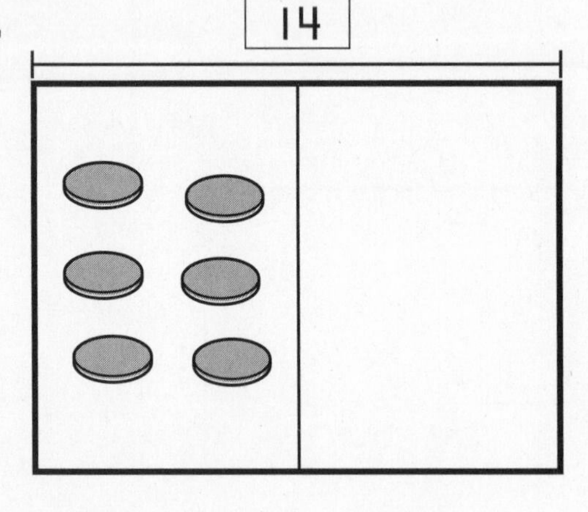

6 + ______ = 14

So 14 − 6 = ______.

7.

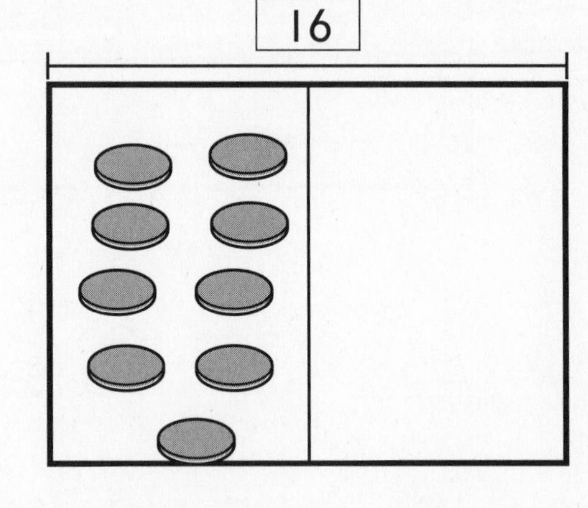

9 + ______ = 16

So 16 − 9 = ______.

Reasoning Write the missing number.

8. 9 + ______ = 15 So 15 − 9 = ______.

9. 8 + ______ = 12 So 12 − 8 = ______.

Name ______________________

Finding the Missing Part

1. 16 in all

7 + __9__ = 16

__9__ are in the basket.

2. 15 in all

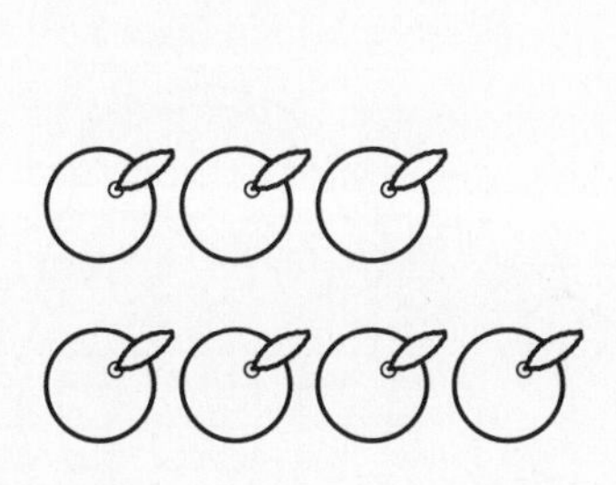

7 + ______ = 15

______ are in the basket.

3. 9 in all

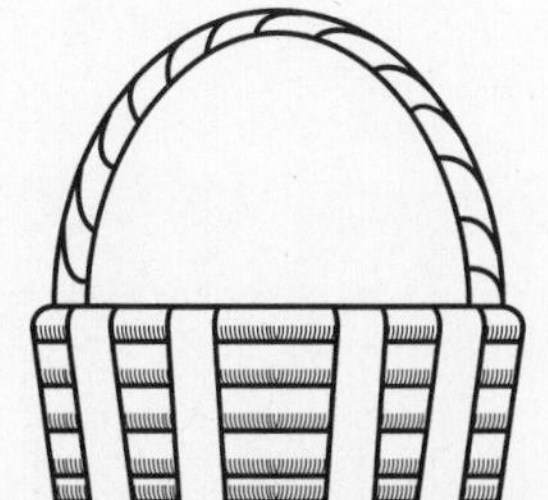

9 + ______ = 9

______ are in the basket.

Materials: Counters, 18 for each child

1. Say: ***Rosita has 16 apples. Seven of the apples are out of the basket. How many apples are in the basket?*** Have children use counters to write and solve the number sentence. 9; 9
2. Say: ***Rameriz has 15 oranges. Seven of the oranges are out of the basket. How many oranges are in the basket?*** Have children use counters to write and solve the number sentence. 8; 8
3. Say: ***Lizzie has 9 strawberries. Nine of the strawberries are out of the basket. How many strawberries are in the basket?*** Have children use counters to write and solve the number sentence. 0; 0

Name ______________________

Finding the Missing Part (continued)

Find how many pieces of fruit are in each basket.

4. Martin has 14 pears.
7 are out of the basket.
How many are in the basket?

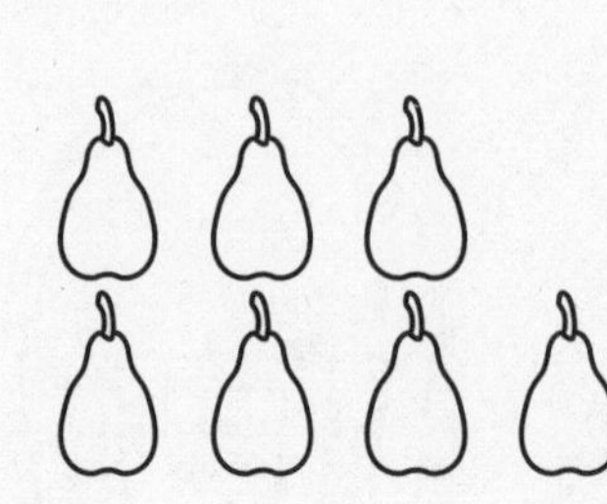

7 + ______ = 14

______ are in the basket.

5. Pauline has 12 lemons.
8 are out of the basket.
How many are in the basket?

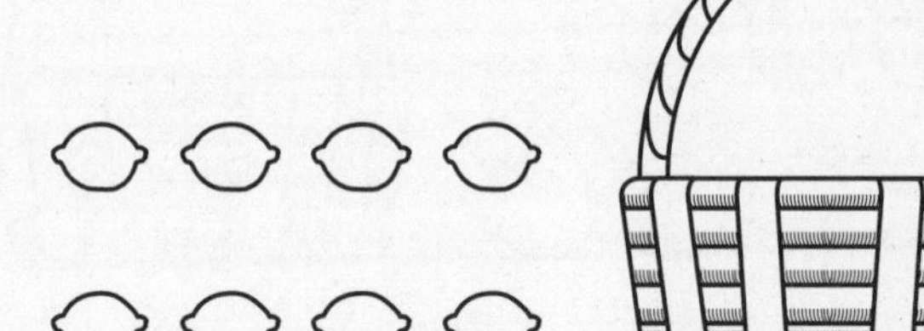

8 + ______ = 12

______ are in the basket.

Reasoning

Find the missing numbers.

6.

4	4	4	4	4
+ ☐	+ ☐	+ ☐	+ ☐	+ ☐
6	8	10	12	14

Name ______________________________

Using Subtraction Strategies

1. $12 - 6$ — **Doubles** (circled) — Count Back — Think Addition

   6

2. $9 - 1$ — Doubles — Count Back — Think Addition

3. $16 - 9$ — Doubles — Count Back — Think Addition

4. $14 - 7$ — Doubles — Count Back — Think Addition

5. $15 - 8$ — Doubles — Count Back — Think Addition

6. $11 - 2$ — Doubles — Count Back — Think Addition

1. Say: ***Until you memorize the subtraction facts, you can use doubles, counting back, or thinking addition to find the differences.*** Have children solve 12 − 6. Ask several children to explain how they solved the problem. Discuss as a class why "Doubles" is the easiest way to solve 12 − 6. Have students circle "Doubles".
2. Have children solve 9 − 1. Ask several children to explain how they solved the problem. Discuss as a class why "Counting Back" is the easiest way to solve 9 − 1. Have students circle "Count Back".
3. Have children solve 16 − 9. Ask several children to explain how they solved the problem. Discuss as a class why "Think Addition" is the easiest way to solve 16 − 9. Point out that 9 is too much to count back and 9 + 7 is not a double. Say: ***When no other strategy works, think addition.*** Have students circle "Think Addition".
4. Have children solve the other problems and circle which way they solved.

Name ______________________________

Using Subtraction Strategies (continued)

Subtract.
Circle the easiest way to find the difference.

7. $10 - 2$ = ____ Doubles / Count Back / Think Addition

8. $18 - 9$ = ____ Doubles / Count Back / Think Addition

9. $15 - 9$ = ____ Doubles / Count Back / Think Addition

10. $14 - 8$ = ____ Doubles / Count Back / Think Addition

11. $10 - 5$ = ____ Doubles / Count Back / Think Addition

12. $8 - 1$ = ____ Doubles / Count Back / Think Addition

Subtract.

13. $9 - 2$ = ____ $10 - 1$ = ____ $15 - 6$ = ____ $12 - 4$ = ____ $13 - 9$ = ____ $12 - 8$ = ____

14. $16 - 8$ = ____ $17 - 9$ = ____ $12 - 5$ = ____ $11 - 3$ = ____ $15 - 7$ = ____ $6 - 1$ = ____

Name ______________________________

Subtraction Facts with 10

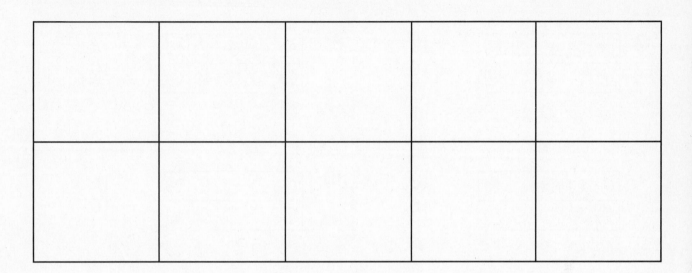

1. 16 − 10 = 6
2. 20 − 10 = ______
3. 18 − 8 = ______
4. 19 − 9 = ______
5. 12 − 10 = ______
6. 15 − 10 = ______

Materials: Counters, 20 for each child

1. Have children fill the ten-frame with yellow counters. Have them put six red counters below the frame. Ask: ***What is an easy way to find 16 minus 10?*** Take away all the counters in the ten-frame. Have children remove all 10 counters from the ten-frame and count how many are left. Have children write 6. Do 20 − 10 similarly.
2. Have children show 18 with 10 counters in the ten-frame and 8 counters below it. Ask: ***What is an easy way to find 18 minus 8?*** Have children remove all the counters below the ten-frame. Ask: ***How many counters are left?*** Have children write 10. Do 19 − 9 similarly.
3. Have children use the ten-frame to find the other differences.
4. Ask: ***How could you find 14 − 10 without counters?*** Since 14 is one ten and 4 ones, when you take away 10, the 4 ones are left. ***How could you find 15 − 5 without counters?*** Since 15 is one ten and 5 ones, when you take away the 5 ones, only the ten is left.

Name ___________________________

Subtraction Facts with 10 (continued)

Cross out to subtract.

7. 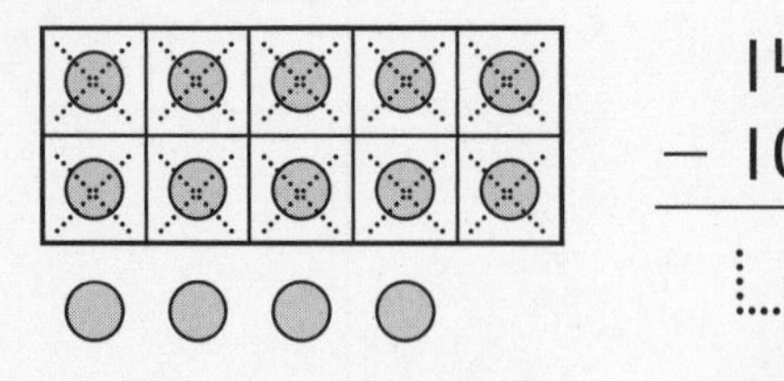

$$\begin{array}{r} 14 \\ -\ 10 \\ \hline 4 \end{array}$$

8. 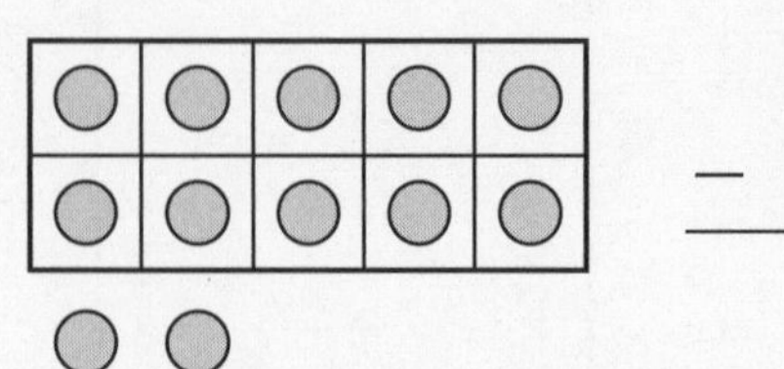

$$\begin{array}{r} 12 \\ -\ 10 \\ \hline \end{array}$$

9. 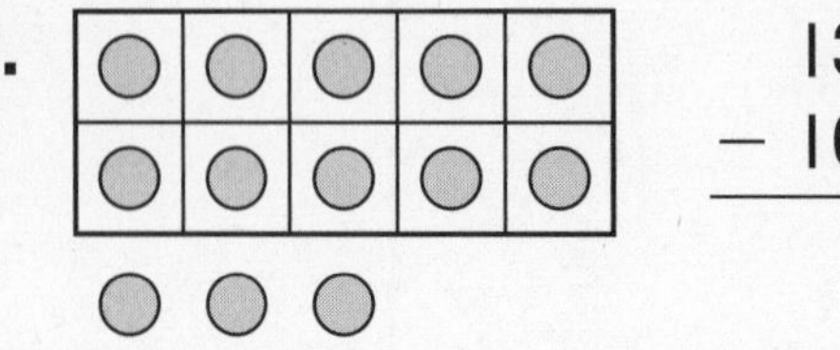

$$\begin{array}{r} 13 \\ -\ 10 \\ \hline \end{array}$$

10. 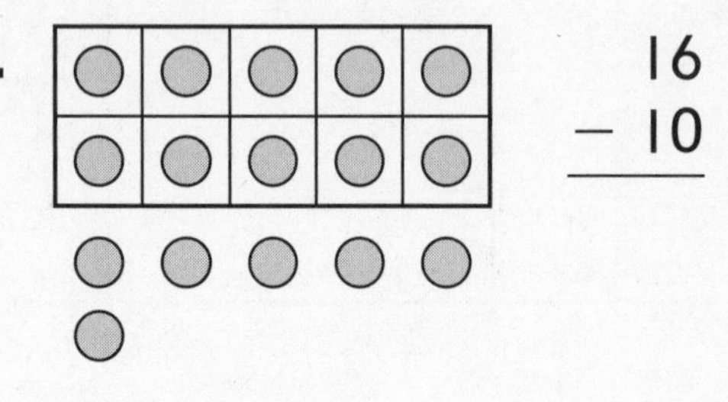

$$\begin{array}{r} 16 \\ -\ 10 \\ \hline \end{array}$$

Subtract.

11. $\begin{array}{r} 17 \\ -\ 10 \\ \hline \end{array}$ $\begin{array}{r} 15 \\ -\ 10 \\ \hline \end{array}$ $\begin{array}{r} 20 \\ -\ 10 \\ \hline \end{array}$ $\begin{array}{r} 18 \\ -\ 10 \\ \hline \end{array}$ $\begin{array}{r} 19 \\ -\ 10 \\ \hline \end{array}$

12. **Reasoning** Look at the subtraction sentences.

$11 - 10 = 1$ $12 - 10 = 2$ $13 - 10 = 3$

$14 - 10 = 4$ $15 - 10 = 5$ $16 - 10 = 6$

Tell what happens when you subtract $19 - 10$.

Name ______________________

Addition Properties

Materials 4 half sheets of paper, 24 color tiles (8 each of 3 colors) per pair

1. Show 2 + 5 and 5 + 2 by placing the tiles on the paper.

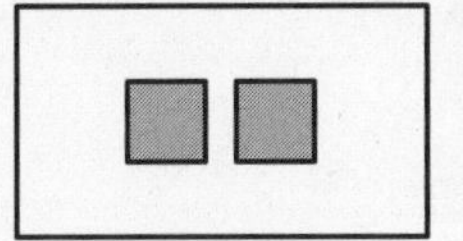 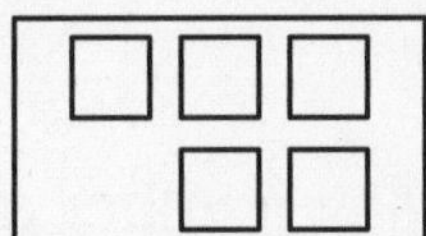 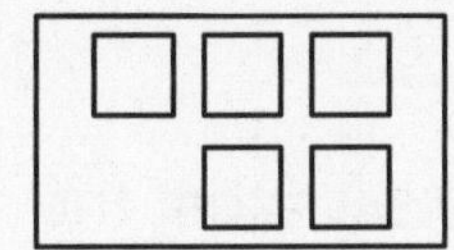 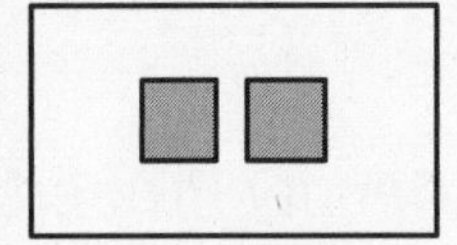

2. Add. 2 + 5 = ________ and 5 + 2 = ________

3. The Commutative Property says that you can change the order of the addends and the sum will be the same.

So, 2 + 5 = 5 + ________.

4. Use the tiles to show (4 + 3) + 1. Use 3 different colors of tiles.

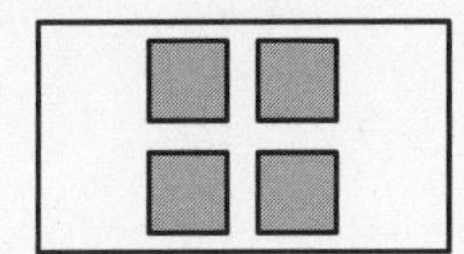 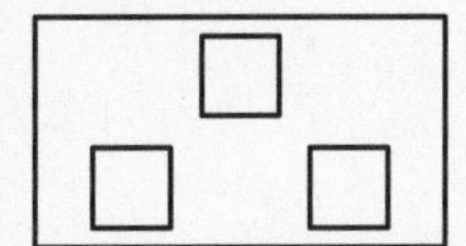 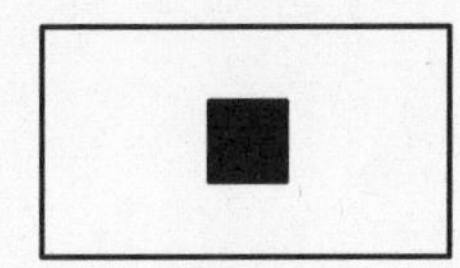

5. Add. Remember the parentheses show which numbers to add first.

(4 + 3) + 1 = ________ + 1 = ________

6. Move the paper with 3 tiles closer to the paper with 1 tile to show 4 + (3 + 1).

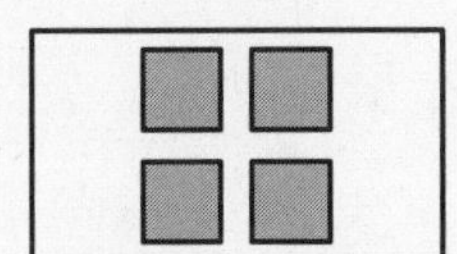 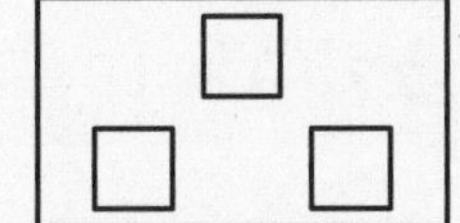 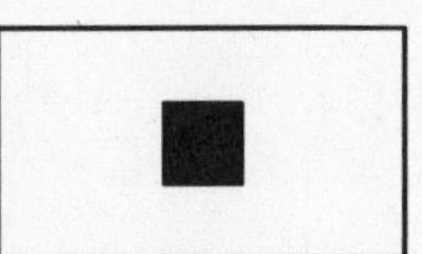

7. Add. 4 + (3 + 1) = 4 + ________ = ________

8. The Associative Property says that you can group addends in any way and the sum will be the same.

So, (4 + 3) + 1 = 4 + (________ + ________).

Name ______________________________

Addition Properties (continued)

9. Use tiles to show 3 + 0.

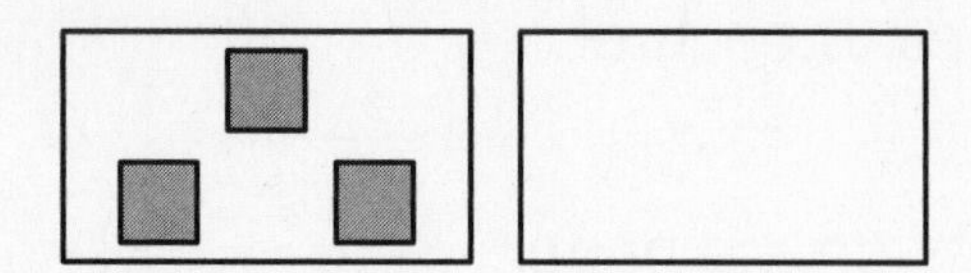

10. Add: 3 + 0 = ________.

11. The Identity Property says that the sum of any number and 0 is that number.

So, 3 + 0 = ________.

Find each sum.

12. (4 + 6) + 2 = _____ + 2 = _____

4 + (6 + 2) = 4 + _____ = _____

13. (7 + 1) + 2 = _____ + 2 = _____

7 + (1 + 2) = 7 + _____ = _____

14. 9 + 3 = _____

3 + 9 = _____

15. 5 + 8 = _____

8 + 5 = _____

16. 6 + 9 = _____

9 + 6 = _____

17. 7 + 0 = _____

18. 0 + 13 = _____

19. 45 + 0 = _____

Write each missing number.

20. 4 + 6 = 6 + _____

21. 7 + 4 = _____ + 7

22. 6 + 9 = 9 + _____

23. 4 + _____ = 4

24. 0 + _____ = 8

25. 7 + _____ = 7

26. (7 + 8) + 2 = 7 + (8 + _____)

27. 9 + (1 + 8) = (9 + 1) + _____

28. Reasoning Carla ate 2 bananas and 10 raisins. The next day she ate 10 raisins and 2 bananas. Did Carla eat the same number of pieces of fruit each day? Explain.

Name ______________________

Relating Addition and Subtraction

Materials 16 counters per student

1. Use counters to show each number sentence in the table. Find the missing number. Draw the counters you used in the table.

Addition	Subtraction
3 + _______ = 8	8 − 5 = _______
Addition	**Subtraction**
_______ + 3 = 8	_______ − 3 = 5

2. Related addition and subtraction facts have the same numbers. These same numbers are called a fact family. What three numbers were used in the fact family above? _______________

3. Fill in the blanks to complete the fact family.

_______ + 7 = 13   13 − 7 = _______

_______ + 6 = _______   _______ − 6 = 7

4. What three numbers were used in the fact family in Question 3? _______________

Name ________________

Relating Addition and Subtraction (continued)

Complete the related addition and subtraction facts.

5.

$3 + 7 =$ ____ $7 + 3 =$ ____

$10 - 3 =$ ____ $10 - 7 =$ ____

6.

____ $+ 7 = 12$ $7 +$ ____ $= 12$

$12 - 7 =$ ____ $12 -$ ____ $= 7$

Complete each fact family. You may use counters to help.

7. $4 + 8 =$ ____ $12 -$ ____ $= 8$

____ $+ 4 = 12$ ____ $- 8 = 4$

8. $5 + 9 =$ ____ ____ $- 5 = 9$

$9 +$ ____ $= 14$ $14 -$ ____ $= 5$

9. $8 + 3 =$ ____ $11 - 8 =$ ____

$3 +$ ____ $= 11$ ____ $- 3 = 8$

10. $6 +$ ____ $= 13$ $13 -$ ____ $= 7$

$7 +$ ____ $= 13$ ____ $- 7 = 6$

11. Reasoning John has 14 pencils. He gives some to Sonja. He has 8 left. How many pencils did John give to Sonja? ____

12. Write two facts that are related to the subtraction fact $14 - 8 = 6$.

Name ______________________

Multiplication as Repeated Addition

Materials 24 counters and 4 half-sheets of paper per student or pair

Freyja has 4 plates. Each plate has 5 cherries. Answer 1 to 6 to find how many cherries she has in all.

You can use multiplication to find how many in all when you have equal groups.

1. Show 4 plates with 5 cherries on each using counters.

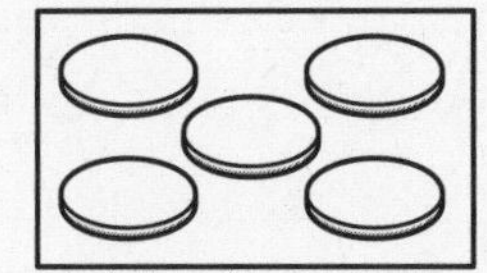 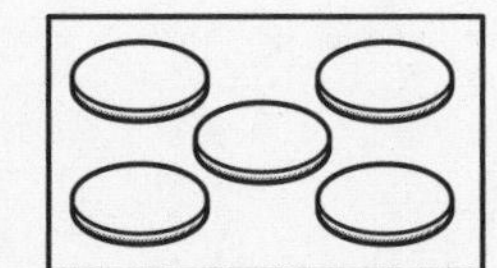 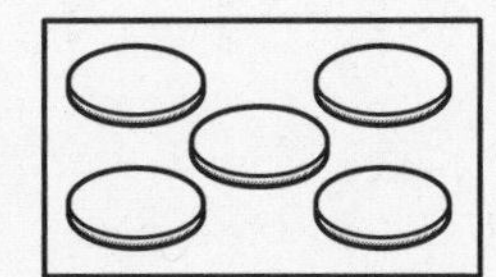 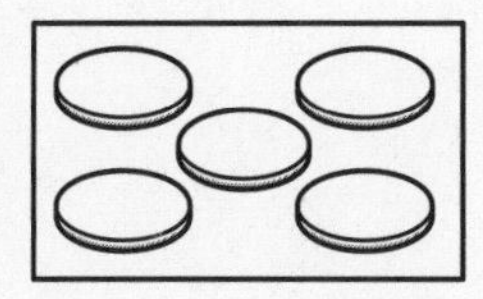

2. Use addition to find how many cherries Freyja has.

_____ + _____ + _____ + _____ = 20

3. How many plates? _____

4. How many cherries on each plate? _____

5. Use multiplication to find how many cherries Freyja has in all.

_________ × _________ = 20

Number of Plates   Number of Cherries on Each Plate

6. How many cherries does Freyja have in all? _____

7. Use counters and repeated addition to find 3×8.

$3 \times 8 = 8 +$ _____ + _____

= _____

Name ______________________________

Multiplication as Repeated Addition (continued)

Add. Then multiply. Use counters if you like.

8. 

$3 + 3 =$ ______

$2 \times 3 =$ ______

9.

$2 + 2 + 2 + 2 =$ ______

$4 \times 2 =$ ______

Use the pictures to fill in the blanks.

10. 

3 groups of ______

$4 +$ ______ $+$ ______ $=$ ______

$3 \times$ ______ $=$ ______

11. 

3 groups of ______

$6 +$ ______ $+$ ______ $=$ ______

$3 \times$ ______ $=$ ______

Fill in the blanks to make each number sentence true.

12. ______ $+$ ______ $+$ ______ $+$ ______ $+$ ______ $+$ ______ $= 6 \times 8$

13. $9 + 9 +$ ______ $+$ ______ $=$ ______ $\times 9$

14. Reasoning Melissa says that $5 + 5 + 5 + 3$ is the same thing as 4×5. Explain why Melissa is wrong.

Name ______________________________

Arrays and Multiplication

Materials 16 counters per student

1. Show an array of 4 rows with 2 counters in each row.

2. Write a multiplication sentence for the array.

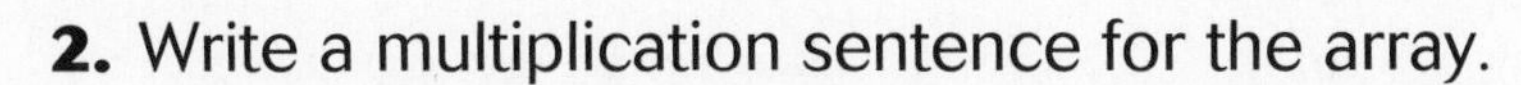

______ $\times$ ______ $=$ ______

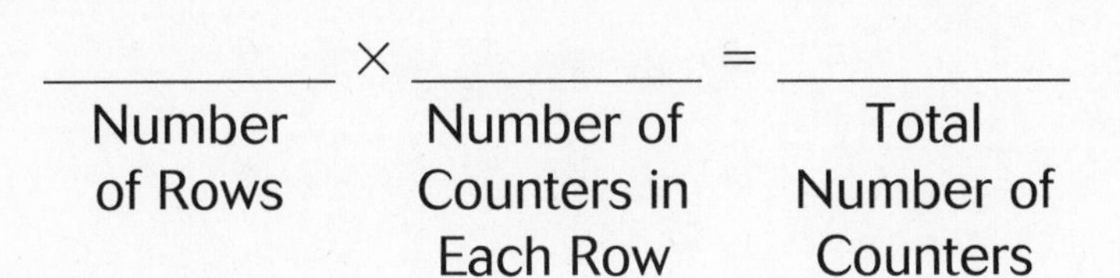

Number of Rows	Number of Counters in Each Row	Total Number of Counters

3. How many counters are in the array? ______

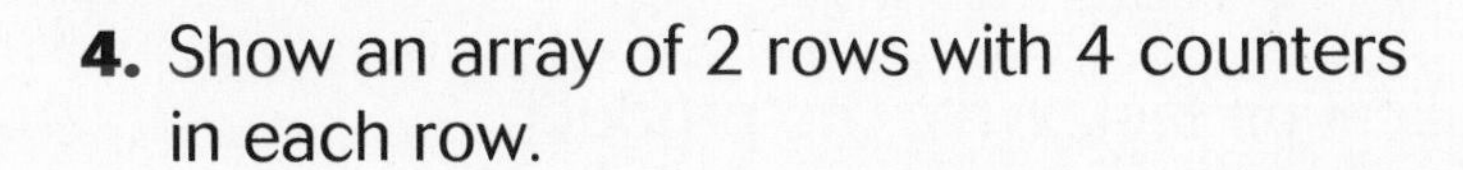

4. Show an array of 2 rows with 4 counters in each row.

5. Write a multiplication sentence for this array.

______ $\times$ ______ $=$ ______

Number of Rows	Number of Counters in Each Row	Total Number of Counters

6. How many counters are in this array? ______

7. Both arrays have 8 counters.

   So, $4 \times 2 = 2 \times$ ______

8. Since both arrays have 8 counters then you can say,

   $4 \times 2 = 8$, and $2 \times 4 =$ ______

Knowing one multiplication fact means you know another.

9. If you know $3 \times 8 = 24$, then you know $8 \times 3 =$ ______.

Name ______________________

Arrays and Multiplication (continued)

Write a multiplication sentence for each array.

10. ☆ ☆ ☆ ☆ ☆
☆ ☆ ☆ ☆ ☆
☆ ☆ ☆ ☆ ☆
☆ ☆ ☆ ☆ ☆
☆ ☆ ☆ ☆ ☆
☆ ☆ ☆ ☆ ☆

____

11. ❀ ❀ ❀ ❀ ❀ ❀ ❀
❀ ❀ ❀ ❀ ❀ ❀ ❀
❀ ❀ ❀ ❀ ❀ ❀ ❀
❀ ❀ ❀ ❀ ❀ ❀ ❀
❀ ❀ ❀ ❀ ❀ ❀ ❀

____

Draw an array to find each multiplication fact. Write the product.

12. $3 \times 5 =$ ______

13. $2 \times 6 =$ ______

Fill in the blanks.

14. $4 \times 8 = 32$, so $8 \times 4 =$ ______

15. $9 \times 2 = 18$, so ______ $\times 9 = 18$

16. $5 \times 7 = 35$, so $7 \times$ ______ $= 35$

17. $3 \times 6 = 18$, so ______ $\times 3 = 18$

18. $2 \times 4 = 8$, so $4 \times$ ______ $= 8$

19. $1 \times 6 = 6$, so $6 \times 1 =$ ______

20. Reasoning How does an array show equal groups?

Name ______________________________

Using Multiplication to Compare

Materials 12 counters per student

Alicia has 2 stickers. Pedro has 3 times as many stickers as Alicia. How many stickers does Pedro have?

1. Show Alicia's stickers with counters.

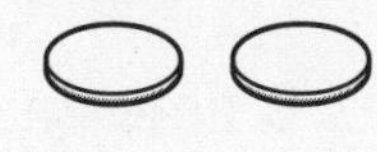

2. Show Pedro's stickers with counters.

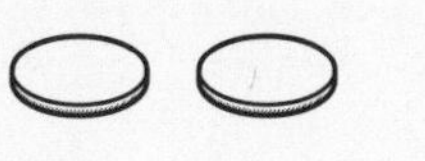
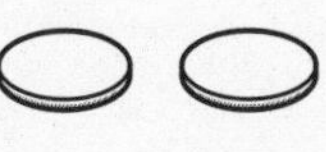

3. Write a multiplication sentence.

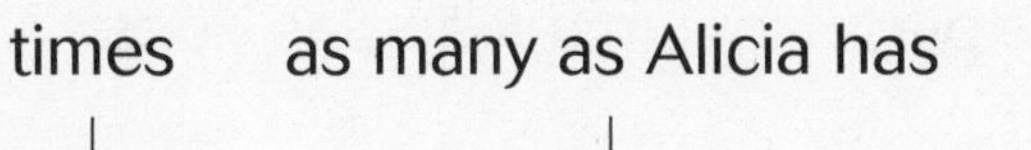
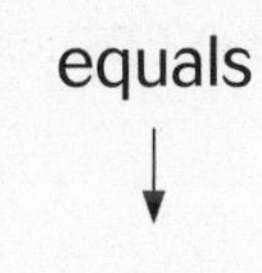

3	times	as many as Alicia has	equals	number Pedro has
↓	↓	↓	↓	↓
______	×	______	=	______

4. How many stickers does Pedro have? ______

Mia has 4 yo-yos. Flo has twice as many as Mia. How many yo-yos does Flo have?

The word **twice** in a word problem means 2 times as many.

5. Show Mia's yo-yos with counters.

6. Show Flo's yo-yos with counters.

7. Write a multiplication sentence.

2	times	as many as Mia has	equals	number Flo has
↓	↓	↓	↓	↓
______	×	______	=	______

8. How many yo-yos does Flo have? ______

Name ______________________________

Using Multiplication to Compare (continued)

Solve. You may use drawings or counters to help.

9. Janos has 3 stickers. Lucy has twice as many stickers as Janos. How many stickers does Lucy have?

____

10. Rob has 4 model airplanes. Julio has 3 times as many model airplanes as Rob. How many model airplanes does Julio have?

____

11. Mr. King has 5 apples left in his store. Ruth needs twice as many apples to bake apple pies. How many apples does Ruth need?

____

Use the recipe to answer Exercises 12–15.

Fruit Smoothie

3 large bananas
2 cups strawberries
1 cup orange juice
1 cup cranberry juice
1 cup ice cubes

Blend until smooth.
Makes 5 servings.

12. The recipe serves 5 people. Joan wants to make the recipe for 15 people. How many times more is this?

____

13. How many bananas will Joan need to make the recipe for 15 people?

____

14. How many cups of strawberries will Joan need to make the recipe for 15 people?

____

15. Reasoning If Joan wants to make twice as much as the recipe in the chart, what will she need to do to all of the ingredients?

Name ______________________________

Writing Multiplication Stories

Follow 1 to 5 below to write a multiplication story for 5×4 that is about hamburgers and pickle slices.

1. 5×4 means ______ groups of ______.

2. So, 5×4 might mean ______ hamburgers with ______ pickle slices each.

3. Write a story about 5 hamburgers with 4 pickle slices each.

Mrs. ________________ went through a drive thru and

bought ______ hamburgers. Each hamburger had ______

pickle slices. How many ______________ were there in all?

4. Draw a picture to find how many pickle slices there were in all.

$5 \times 4 =$ ______

5. How many pickle slices were there in all? ______

6. Write a multiplication story for 6×3 about nests and eggs.

Mr. ________________ found ______ nests. Each nest had

______ eggs. How many ______________ did he find in all?

7. Draw a picture to find how many eggs he found in all.

$6 \times 3 =$ ______

8. How many eggs did he find in all? ______

Name ______________________________

Writing Multiplication Stories (continued)

Write a multiplication story. Then find the product.

9.

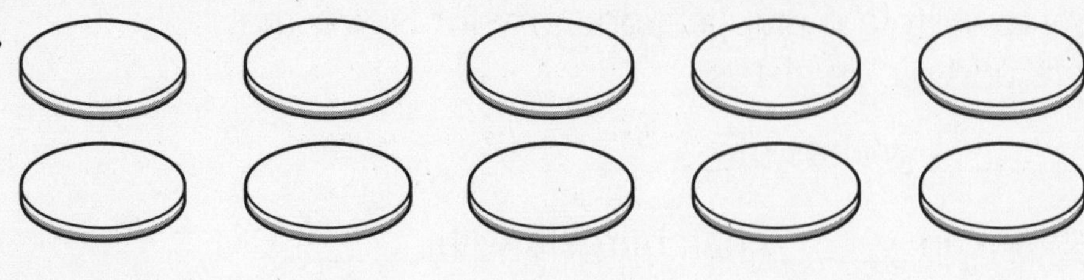

$2 \times 5 =$ ______

Write a multiplication story for Exercises 10 and 11. Draw a picture to find each product.

10. $6 \times 6 =$ ______

11. $4 \times 5 =$ ______

12. There are 4 houses on Oak Street. Four people live in each house. How many people live on Oak Street?

Name ______________________________

Multiplying by 2 and 5

1. Continue skip counting by 2s on the number line below.

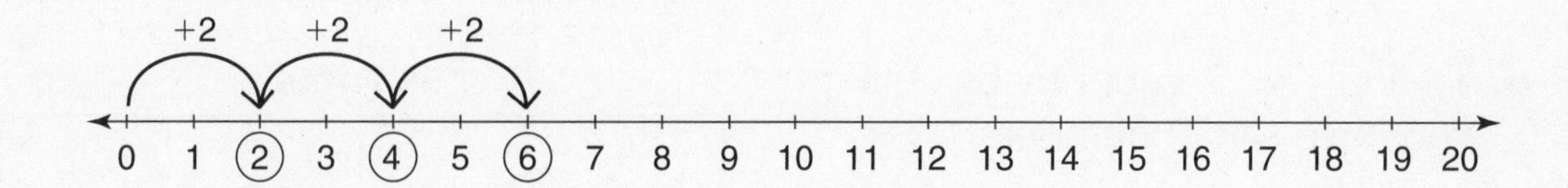

2. Each number that a hop lands on is a **multiple** of two. Circle each multiple of 2 on the number line. Then list them in the blanks below.

_____ _____ _____ _____ _____ _____ _____ _____ _____ _____

3. To find 6×2, count by 2s until you have said 6 numbers.

2, 4, _____, _____, 10, _____

So, $6 \times 2 =$ _____.

4. Repeat 3 above for each of the 2s facts in the table. Complete the table.

2s Facts

$0 \times 2 = 0$	$5 \times 2 =$ _____
$1 \times 2 =$ _____	$6 \times 2 = 12$
$2 \times 2 =$ _____	$7 \times 2 =$ _____
$3 \times 2 =$ _____	$8 \times 2 =$ _____
$4 \times 2 =$ _____	$9 \times 2 =$ _____

5. Reasoning What is the pattern in the products of the 2s facts?

All of the multiples of 2 end in 0, 2, _____, _____, or _____.

6. Continue skip counting by 5s on the number line below. Circle each multiple of 5 on the number line.

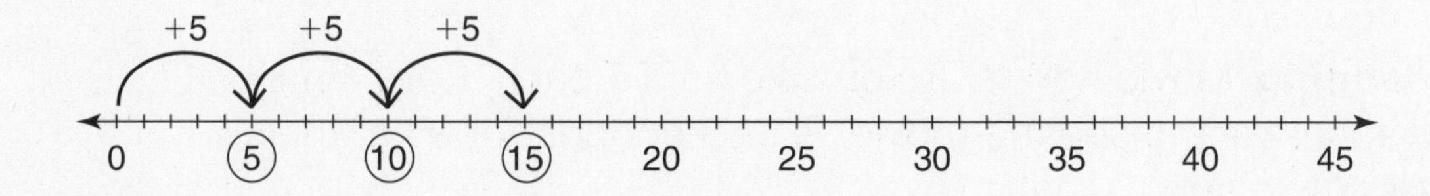

Name ____________________

Multiplying by 2 and 5 (continued)

7. Circle each multiple of 5 on the number line. Then list them in the blanks below.

____ ____ ____ ____ ____ ____ ____ ____ ____

8. To find 7×5, count by 5s until you have said 7 numbers.

5, 10, 15, ____, ____,

____, ____

So, $7 \times 5 =$ ____.

9. Repeat 8 above for each of the 5s facts in the table.

5s Facts

$0 \times 5 = 0$	$5 \times 5 =$ ____
$1 \times 5 =$ ____	$6 \times 5 =$ ____
$2 \times 5 =$ ____	$7 \times 5 = 35$
$3 \times 5 =$ ____	$8 \times 5 =$ ____
$4 \times 5 =$ ____	$9 \times 5 =$ ____

10. Reasoning What is the pattern in the products of the 5s facts?

All of the multiples of 5 end in ____ or ____.

Complete each multiplication problem.

11. 2×3

12. 2×6

13. 2×2

14. 2×1

15. 7×2

16. 7×5

17. 5×3

18. 8×5

19. 5×4

20. 1×5

21. 2×4

22. 5×2

23. Reasoning Movie tickets are on sale for $5 each. Ross, Emily, and John want to see the movie. Is $18 enough for all of their tickets? Explain.

Name ___________________________

Multiplying by 9

Learn how to multiply by 9 by answering 1 to 5.

1. Complete the table.

Fact	Product	Two Digits in the Product	Sum of the Two Digits in the Product
$0 \times 9 =$	0	0 and 0	$0 + 0 = 0$
$1 \times 9 =$	9	0 and 9	$0 + 9 = 9$
$2 \times 9 =$	18		
$3 \times 9 =$	27	2 and 7	$2 + 7 = 9$
$4 \times 9 =$	36		
$5 \times 9 =$	45	4 and 5	
$6 \times 9 =$	54		
$7 \times 9 =$	63		
$8 \times 9 =$	72		
$9 \times 9 =$	81		$8 + 1 = 9$

2. Reasoning Besides the product of 0×9, what pattern do you see in the sums of the digits of each product?

3. Look at the number being multiplied by 9 in each product and the tens digit of that product.

When 3 is multiplied by 9, what is the tens digit of the product? _______.

When 6 is multiplied by 9, what is the tens digit of the product? _______.

Name ______________________________

Multiplying by 9 (continued)

4. **Reasoning** Complete to describe the pattern you see in the tens digits of the products when a factor is multiplied by 9.

   The tens digit of the product is ______ less than the other factor.

5. Complete the following to find 7×9.

   The tens digit is $7 - 1 =$ ______.

   The ones digit is $9 - 6 =$ ______.

   So, $7 \times 9 =$ ______ and $9 \times 7 =$ ______.

Find each product.

6. 1×9

7. 9×2

8. 9×4

9. 9×0

10. 6×9

11. 9×9

12. 8×9

13. 5×9

14. 9×7

15. 3×9

16. 2×9

17. 9×6

18. **Reasoning** Joshua and his sister have each saved $9. They wish to buy a new game that costs $20. If they put their savings together, do they have enough money to buy the game?

19. **Reasoning** Jane said that $7 \times 9 = 62$. Explain how you know this is incorrect.

Name ______________________

Math Diagnosis and Intervention System
Intervention Lesson **B49**

Multiplying by 1 or 0

Materials 9 counters and 9 half sheets of paper per student

Complete 1 to 6 to discover that when you multiply any number by 1, the product is the other number.

Use the paper to show groups and the counters to show the number in each.

1. Show 5×1.

 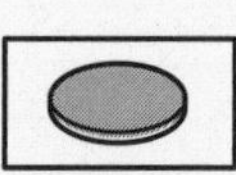 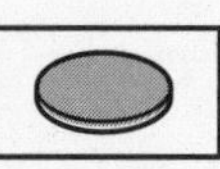  

2. How many counters in all? ______ $5 \times 1 =$ ______

3. Show 4×1.

4. How many counters in all? ______ $4 \times 1 =$ ______

5. Use the paper and counters to complete the table on the right.

6. **Reasoning** What pattern do you see in the table?

1s Facts

$0 \times 1 = 0$	$5 \times 1 = 5$
$1 \times 1 =$ ______	$6 \times 1 =$ ______
$2 \times 1 =$ ______	$7 \times 1 =$ ______
$3 \times 1 =$ ______	$8 \times 1 =$ ______
$4 \times 1 = 4$	$9 \times 1 =$ ______

Complete 7 to 12 to discover that when you multiply any number by 0, the product is 0.

7. Show 3×0.

8. How many counters in all? ______

9. Show 6×0.

  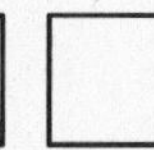 

10. How many counters in all? ______

Name ______________________________

Multiplying by 1 or 0 (continued)

11. Use the paper and counters to complete the table on the right.

12. Reasoning What pattern do you see in the table?

0s Facts

$0 \times 0 = 0$	$5 \times 0 =$ _____
$1 \times 0 =$ _____	$6 \times 0 = 0$
$2 \times 0 =$ _____	$7 \times 0 =$ _____
$3 \times 0 = 0$	$8 \times 0 =$ _____
$4 \times 0 =$ _____	$9 \times 0 =$ _____

Find each product.

13. $2 \times 1 =$ _____ **14.** $4 \times 0 =$ _____ **15.** $6 \times 1 =$ _____

16. $1 \times 9 =$ _____ **17.** $1 \times 2 =$ _____ **18.** $4 \times 1 =$ _____

19. 3×0 **20.** 0×9 **21.** 8×1 **22.** 1×8 **23.** 9×1

24. 5×1 **25.** 5×0 **26.** 1×1 **27.** 1×0 **28.** 7×1

29. Reasoning Explain why $1 \times 0 = 0$.

Name ______________________

Multiplying by 3

Materials 18 counters, 6 inch piece of yarn per student

Use 1s facts and 2s facts to multiply by 3.

1. Show a 3×6 array.

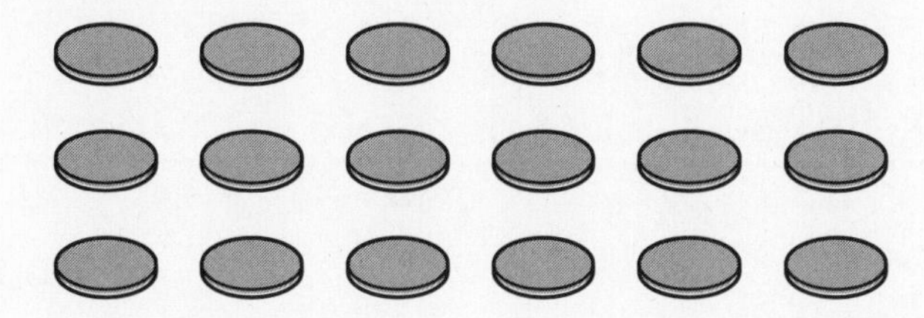

2. Place the piece of yarn between the first and second row of the array. Fill in the blanks.

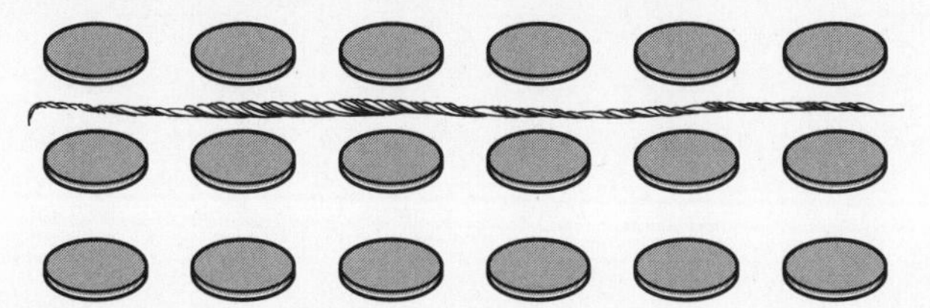

$1 \times$ ______ $=$ ______

______ $\times 6 =$ ______

3. So, $3 \times 6 = 6 + 12 =$ ______.

4. Use 1s and 2s facts to find 3×7 by doing the following.

$1 \times 7 =$ ______

$2 \times 7 =$ ______

So, $3 \times 7 =$ ______ $+$ ______ $=$ ______.

5. Use 1s and 2s facts to find 3×8 by doing the following.

$1 \times 8 =$ ______

$2 \times 8 =$ ______

So, $3 \times 8 =$ ______ $+$ ______ $=$ ______.

Name ______________________________

Multiplying by 3 (continued)

Find each product.

6. $2 \times 3 =$ ______ **7.** $1 \times 3 =$ ______ **8.** $7 \times 3 =$ ______

9. $3 \times 4 =$ ______ **10.** $3 \times 6 =$ ______ **11.** $3 \times 7 =$ ______

12. 5×3 **13.** 8×3 **14.** 3×8 **15.** 3×6 **16.** 3×1

17. 3×2 **18.** 3×3 **19.** 4×3 **20.** 3×5 **21.** 9×3

22. The weatherman says the temperature is rising 3 degrees every hour. How much hotter is it after 2 hours have passed? ______

23. Mrs. Hernandez's class is raising money by selling boxes of cookies for $3 each. Alex sold 4 boxes to her mother and 2 more to her neighbor. How much money did Alex raise? ______

24. Reasoning If 3×6 can be solved by separating an array into a 1×6 and a 2×6 array, explain how 4×6 can be separated so that it can be solved with known facts? Then find 4×6.

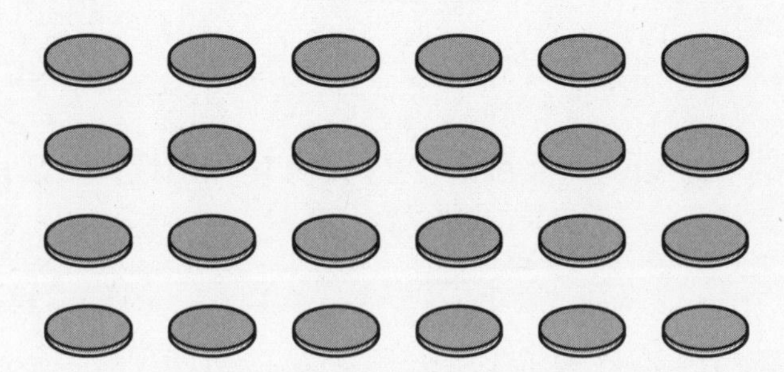

Name ______________________________

Multiplying by 4

Materials 24 counters, 6 inch piece of yarn per student

Use 2s facts to multiply by 4.

1. Show a 4×6 array.

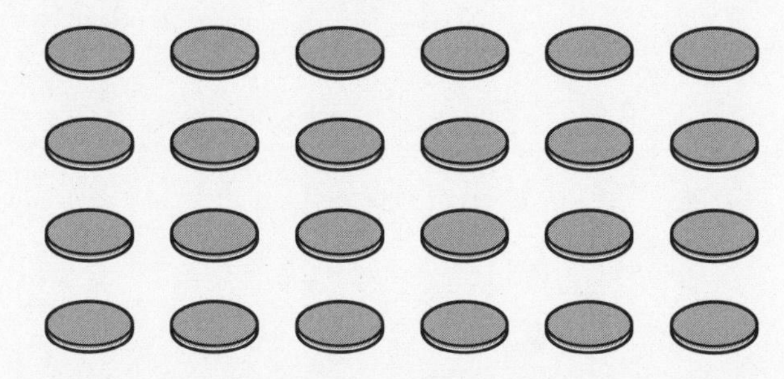

2. Place the piece of yarn between the second and third row of the array. Fill in the blanks.

_____ $\times 6 =$ _____

$2 \times$ _____ $=$ _____

3. So, 4×6 is double the product of 2×6.

$2 \times 6 =$ _____

Double the product: $12 + 12 =$ _____ So, $4 \times 6 =$ _____.

4. Use 2s facts to find 4×7 by doing the following.

Find the product of 2×7. $2 \times 7 =$ _____

Double the product: $14 + 14 =$ _____ So, $4 \times 7 =$ _____.

5. Use 2s facts to find 4×4 by doing the following.

Find the product of 2×4. $2 \times 4 =$ _____

Double the product: $8 + 8 =$ _____ So, $4 \times 4 =$ _____.

Name ______________________________

Multiplying by 4 (continued)

Find each product.

6. $8 \times 4 =$ ______ **7.** $3 \times 4 =$ ______ **8.** $1 \times 4 =$ ______

9. 4×4 **10.** 4×8 **11.** 9×4 **12.** 7×4 **13.** 6×4

14. 4×6 **15.** 4×1 **16.** 4×2 **17.** 4×5

18. 5×4 **19.** 4×7 **20.** 2×4 **21.** 4×3

22. Reasoning If $9 \times 4 = 36$, then $4 \times$ ______ $= 36$.

23. Helen is planting a garden. She buys 3 trays of tomato plants. Each tray has 4 plants and costs $2. How many tomato plants did Helen buy? ______

24. Jean reads 5 pages in a book before bedtime each night. Bedtime is at 9:00 P.M. How many pages does Jean read in 4 nights? ______

25. How can you find 4×8 without using two 4×4 arrays?

Name ______________________________

Multiplying by 6 or 7

Materials 56 counters, 6 inch piece of yarn per student or pair

Use 1s facts and 5s facts to multiply by 6.

1. A 6×7 array is 6 rows of ______.

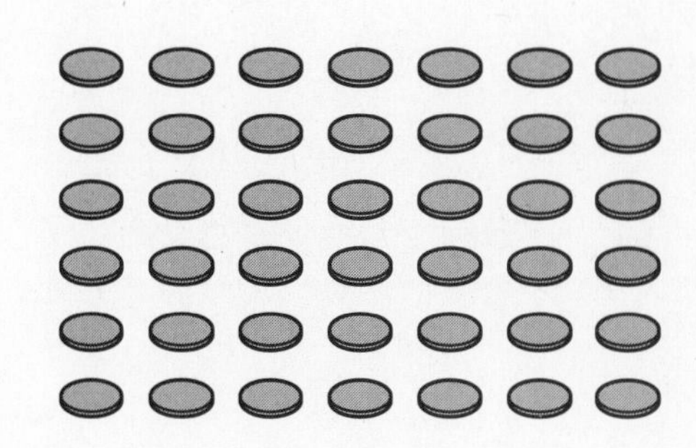

2. Draw a line to separate the 6×7 array into 1 row of 7 and 5 rows of 7.

$1 \times 7 =$ ______ $5 \times 7 =$ ______

So, $6 \times 7 = 7 +$ ______ $=$ ______.

Use 2s facts and 5s facts to multiply by 7.

3. A 7×8 array is 7 rows of ______.

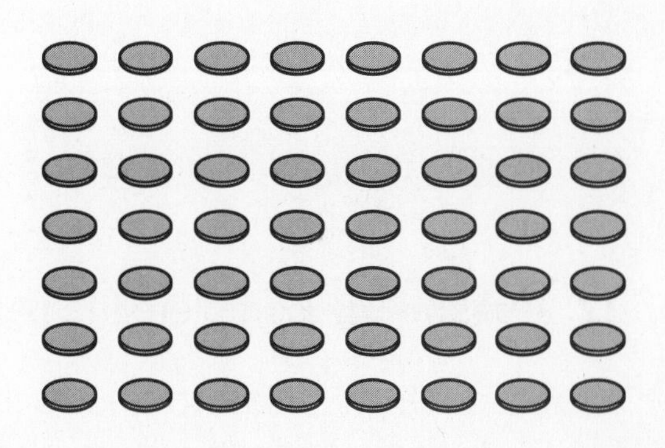

4. Draw a line to separate the 7×8 array into 2 rows of 8 and 5 rows of 8.

$2 \times 8 =$ ______ $5 \times 8 =$ ______

So, $7 \times 8 = 16 +$ ______ $=$ ______.

5. $6 \times 8 = 8 +$ ______ $=$ ______

6. $7 \times 7 = 14 +$ ______ $=$ ______

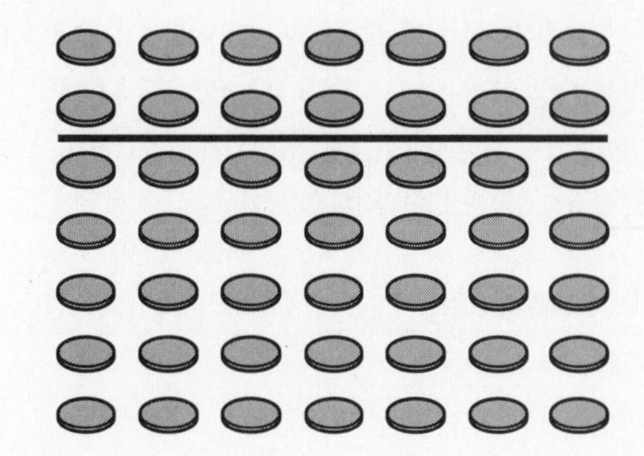

Name ______________________

Multiplying by 6 or 7 (continued)

Find each product.

7. 1×7

8. 6×3

9. 6×8

10. 9×7

11. 6×9

12. 7×4

13. 4×6

14. 3×7

15. 7×7

16. 2×7

17. 6×6

18. 6×2

19. $6 \times 1 =$ ______

20. $7 \times 8 =$ ______

21. $6 \times \$6 =$ ______

22. Reasoning Complete the pattern. 6, 12, 18, ______, 30, ______

23. Students in a classroom are in groups with 7 students in each group. There are 5 groups of students. How many students are there in the classroom? ______

24. A parking lot has 7 rows of parking spaces. There are six cars in each row. The charge to park in this lot is $2 each day. How many cars are in the parking lot? ______

25. Reasoning How does knowing $3 \times 8 = 24$ help you find 6×8?

Name ______________________________

Multiplying by 8

Use 4s facts to multiply by 8.

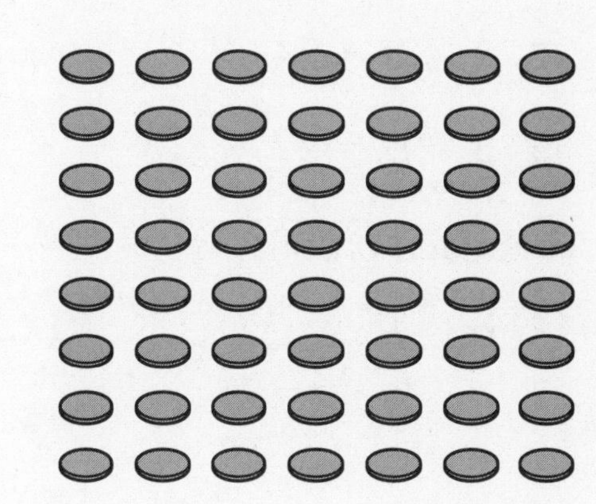

1. An 8×7 array is ______ rows of ______.

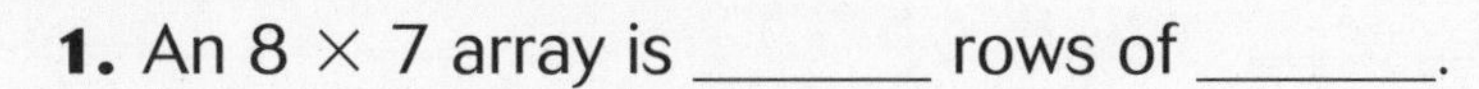

2. Draw a line to separate the 8×7 array into two arrays with 4 rows of 7.

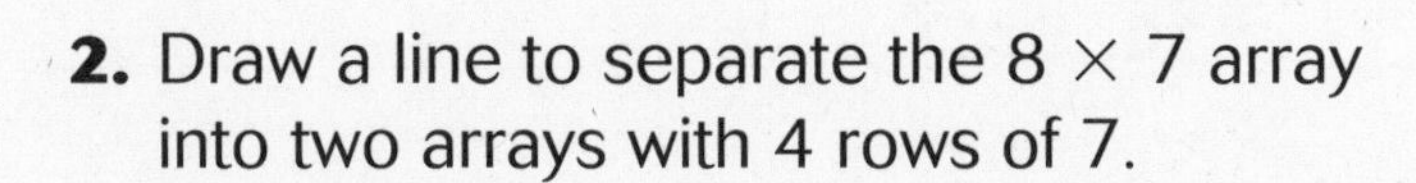

3. Since the 8×7 array is the same thing as two 4×7 arrays, you can find the product of 4×7 and then double it.

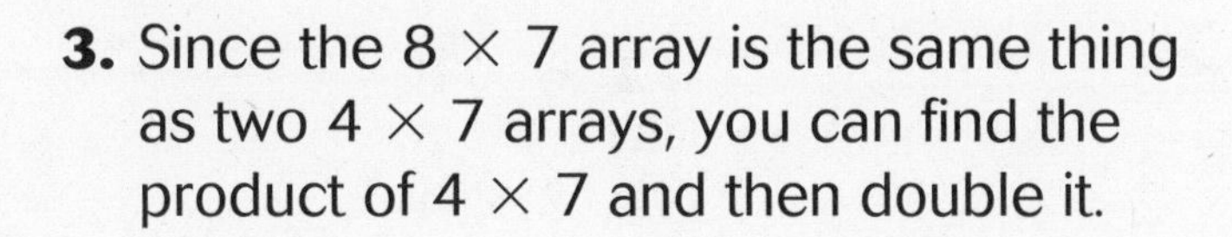

$4 \times 7 =$ ______

Double the product:

$$\begin{array}{r} 28 \\ +\ 28 \\ \hline \end{array}$$

So, $8 \times 7 =$ ______.

You can also use 3s facts and 5s facts to multiply by 8.

4. Draw a line to separate the 8×7 array into a 3×7 array and a 5×7.

$3 \times 7 =$ ______

$5 \times 7 =$ ______

5. Since the 8×7 array is the same thing as a 3×7 array plus a 5×7 array, add the products.

$8 \times 7 = 21 +$ ______

$=$ ______

So, $8 \times 7 =$ ______.

6. **Reasoning** Explain two ways to find 8×6.

Name ______________________________

Multiplying by 8 (continued)

In Exercises 7–10, use 3s facts, 4s facts and 5s facts to fill in the blanks and find the product.

7. $8 \times 8 = 24 +$ ______ = ______

8. $8 \times 8 = 32 +$ ______ = ______

9. $8 \times 9 = 27 +$ ______ = ______

10. $8 \times 9 = 36 +$ ______ = ______

Find each product.

11. $8 \times 1 =$ ______

12. $2 \times 8 =$ ______

13. $6 \times 8 =$ ______

14. $0 \times 8 =$ ______

15. $8 \times 2 =$ ______

16. $8 \times 4 =$ ______

17. 1×8

18. 8×3

19. 8×6

20. 9×8

21. 7×8

22. 8×5

23. 8×8

24. 4×8

25. There are 8 ounces in each cup of water. A recipe calls for 3 cups of water. How many ounces of water are needed for the recipe? ______

26. Each chapter in a book has 8 pages and 3 pictures. There are 6 chapters in the book. How many pages are there in the book? ______

27. Reasoning If $9 \times 8 = 72$, then $8 \times 9 =$ ______.

28. Reasoning Find 8×5. Tell how you found it.

Name ________________________________

Multiplying by 10

Answer 1 to 5 to learn how to multiply by 10.

1. Continue skip counting by 10s on the number line below.

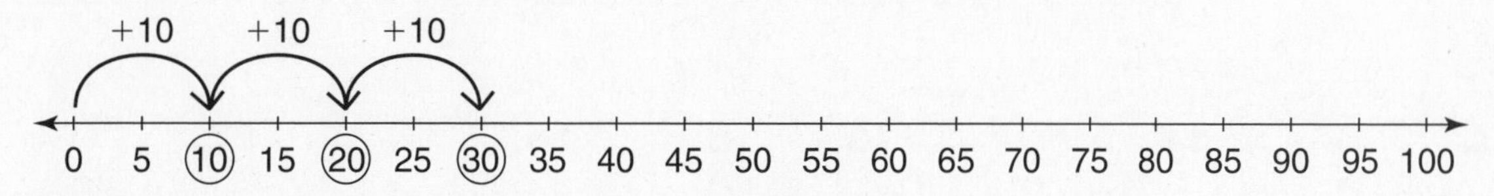

2. Each number a hop lands on is a **multiple** of ten. Circle each multiple of 10 on the number line. Then list them in the blanks below.

_____ _____ _____ _____ _____ _____ _____ _____ _____ _____

3. To find 6×10, count by 10s until you have said 6 numbers.

10, 20, _____, _____,

_____, _____

So, $6 \times 10 =$ _____.

4. Do this for each of the 10s facts. Complete the table.

5. Reasoning Complete to describe the patterns in the products of the 10s facts.

10s Facts

$0 \times 10 = 0$	$6 \times 10 =$ _____
$1 \times 10 =$ _____	$7 \times 10 =$ _____
$2 \times 10 =$ _____	$8 \times 10 =$ _____
$3 \times 10 =$ _____	$9 \times 10 =$ _____
$4 \times 10 =$ _____	$10 \times 10 =$ _____
$5 \times 10 =$ _____	

All the multiplies of 10 end in what number? _____

So, when you multiply a number by 10,

you just write the number and a _____.

6. Reasoning What is 10×7? Explain how you know.

Name ____________________

Multiplying by 10 (continued)

Find each product.

7. $2 \times 10 =$ ______ **8.** $4 \times 10 =$ ______ **9.** $6 \times 10 =$ ______

10. $10 \times 6 =$ ______ **11.** $10 \times 2 =$ ______ **12.** $10 \times 5 =$ ______

13. 3×10 **14.** 10×9 **15.** 8×10 **16.** 10×8 **17.** 9×10

18. 5×10 **19.** 10×3 **20.** 10×1 **21.** 1×10 **22.** 7×10

23. There are 8 markers in one box. How many markers are in 10 boxes? ______

24. Reasoning Complete the pattern. 10, 20, ______,

______, 50, ______, 70

25. Reasoning Seven friends get together to play a marble game. Sixty marbles are needed to play this game. Each friend brings ten marbles. Are there enough marbles to play the game?

26. Reasoning Jake said that 10×4 is 100. Is Jake correct? Explain.

Name ______________________________

Multiplying by 11 and 12

When multiplying by 11, multiply the factor that is not 11 by 10. Then add that factor to the product.

Find 4×11 by answering 1 to 4.

1. What is the factor that is not 11? ______

2. Multiply the factor that is not 11 by 10. $4 \times 10 =$ ______

3. Add the factor that is not 11 to the product. $40 + 4 =$ ______

4. So, $4 \times 11 =$ ______

When multiplying by 12, break the 12 into $10 + 2$. Multiply the factor that is not 12 by 10 and by 2. Then, add the two products.

Find 8×12 by answering 5 to 9.

5. What is the factor that is not 12? ______

6. Multiply the factor that is not 12 by 10. $8 \times 10 =$ ______

7. Multiply the factor that is not 12 by 2. $8 \times 2 =$ ______

8. Add the products together. $80 + 16 =$ ______

9. So, $8 \times 12 =$ ______.

10. Find 11×12.

$10 \times 12 =$ ______ $1 \times 12 =$ ______ $120 + 12 =$ ______

So, $11 \times 12 =$ ______.

11. To find 12×12, add 10×12 and 2×12, so ______ + ______.

So, $12 \times 12 =$ ______.

Name ______________________________

Multiplying by 11 and 12 (continued)

Find each product.

12. 7×11

$7 \times 10 =$ ______

$7 \times 1 =$ ______

$7 \times 11 =$ ______

13. 5×12

$5 \times 10 =$ ______

$5 \times 2 =$ ______

$5 \times 12 =$ ______

14. $3 \times 12 =$ ______ **15.** $5 \times 11 =$ ______ **16.** $7 \times 12 =$ ______

17. $10 \times 11 =$ ______ **18.** $12 \times 4 =$ ______ **19.** $11 \times 12 =$ ______

20. $11 \times 6 =$ ______ **21.** $3 \times 11 =$ ______ **22.** $12 \times 6 =$ ______

23. $9 \times 11 =$ ______ **24.** $12 \times 9 =$ ______ **25.** $5 \times 11 =$ ______

26. $11 \times 12 =$ ______ **27.** $8 \times 11 =$ ______ **28.** $10 \times 12 =$ ______

29. There are 2 baseball teams with 12 players on each team. How many players are playing baseball? ______

30. Twelve eggs are in a carton. Twelve cartons are in a case. How many eggs are in one case? ______

31. Reasoning Complete the pattern using multiples of 11, up to 9×11.

11, 22, 33, ______, ______, 66, ______, ______, 99

32. Reasoning Explain how to find 9×12.

Name ______________________

Multiplying Three Numbers

Does it matter how you multiply $5 \times 2 \times 3$? Answer 1–8 to find out.

To show the factors you are multiplying first, use parentheses as grouping symbols.

1. Group the first two factors together. $(\_\_\_\_ \times \_\_\_\_) \times 3$

2. Multiply what is in the parentheses first. $5 \times 2 = \_\_\_\_$

3. Then, multiply the product of what is in parentheses by the third factor. $10 \times 3 = \_\_\_\_$

4. So, $(5 \times 2) \times 3 = \_\_\_\_$.

5. Start again and group the last two factors together. $5 \times (\_\_\_\_ \times \_\_\_\_)$

6. Multiply what is in the parentheses first. $2 \times 3 = \_\_\_\_$

7. Then, multiply 5 by the product of what is in parentheses. $5 \times 6 = \_\_\_\_$

8. So, $5 \times (2 \times 3) = \_\_\_\_$.

It does not matter how the factors are grouped; the product will be the same.

9. $5 \times (2 \times 3) = (5 \times \_\_\_\_) \times 3$

Find $3 \times 2 \times 4$ two different ways.

10. Do the 3×2 first.

$3 \times 2 = \_\_\_\_$ $6 \times 4 = \_\_\_\_$ So, $(3 \times 2) \times 4 = \_\_\_\_$.

11. Do the 2×4 first.

$2 \times 4 = \_\_\_\_$ $3 \times 8 = \_\_\_\_$ So, $3 \times (2 \times 4) = \_\_\_\_$.

Name ______________________________

Multiplying Three Numbers (continued)

Find each product two different ways.

12. $(1 \times 3) \times 6 =$ _____

$1 \times (3 \times 6) =$ _____

13. $(5 \times 2) \times 4 =$ _____

$5 \times (2 \times 4) =$ _____

14. $(2 \times 4) \times 1 =$ _____

$2 \times (4 \times 1) =$ _____

15. $(2 \times 2) \times 5 =$ _____

$2 \times (2 \times 5) =$ _____

Find each product.

16. $2 \times 4 \times 3 =$ _____

17. $7 \times 1 \times 3 =$ _____

18. $3 \times 3 \times 2 =$ _____

19. $3 \times 2 \times 6 =$ _____

20. $(4 \times 2) \times 2 =$ _____

21. $3 \times (0 \times 7) =$ _____

22. $1 \times 7 \times 9 =$ _____

23. $8 \times (2 \times 3) =$ _____

24. $(2 \times 5) \times 6 =$ _____

25. $9 \times 0 \times 3 =$ _____

26. $4 \times 5 \times 1 =$ _____

27. $(3 \times 6) \times 1 =$ _____

28. Reasoning When multiplying three numbers, if one of the factors is zero, what will the answer be? ______________

29. A classroom of students is getting ready to take a test. There are 5 rows of desks in the room and 4 students are in each row. Each student is required to have 2 pencils. How many pencils are needed? ______________

Name ______________________________

Meanings for Division

Materials 15 counters and 3 half sheets of paper, per pair

Martina has 15 dolls. She put them into 3 equal groups. Answer 1 to 3 to find how many dolls were in each group.

1. Count out 15 counters. Place the counters on the sheets of paper to form 3 equal groups.

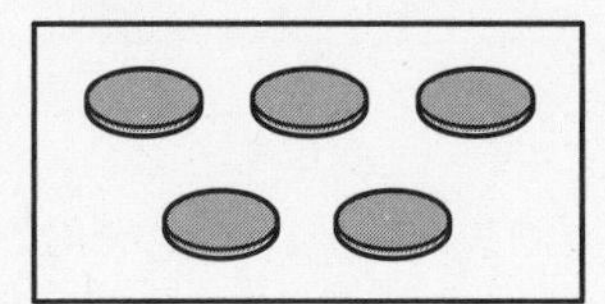  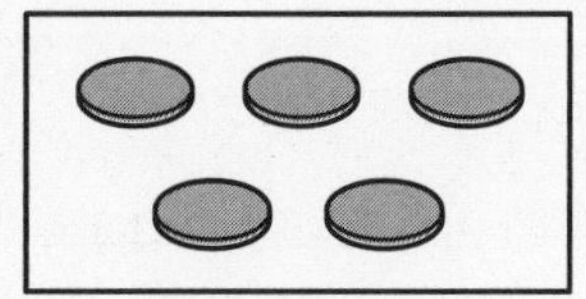

2. Write a number sentence to show division as sharing.

_______ ÷ _______ = _______

Total | Number of equal groups | Number in each group

3. How many dolls were in each group? _______

Mrs. Gentry had only 6 tokens. As the students left her room, she gave each student 2 tokens. Answer 4 to 6 to find how many students got tokens.

4. Show 6 tokens.     

5. Find the number of times 2 can be subtracted from 6 until nothing is left.

$6 - 2 = 4$ 1 time
$4 - 2 = 2$ 2 times
$2 - 2 = 0$ 3 times

6. Write a number sentence to show division as repeated subtraction.

_______ ÷ _______ = _______

Total | Number subtracted each time | Number of times 2 was subtracted

7. How many students got tokens? _______

Name ______________________

Meanings for Division (continued)

Draw pictures to solve each problem.

8. Put 20 counters into 5 equal groups. How many counters are in each group?

____

9. Put 12 counters in a row. How many times can you subtract 4 counters?

____

10. You put 24 cards into 4 equal piles. How many cards are in each pile?

____

11. You put 21 chairs into rows of 7. How many rows do you make?

____

12. You have 30 oranges. If you need 6 oranges to fill a bag, how many bags can you fill?

____

13. You put 10 marbles into equal groups of 5. How many groups are there?

____

14. Eight people went to the museum in two cars. The same number of people went in each car. How many people went in each car? ______________

15. Reasoning How can you use repeated subtraction to find $30 \div 5$?

Name ______________________________

Writing Division Stories

Materials counters, 18 per student or pair of students

To write a division story for 18 ÷ 3 that is about 18 grapes and 3 sisters, fill in the blanks below.

1. Mrs. ______________ put ______ grapes into

a bowl. Mrs. ______________'s daughters,

______________, ______________, and

______________ shared the grapes equally. How

many ______________ did each sister get?

3. Use counters to show how many grapes there were in all.

4. Divide the 18 counters into 3 equal groups.

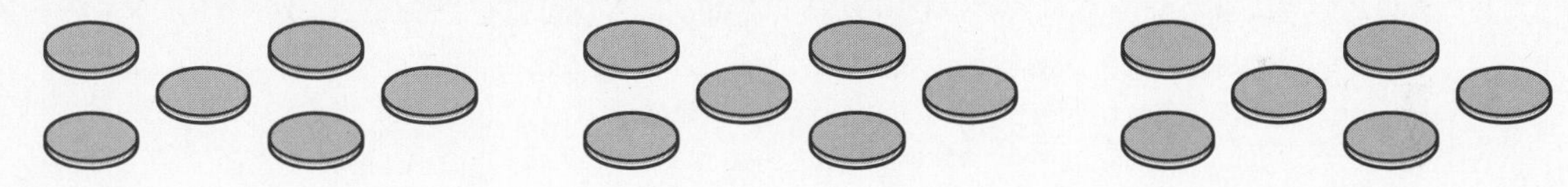

5. How many grapes did each sister get? ______ grapes

6. Write a division story for 10 ÷ 5 about apples and bags.

Mr. ______________ bought ______ apples. He

put ______ apples into each bag. How many ________

did he use?

7. Use counters to show how many apples he bought.

8. Divide the 10 counters into groups with 5 in each group.

9. How many bags did he use? ______ bags

Name ______________________________

Writing Division Stories (continued)

Write a division story for each number sentence below. Use the pictures to help. Then use counters or draw a picture to solve.

10. $15 \div 5 =$ ______

11. $12 \div 3 =$ ______

Write a division story. Then use counters or draw a picture to solve.

12. $14 \div 2 =$ ______

Name ______________________

Relating Multiplication and Division

Materials 36 color tiles per pair

1. Partner A show an array for 2×9, or 2 rows of 9.

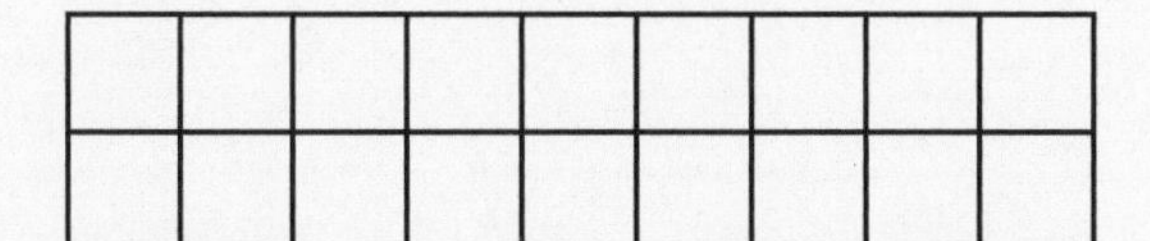

2. Partner B show $18 \div 2$, by showing a total of 18 tiles in 2 rows.

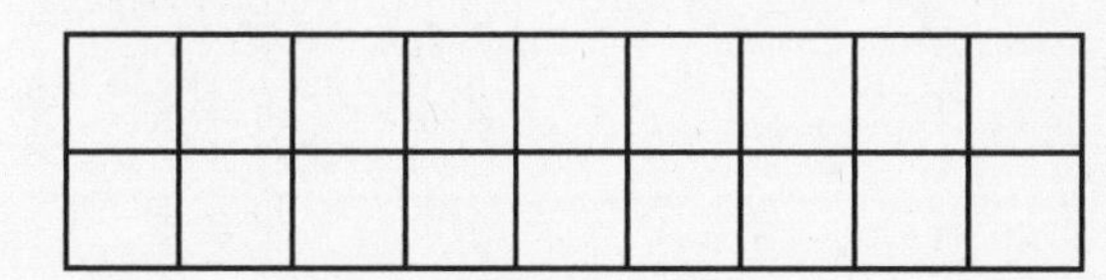

3. What do you notice about the arrays each partner made?

4. Partner A's tiles show:

   $2 \times 9 =$ _______

5. Partner B's tiles show:

   $18 \div 2 =$ _______

6. What do you notice about the numbers used in each number sentence?

Multiplication and division are related to each other. A **fact family** shows how they are related.

A fact family has two multiplication and two division number sentences written with the same 3 numbers.

Fact family for 2, 9, and 18

$2 \times 9 = 18$	$18 \div 2 = 9$
$9 \times 2 = 18$	$18 \div 9 = 2$

You can use multiplication to help you divide.

Find $30 \div 6$.

7. To find $30 \div 6$, think about the related multiplication problem.

   6 times what number equals 30? $6 \times$ _______ $= 30$

8. Since you know $6 \times 5 = 30$, then you know $30 \div 6 =$ _______.

Name ______________________________

Relating Multiplication and Division (continued)

Use the array to complete each sentence.

9.

$4 \times \underline{\qquad} = 20$

$20 \div 4 = \underline{\qquad}$

10. 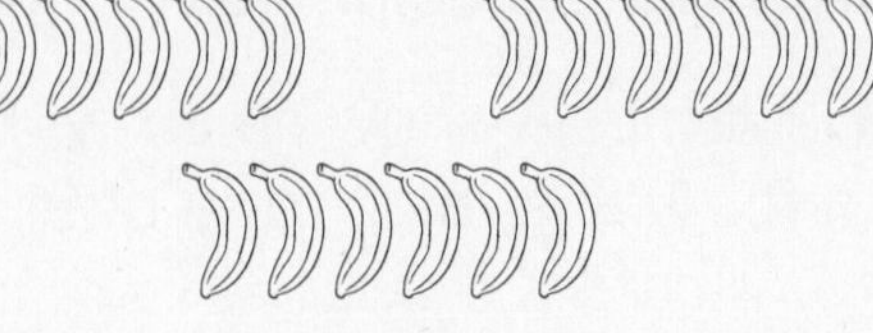

$3 \times \underline{\qquad} = 18$

$18 \div 3 = \underline{\qquad}$

11.

$3 \times \underline{\qquad} = 9$

$9 \div 3 = \underline{\qquad}$

12. 

$6 \times \underline{\qquad} = 12$

$12 \div 6 = \underline{\qquad}$

Write a fact family for each product.

13. $3 \times 7 = 21$

____

____

____

14. $2 \times 4 = 8$

____

____

____

15. $3 \times 5 = 15$

____

____

____

16. Reasoning Why does the fact family for $3 \times 3 = 9$ only have 2 facts?

Name ______________________________

Dividing by 2 Through 5

Materials Have counters available for students to use.

You can use multiplication facts to help you divide.

Anna Maria has 24 leaves in her collection. She puts 4 leaves on each page in her scrap book. How many pages does she need for all her leaves?

Find $24 \div 4$.

1. To find $24 \div 4$, think about the related multiplication problem.

4 times what number equals 24? $4 \times$ ______ $= 24$

2. Since you know $4 \times 6 = 24$, then you know $24 \div 4 =$ ______.

3. How many pages does Anna Maria need for all her leaves? ______

Find $45 \div 5$.

4. 5 times what number equals 45? $5 \times$ ______ $= 45$

5. Since you know $5 \times 9 = 45$, then you know $45 \div 5 =$ ______.

A division problem can be written two different ways.

$30 \div 5 = 6$ $\qquad$ $5\overline{)30}$ with quotient 6

Both problems are read "30 divided by 5 equals 6."

6. Think: $3 \times$ ______ $= 15$ So, $3\overline{)15} =$ ______.

7. Think: $4 \times$ ______ $= 16$ So $16 \div 4 =$ ______.

8. Think: $2 \times$ ______ $= 18$ So $18 \div 2 =$ ______.

Name ______________________________

Dividing by 2 Through 5 (continued)

Use the multiplication fact to find each quotient.

9. $4 \times$ ______ $= 24$

$24 \div 4 =$ ______

10. $6 \times$ ______ $= 30$

$30 \div 6 =$ ______

11. $2 \times$ ______ $= 12$

$12 \div 2 =$ ______

12. $5 \times$ ______ $= 25$

$25 \div 5 =$ ______

13. $3 \times$ ______ $= 27$

$27 \div 3 =$ ______

14. $4 \times$ ______ $= 28$

$28 \div 4 =$ ______

Find each quotient.

15. $25 \div 5 =$ ______

16. $20 \div 4 =$ ______

17. $12 \div 3 =$ ______

18. $5\overline{)35}$

19. $4\overline{)36}$

20. $3\overline{)21}$

21. Mario has 15 eggs. He wants to share them equally with 3 friends. How many eggs will each friend get?

Think: $3 \times 5 = 15$. So, $15 \div 3 =$ ______ eggs.

22. Todd has 40 whistles. He wants to divide them evenly between his 5 friends. How many whistles will each friend get? ______________

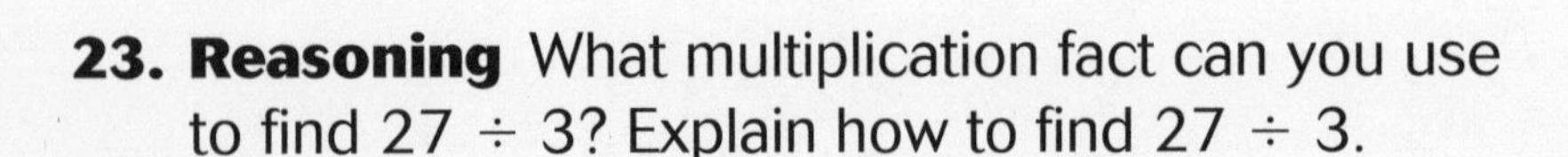

23. Reasoning What multiplication fact can you use to find $27 \div 3$? Explain how to find $27 \div 3$.

24. If $4 \times 10 = 40$, then what is $40 \div 4$? ______

Name ______________________________

Dividing by 6 and 7

Materials Have counters available for students to use.

You can use multiplication facts to help you divide.

Ahmed has 24 bugs to put on 6 boards. He wants the same number of bugs on each board. How many bugs should he put on each board?

Find $24 \div 6$.

1. To find $24 \div 6$, think about the related multiplication problem.

6 times what number equals 24? $6 \times$ ______ $= 24$

2. Since you know $6 \times 4 = 24$, then you know $24 \div 6 =$ ______.

3. How many bugs should Ahmed put on each board? ______

Find $21 \div 7$.

4. To find $21 \div 7$, think about the related multiplication problem.

7 times what number equals 21? $7 \times$ ______ $= 21$

5. Since you know $7 \times 3 = 21$, then you know $21 \div 7 =$ ______.

6. Think: $6 \times$ ______ $= 30$ So, $6\overline{)30} =$ ______.

7. Think: $7 \times$ ______ $= 49$ So $49 \div 7 =$ ______.

8. Think: $6 \times$ ______ $= 48$ So $48 \div 6 =$ ______.

9. Reasoning Explain how to find $63 \div 7$.

Name ______________________________

Dividing by 6 and 7 (continued)

Use the multiplication fact to find each quotient.

10. $6 \times 5 = 30$

$30 \div 6 =$ ______

11. $7 \times 2 = 14$

$14 \div 7 =$ ______

12. $6 \times 1 = 6$

$6 \div 6 =$ ______

13. $7 \times 5 = 35$

$35 \div 7 =$ ______

14. $6 \times$ ______ $= 36$

$36 \div 6 =$ ______

15. $7 \times$ ______ $= 56$

$56 \div 7 =$ ______

16. $6 \times$ ______ $= 24$

$24 \div 6 =$ ______

17. $6 \times 9 = 54$

$54 \div 6 =$ ______

18. $6 \times 7 = 42$

$42 \div 6 =$ ______

Find each quotient.

19. $6\overline{)54}$

20. $7\overline{)42}$

21. $6\overline{)30}$

22. $7\overline{)7}$

23. $6\overline{)42}$

24. $7\overline{)70}$

25. $6\overline{)12}$

26. $7\overline{)14}$

27. $6\overline{)60}$

28. Mrs. Carpenter's class is dividing into groups for group work. There are 28 students in the class and 35 desks. How many students will be in each group if there are 7 groups? ______________

29. Reasoning If you know that $6 \times 12 = 72$, then what is $72 \div 6$? ______________

Name ____

Dividing by 8 and 9

Materials Have counters available for students to use.

You can use multiplication facts to help you divide.

At the museum, 32 students are divided into 8 equal groups.
How many students are in each group?

Find $32 \div 8$.

1. To find $32 \div 8$, think about the related multiplication problem.

8 times what number equals 32? $8 \times$ ______ $= 32$

2. Since you know $8 \times 4 = 32$, then you know $32 \div 8 =$ ______.

3. How many students are in each group at the museum? ______ students

Find $36 \div 9$.

4. To find $36 \div 9$, think about the related multiplication problem.

9 times what number equals 36? $9 \times$ ______ $= 36$

5. Since you know $9 \times 4 = 36$, then you know $36 \div 9 =$ ______.

Find $8\overline{)80}$.

6. To find $8\overline{)80}$, think about the related multiplication problem.

8 times what number equals 80? $8 \times$ ______ $= 80$

7. Since you know $8 \times 10 = 80$, then you know $8\overline{)80} =$ ______.

8. Reasoning Explain how to find $56 \div 8$.

Name ______________________________

Dividing by 8 and 9 (continued)

Use the multiplication fact to find each quotient.

9. $8 \times 2 = 16$

$16 \div 8 =$ ______

10. $9 \times 5 = 45$

$45 \div 9 =$ ______

11. $8 \times 3 = 24$

$24 \div 8 =$ ______

12. $9 \times 6 = 54$

$54 \div 9 =$ ______

13. $8 \times$ ______ $= 32$

$32 \div 8 =$ ______

14. $8 \times$ ______ $= 48$

$48 \div 8 =$ ______

15. $9 \times$ ______ $= 27$

$27 \div 9 =$ ______

16. $9 \times$ ______ $= 90$

$90 \div 9 =$ ______

17. $8 \times$ ______ $= 72$

$72 \div 8 =$ ______

Find each quotient.

18. $9\overline{)63}$

19. $8\overline{)32}$

20. $9\overline{)36}$

21. $8\overline{)64}$

22. $9\overline{)81}$

23. $8\overline{)16}$

24. $9\overline{)45}$

25. $8\overline{)56}$

26. $8\overline{)40}$

27. Reasoning If you know that $8 \times 12 = 96$, then what is $96 \div 8$? ______

28. Nine friends go to lunch and split the $54 ticket evenly. How much does each friend pay? ______

Name ______________________________

0 and 1 in Division

Think about related multiplication facts to help you divide.

Find $5 \div 1$.

1. Think: 1 times what number equals 5? $1 \times$ ______ $= 5$

2. Since you know $1 \times 5 = 5$, then you know $5 \div 1 =$ ______.

3. If Karina had 5 oranges to put equally in 1 basket, how many oranges would go in each basket? ______ oranges

Find $9 \div 1$.

4. $1 \times$ ______ $= 9$ So, $9 \div 1 =$ ______.

5. What is the result when any number is divided by 1? ______________

Find $0 \div 7$.

6. Think: 7 times what number equals 0? $7 \times$ ______ $= 0$

7. Since you know $7 \times 0 = 0$, then you know $0 \div 7 =$ ______.

8. If Karina had 0 oranges to put equally in 7 baskets, how many oranges would go in each basket? ______ oranges

Find $0 \div 2$.

9. $2 \times$ ______ $= 0$ So, $0 \div 2 =$ ______.

10. What is the result when zero is divided by any number (except 0)? ______

Find $5 \div 0$.

11. **Reasoning** If Karina had 5 oranges to put equally in 0 baskets, how many oranges would go in each basket? Explain.

You cannot divide a number by 0.

Name ________________________________

0 and 1 in Division (continued)

Find 4 ÷ 4.

12. Think: 4 times what number equals 4? 4 × _______ = 4

13. Since you know 4 × 1 = 4, then you know 4 ÷ 4 = _______.

14. If Karina had 4 oranges to put equally in 4 baskets, how many oranges would go in each basket? _______ orange

Find 8 ÷ 8.

15. 8 × _______ = 8 So, 8 ÷ 8 = _______.

16. What is the result when any number (except 0) is divided by itself? _______

Find each quotient.

17. 4 ÷ 1 = _______ **18.** 0 ÷ 5 = _______ **19.** 6 ÷ 6 = _______

20. $3\overline{)0}$ **21.** $9\overline{)9}$ **22.** $5\overline{)5}$

23. $1\overline{)6}$ **24.** $1\overline{)1}$ **25.** $8\overline{)0}$

26. Reasoning Use the rule for division by 1 to find 247 ÷ 1. Explain.

27. Larry has 3 friends who would like some cookies but he has no cookies to give them. How many cookies can Larry give each friend?